Experiments in Digital Fundamentals with VHDL

To Accompany FLOYD, DIGITAL FUNDAMENTALS with VHDL

David Buchla
Yuba College

Douglas A. Joksch
Yuba College

PEARSON

Prentice Hall

Upper Saddle River, New Jersey
Columbus, Ohio

NOTICE TO THE READER

The publisher and the authors do not warrant or guarantee any of the products and/or equipment described herein nor has the publisher or the authors made any independent analysis in connection with any of the products, equipment, or information used herein. The reader is directed to the manufacturer for any warranty or guarantee for any claim, loss, damages, costs, or expense, arising out of or incurred by the reader in connection with the use or operation of the products and/or equipment.

The reader is expressly advised to adopt all safety precautions that might be indicated by the activities and experiments described herein. The reader assumes all risks in connection with such instructions.

Editor in Chief: Stephen Helba
Acquisitions Editor: Dennis Williams
Development Editor: Kate Linsner
Production Editor: Rex Davidson
Cover Photo: PhotoDisc
Design Coordinator: Karrie Converse-Jones
Cover Designer: Thomas Borah
Production Manager: Pat Tonneman
Marketing Manager: Ben Leonard

This book was set in Times Roman by Carlisle Communications, LTD. and was printed and bound by Courier Kendallville, Inc. The cover was printed by Phoenix Color Corp.

Altera® is a registered trademark of Altera Corporation

MAX+plus®II is a registered trademark of Altera Corporation

Xilinx® is a registered trademark of Xilinx, Inc.

PLDT-1™, PLDT-2™, and PLDT-3™ are trademarks of RSR Electronics

Pearson Education Ltd.
Pearson Education Singapore Pte. Ltd.
Pearson Education Canada, Ltd.
Pearson Education—Japan

Pearson Education Australia Pty. Limited
Pearson Education North Asia Ltd.
Pearson Educación de Mexico, S.A. de C.V.
Pearson Education Malaysia Pte. Ltd.

10 9 8 7 6 5 4 3 2 1
ISBN 0-13-045305-6

To our Wives—Lorraine and Tina

Contents

Preface

Experiments in Digital Fundamentals with VHDL provides laboratory exercises that support *Digital Fundamentals with VHDL* by Tom Floyd. The manual contains 27 experiments using both traditional TTL/CMOS logic and programmable logic using VHDL. Although the implementation of traditional logic is different from VHDL, the focus in both cases is logic. The VHDL experiments are simply an alternate tool for teaching logic; we are not attempting to teach the detailed syntax of VHDL. Nearly all of the experiments with VHDL include the required programs with only some logic statements left for the student to complete. Abundant examples are provided.

Programmable logic devices have changed the way digital logic is implemented. Today, designers usually specify logic functions with a hardware description language (HDL) and download the description to a programmable integrated circuit. One of the most popular hardware description languages is called VHDL [for Very High-Speed Integrated Circuit (VHSIC) Hardware Description Language].

VHDL has been slow catching on with technician-level courses, partly because it is a very sophisticated language and training materials have been lacking. Although several well-designed stand-alone project boards are available for schools, lab manuals that support these boards by showing the underlying VHDL program have not been available. The approach we have taken is to include the programs as part of the exercise rather than simply pasting graphics to the screen.

We have tried to maximize the flexibility of this manual by bridging fixed-function logic (standard TTL and CMOS ICs) and VHDL logic. To accomplish this bridging, we show two procedures for most experiments. The two procedures are independent of each other; you can choose to use one or the other or (time permitting) use both procedures. The first procedure for the fixed-function logic section, marked with a TTL or CMOS icon, applies traditional TTL or CMOS logic to teach a concept; the same steps are basically identical to those in the parallel experiment found in *Experiments in Digital Fundamentals*, which has been used by thousands of students to learn traditional IC logic. The second procedure, marked with a VHDL icon, implements essentially the same logic in a PLD using the VHDL program and one of the programmable logic device project boards supported by this manual. Depending on the objectives of your course, a mix of traditional and VHDL logic can be accommodated with this manual. In a few cases, we made minor changes in the implementation of the VHDL program to show the versatility of VHDL or to accommodate differences in hardware and software. One good example of the difference in hardware and software is a method shown in step 12 of Experiment 19 for implementing a counter. The VHDL implementation in this step has no equivalent component implementation (such as a D flip-flop) but shows an important program construction. It also emphasizes why showing the program is important to understanding VHDL.

In general, the VHDL procedure includes the necessary VHDL program, except that a small part of the program is left as a student exercise in many experiments. The part left for students deals directly with the logic, as opposed to the syntax of VHDL. The VHDL programs tend to be progressively more involved, so it is best to start with earlier, more tutorial type experiments before attempting the later ones. All VHDL programs can be used with any one of the five project boards that are supported by the lab manual. These boards are the PLDT-1*, PLDT-2, and PLDT-3 boards from RSR Electronics, the DeVry University eSOC board, and the Altera University Program board.

Each of the five project boards uses software supplied by either Altera or Xilinx, depending on the board. The software is available free on the Internet. Each board has certain common characteristics, such as input switches and output LEDs, which are described in the section entitled *Project Board Familiarization*. In this section tables describe the specific characteristics of each board, such as the location of inputs and outputs as well as pin numbering information. The student will need to read the data for his or her specific board from the appropriate table. These tables are referenced throughout the experiments for necessary pin assignments.

In addition to detailed hardware descriptions, we have included two tutorial exercises—one for each of the two compilers (Xilinx and Altera). The tutorials are in the section entitled *VHDL Software Familiarization*. These tutorials are designed to teach the steps needed to implement the programs included in the VHDL experiments. In this section, we provide a "guided tour" of how to write a program, download it, and run it. The tutorials are self-paced and could be run as a separate laboratory exercise or assigned for homework.

We have also made provision for the difference in board design by including two versions of all of the software. Some boards use an active-HIGH convention for outputs; that is, LEDs and seven-segment displays are turned on with a logic 1. Boards with active-HIGH outputs are the PLDT-1, PLDT-2, and PLDT-3 boards and the Altera University Program board. Another convention is to use an active-LOW output where LEDs and seven-segment displays are turned on with a logic 0. The DeVry University eSOC board is in this category. The software listings given in the manual are always shown with the active-HIGH convention, but the accompanying CD has student program listings, in separate folders, for both active-HIGH and active-LOW. The only difference in the two program listings is in how the outputs are defined. Students using an active-LOW board will see the same results in their experiments as those using an active-HIGH board.

We like the concept of building programs toward a realistic project as was done in the Floyd text for the traffic light control system. Experiment 13 and Experiment 14 have components of a traffic light that are used in the final composite program for the traffic light in Experiment 22. Experiment 14 is strictly a VHDL experiment that goes with Floyd's chapter 7, "*Additional VHDL Topics and Applications.*" This experiment contains the timer program for a traffic light. Likewise, the TTL experiments build toward a completed system by learning about the composite pieces in earlier experiments.

The experiments themselves closely track the level and materials in Floyd's *Digital Fundamentals with VHDL* text. The text includes descriptions of traditional logic along with VHDL. There are experiments available for every chapter of the text and reading references are coordinated to the text, but the emphasis is on the first ten chapters that include the VHDL material. All experiments start with Objectives, Reading, Summary of Theory, and Pre-lab Questions. These features are intended to be used with *both* the traditional logic and the VHDL approach, and include both icons on the first page of the experiment, where applicable. For most experiments, the Pre-lab Questions are followed by a TTL or CMOS experiment and Report section, which concludes the traditional part of the experiment. Following this, most experiments then have a VHDL Program Overview, a Procedure section, and a Report. The VHDL experiment can be used alone or in conjunction with the traditional experiment; it uses one of the five boards mentioned previously. Except for Experiments 15 and 16, the VHDL experiment does not require materials other than one of the project boards, a function generator with a TTL pulse output, and an oscilloscope. Experiment 15 uses a fixed-function (TTL) delay circuit that can be constructed easily on a small protoboard and connected to the project board to add a hands-on circuit to the VHDL experience, and Experiment 16 uses two CdS light sensors.

The VHDL procedure section tends to be tutorial in nature, as most of the VHDL programs are complete, as mentioned. The programs include comments and sidebar information (labeled "Code Tip") about the programs in order that students will see the reason for certain program structures and develop good programming habits. When the program is entered into the board, the logic is tested much like traditional logic, with input switches and output LEDs for most experiments. Specific instructions are provided in the section entitled *Project Board Familiar-*

---

*Although the PLD-1 board is no longer in production, we have included it because many are still in use.

ization, which shows how to connect pulse generators and oscilloscopes, so that students can observe waveforms in sequential logic experiments. Color photos of these connections are on the back cover for reference.

The labs themselves emphasize small projects, which make electronics so exciting and interesting. For projects to work in a limited lab period, they must be relatively small but illustrate an important concept. Examples of these projects include a logic probe, a change machine, a burglar alarm, a traffic light simulation, and a digital light meter.

In addition to the flexibility of traditional and VHDL procedures, all experiments include a *For Further Investigation* section in both the TTL/CMOS procedure and the VHDL procedure. These are intended to be used as an enhancement or as part of the experiment depending on time constraints in the laboratory. The *For Further Investigation* sections tend to include predominantly open-ended investigations, frequently with a design problem associated with them. (For example, the traffic light in Experiment 22 has a pedestrian "pushbutton" latch for the student to design.)

Although there are more experiments than most digital courses can use, they are given to provide a variety of choices for instructors, as well as a series of interesting circuits that can be used for class discussion. Appendix A contains selected manufacturer's data sheets; ones not shown are available on the Internet directly from the manufacturer.

All of the traditional TTL/CMOS experiments are designed to fit onto one 47-row protoboard available from Radio Shack and other suppliers. The VHDL experiments need to be run on a computer with Windows 95, 98, or XP; it is not recommended to use Windows ME for Xilinx. The VHDL experiments require a TTL-compatible, variable-frequency pulse generator, a multimeter, and a dual-channel oscilloscope. In addition, Experiment 15 requires a protoboard to construct a delay circuit. Experiment 27 also requires a -12 V supply.

Experiment 26, *Introduction to the Intel Processors,* uses a different format than the other experiments. It requires a PC to explore the architecture of microprocessors and provides a "bridge" to a microprocessor course. The experiment is tutorial in nature and spaces are left within the procedure for students' answers and observations.

Other supporting material for this manual include the following:

• Free student software is available from Altera and Xilinx to support the project boards in this manual. The software can be downloaded from **www. Altera.com** and **www.Xilinx.com**. You will need to obtain a student license from the manufacturer's web site.

• Two new tutorial exercises (one for each compiler) are included to illustrate the specific steps needed to implement the VHDL programs in this manual.

• A CD with student versions of the VHDL source listings (as given in the experiments) is packaged with this manual. Users of this manual may cut and paste these programs into the VHDL editor to save typing time. Students should be encouraged to read the programs to understand how they implement the logic of the experiment. In addition, the CD contains Electronics Workbench/Multisim exercises described in the next paragraph.

• Electronics Workbench/Multisim exercises are on the CD packaged with this manual. The philosophy of learning by doing is behind all laboratory work, and we believe there is no substitute for constructing and testing circuits as a part of digital electronics. That being said, computers and electronics simulation software offer excellent supplementary teaching tools. Because many schools use Electronics Workbench, troubleshooting exercises are available for several of the laboratory experiments. The circuit files are used with either the Electronics Workbench (EWB) program or the Multisim 2001 program. Multisim 2001 is the new name for the program previously associated with Electronics Workbench, Version 5. Files from EWB and Multisim are not mutually compatible. For this reason, both EWB and Multisim files are included on the disk that accompanies this manual for schools still using EWB. Multisim circuit files have the extension msm, and Electronics Workbench Version 5 files have the extension ewb. In addition to the EWB (.ewb) circuit files and the Multisim (.msm) circuit files, a copy of the Multisim 2001 program (textbook edition) is included on the CD in the folder MSMTKBK.

• PowerPoint slides have been prepared as a supplement for instructors. The PowerPoint slides support the TTL/CMOS portion of this manual with several slides for most experiments. The slides can be used as a review of the experiment and include Troubleshooting and Related Questions. They are available free of charge to instructors who have adopted *Experiments in Digital Fundamentals with VHDL.*

• **Troubleshooting coverage.** Troubleshooting problems are included in nearly all of the experiments, including simulated fault analysis and "what if" questions. Questions and space for answers are included in the Report section for both the TTL/CMOS and the VHDL reports.

• **Pre-lab questions**. We feel that it is important that students come to lab class prepared to do the experimental work, so we have included two or three questions labeled Pre-lab Questions. These questions can be answered from the material in the **Summary of Theory** before class.

- A **guide to oscilloscopes**. Coverage of analog and digital storage oscilloscopes (DSOs) is included. To simplify teaching the new features found on digital scopes, a generic digital scope is described (with a block diagram) followed by a specific example of a widely used model—the Tektronix TDS220.

- Data sheets are available in Appendix A for the integrated circuits needed in the first 8 experiments (and a few other useful data sheets are given for ready reference). Data sheets for other integrated circuits are available on manufacturers' web sites* and in data books.

---

*A list of manufacturers can be found at http://www.physnet.uni-hamburg.de/home/vms/krey/icman.html.

We have enjoyed working with Tom Floyd and appreciate his suggestions for this manual. As always, it is a pleasure to work with the staff at Prentice Hall. We would like to thank our editors; Dennis Williams, Kate Linsner, and Rex Davidson. We also appreciate the very thorough job of editing from Lois Porter. Finally, we want to express our appreciation to our wives. Without their unwavering teetering support, this lab manual would still be 1s and 0s.

David Buchla

Douglas Joksch

Introduction to the Student

Digital Electronics

Electronics has been and continues to be one of the most dynamic disciplines. Since the introduction of integrated circuits (ICs), and especially microprocessors, changes in the way circuits are implemented have been dramatic. Although implementations change, the fundamental logic remains the same. This lab manual supports Floyd's *Digital Fundamentals with VHDL* by teaching the logic underlying all digital electronics with hands-on experience. The vehicle to teach that logic is either traditional integrated circuits that you will construct on protoboards or a programmable logic device (PLD) using one of the five commercial project boards supported by this manual. Whichever exercise you do, your focus should be on principles of digital logic as described in the Summary of Theory for each experiment.

TTL/CMOS Logic

The two major integrated circuit families are TTL (*Transistor-Transistor Logic*) and CMOS (*Complementary Metal-Oxide Semiconductor*). The TTL and CMOS integrated circuits are fixed-function—that is, each integrated circuit is designed to do a specific logic function and no more. These functions range from basic gates to comparators, adders, counters, and much more. Most practical circuits require several ICs interconnected to make a working system. The connections are done on a printed circuit board or, in the laboratory, on solderless boards called protoboards.

VHDL Logic

VHDL is a programming language that enables you to describe the entire logic for a system in a single programmable integrated circuit called a PLD. It is called a hardware description language because all of the fixed functions such as gates, comparators, adders, and counters can be described in VHDL along with the "glue-logic" to connect the functions together. Knowledge of VHDL is a marketable skill, so it is worthwhile to look carefully at the program examples and exercises in this manual.

In order to begin writing a VHDL program, you would need to know a lot of the syntax for the language. To help you get started, and focus on the logic rather than the syntax, all of the programs you will need for the experiments are either complete or nearly complete (with a few lines left for you to complete, but always with examples). These programs are contained on the CD that accompanies this manual. You can save typing time by doing a "copy and paste" into the text editor. You should read over the Program Overview and the program itself in each experiment and notice how the program was written to learn as much as possible about the VHDL implementation.

While you will undoubtedly learn much of the VHDL syntax in the textbook and by examining the programs in this manual, that is not the main focus of the VHDL experiments. The primary focus is still the fundamentals of digital logic. Both fixed-function and VHDL implementations perform the same logic in these experiments, with a few minor differences. In general, the fixed-function experiment and the VHDL implementation have similar procedures and data.

The programs for VHDL are written for one of two VHDL compilers (Xilinx or Altera). The compiler you will use depends on the specific project board you have, and this manual has a special tutorial exercise for each compiler to familiarize you with the steps needed in performing the experiments. Be sure and go through the tutorial exercise to learn how to download a program to the PLD on your project board. The section *VHDL Software Familiarization* includes the tutorial exercises and shows how to assign pins from the PLD to the inputs and outputs on your project board.

Circuit Wiring

If you are doing one or more of the TTL/CMOS experiments in this manual, you will probably construct it on solderless protoboards ("breadboards") available at Radio Shack and other suppliers of electronic equipment. These boards use #22- or #24-gauge solid core wire for connections, which should have 1/8 inch of the insulation stripped from the ends. Protoboard wiring is not difficult, but it is easy to make a wiring error that is time-consuming to correct. Wires should be kept neat and close to the board. Avoid wiring across the top of integrated circuits (ICs) or using wires much longer than necessary. A circuit that looks like a plate of spaghetti is difficult to follow and worse to troubleshoot.

One useful technique to help avoid errors, especially with larger circuits, is to make a wire list. After assigning pin numbers to the ICs, tabulate each wire in the circuit, showing where it is to be connected and leaving a place to check off when it has been installed. Another method is to cross out each wire on the schematic as it is added to the circuit. Remember the power supply and ground connections, because they frequently are left off logic drawings. Finally, it is useful to "daisy-chain," in the same color, signal wires that are connected to the same electrical point. Daisy-chaining is illustrated in Figure I–1.

Troubleshooting

When the wiring is completed, test the circuit. If it does not work, turn off the power and recheck the wiring. Wiring, rather than a faulty component, is the more likely cause of an error. Check that the proper power and ground are connected to each IC. If the problem is electrical noise, decoupling capacitors between the power supply and ground may help. Good troubleshooting requires the technician to understand clearly the purpose of the circuit and its normal operation. It can begin at the input and proceed toward the output; or it can begin at the output and proceed toward the input; or it can be done by half-splitting the circuit. Whatever procedure you choose, there is no substitute for understanding how the circuit is supposed to behave and applying your knowledge to the observed conditions in a systematic way.

Report Writing

The format of laboratory reports may vary; however, certain requirements are basic to all reports. The

FIGURE I–1

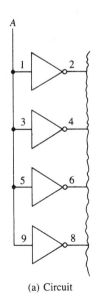

(a) Circuit

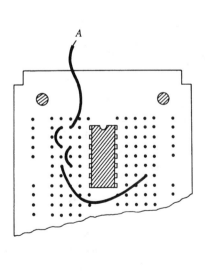

(b) Daisy-chain wiring of *A*

name of the experimenter, date, and purpose of the experiment are entered at the top of each page. All test equipment should be identified by function, manufacturer, and serial number to facilitate reconstruction of the experiment. Test equipment may be identified on a block diagram or circuit drawing rather than an equipment list. References to any books, articles, or other sources that were used in preparing for the experiment are noted. A brief description of the procedure is necessary. The procedure is not a restatement of the instructions in the experiment book but rather is a concise statement about what was done in the experiment. If you write a computer program, the listing may be included in the body of the report if it is a short program, or in an appendix if it is long.

Recording of Data

Data taken in an experiment should be directly recorded in tabular form. When calculations have been applied to data, a sample calculation should be included to indicate clearly what process has been done.

Graphs

A graph is a visual tool that can quickly convey to the reader the relationship between variables. The eye can discern trends in magnitude or slope more easily from graphs than from tabular data. Graphs are constructed with the dependent variable plotted along the horizontal axis (called the abscissa) and the independent variable plotted along the vertical axis (called the ordinate). A smooth curve can be drawn showing the trend of the data. The graph should be labeled on both axes with the variable name and the units used. A figure number should be included as a reference in the written explanation.

Schematics and Block Diagrams

Schematics, block diagrams, waveform drawings, computer listings, and other illustrations are important tools to depict the facts of an experiment. Experiments with circuits need at least a schematic drawing showing the setup and may benefit from other illustrations depending on your purpose. Usually, simple drawings are best; however, sufficient detail must be shown to enable the reader to reconstruct the circuit if necessary.

Figures and Tables

Figures and tables are effective ways to present information. Figures should be kept simple and to the point. Figures should be labeled with a figure number and a brief title. Data tables are useful for presenting data. Usually, data that are presented in a graph or figure should not also be included in a data table. Data tables should be labeled with a table number and short title. The data table should contain enough information to make its meaning clear: The reader should not have to refer to the text.

Suggested Report Format

1. *Title:* A good title must convey the substance of your report by using key words that provide the reader with enough information to decide whether the report should be investigated further.
2. *Contents:* Key headings throughout the report are listed with page numbers.
3. *Abstract:* The abstract is a brief summary of the work, with principal facts and results stated in concentrated form. It is a key factor for a reader to determine if he or she should read further.
4. *Introduction:* The introduction orients your reader to your report. It should briefly state what you did and give the reader a sense of the purpose of the report.
5. *Body of the report:* The body of the report contains the detailed description of what was done. Longer reports should include headings and subheadings. Figures and tables should be labeled and referenced from the body of the report.
6. *Conclusion:* The conclusion summarizes important points or results. It may refer to figures or tables previously discussed in the body of the report to add emphasis to significant points.
7. *References:* References are cited to enable the reader to find information used in developing your report or work that supports your report.

Oscilloscope Guide
Analog and Digital Storage Oscilloscopes

The oscilloscope is the most widely used general-purpose measuring instrument because it presents a graph of the voltage as a function of time in a circuit. Many circuits have specific timing requirements or phase relationships that can be readily measured with a two-channel oscilloscope. The voltage to be measured is converted into a visible display that is presented on a screen.

There are two basic types of oscilloscope: analog and digital. In general, they each have specific characteristics. Analog scopes are the classic "real-time" instruments that show the waveform on a cathode-ray tube (CRT). Digital oscilloscopes are rapidly replacing analog scopes because of their ability to store waveforms and because of measurement automation and many other features such as connections for computers and printers. The storage function is so important that it is usually incorporated in the name, for example, a Digital Storage Oscilloscope (DSO). Some higher end DSOs can emulate an analog scope in a manner that blurs the distinction between the two types. Tektronix, for example, has a line of scopes called DPOs (Digital Phosphor Oscilloscopes) that can characterize a waveform with intensity gradients like an analog scope and gives the benefits of a digital oscilloscope for measurement automation.

Both types of scopes have similar functions and the basic controls are essentially the same for both types (although certain enhanced features are not). In the descriptions that follow, the analog scope is introduced first to familiarize you with basic controls, then a specific digital storage oscilloscope is described (the Tektronix TDS220).

Analog Oscilloscopes

Block Diagram

The analog oscilloscope contains four functional blocks, as illustrated in Figure OG–1. Shown within these blocks are the most important typical controls found on nearly all oscilloscopes. Each of two input channels is connected to the vertical section, which can be set to attenuate or amplify the input signals to provide the proper voltage level to the vertical deflection plates of the CRT. In a dual-trace oscilloscope (the most common type), an electronic switch rapidly switches between channels to send one or the other to the display section. The trigger section samples the input waveform and sends a synchronizing trigger signal at the proper time to the horizontal section. The trigger occurs at the same relative time, thus superimposing each succeeding trace on the previous trace. This action causes the signal to appear to stop, allowing you to examine the signal. The horizontal section contains the time-base (or sweep) generator, which produces a linear ramp, or "sweep," waveform that controls the rate the beam moves across the screen. The horizontal position of the beam is proportional to the time that elapsed from the start of the sweep, allowing the horizontal axis to be calibrated in units of time. The output of the horizontal section is applied to the horizontal

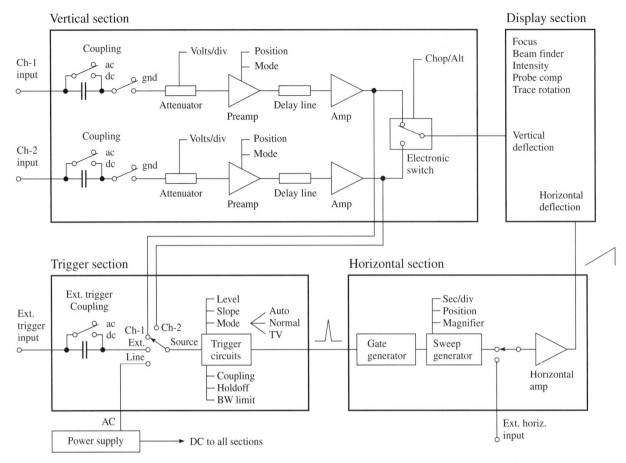

FIGURE OG–1
Block diagram of a basic analog oscilloscope.

deflection plates of the CRT. Finally, the display section contains the CRT and beam controls. It enables the user to obtain a sharp presentation with the proper intensity. The display section usually contains other features such as a probe compensation jack and a beam finder.

Controls

Generally, controls for each section of the oscilloscope are grouped together according to function. Frequently, there are color clues to help you identify groups of controls. Details of these controls are explained in the operator's manual for the oscilloscope; however, a brief description of frequently used controls is given in the following paragraphs. The important controls are shown on the block diagram of Figure OG–1.

Display Controls The display section contains controls for adjusting the electron beam, including FOCUS and INTENSITY controls. FOCUS

and INTENSITY are adjusted for a comfortable viewing level with a sharp focus. The display section may also contain the BEAM FINDER, a control used in combination with the horizontal and vertical POSITION controls to bring the trace on the screen. Another control over the beam intensity is the z-axis input. A control voltage on the z-axis input can be used to turn the beam on or off or adjust its brightness. Some oscilloscopes also include the TRACE ROTATION control in the display section. TRACE ROTATION is used to align the sweep with a horizontal graticule line. This control is usually adjusted with a screwdriver to avoid accidental adjustment. Usually a PROBE COMP connection point is included in the display group of controls. Its purpose is to allow a quick qualitative check on the frequency response of the probe-scope system.

Vertical Controls The vertical controls include the VOLTS/DIV (vertical sensitivity) control and its vernier, the input COUPLING switch, and the vertical POSITION control. There is a duplicate set of these controls for each channel and various switches for selecting channels or other vertical operating modes. The vertical input is connected through a selectable attenuator to a high input impedance dc amplifier. The VOLTS/DIV control on each channel selects a combination of attenuation/gain to determine the vertical sensitivity. For example, a low-level signal will need more gain and less attenuation than a higher level signal. The vertical sensitivity is adjusted in fixed VOLTS/DIV increments to allow the user to make calibrated voltage measurements. In addition, a concentric vernier control is usually provided to allow a continuous range of sensitivity. This knob must be in the detent (calibrated) position to make voltage measurements. The detent position can be felt by the user as the knob is turned because the knob tends to "lock" in the detent position. Some oscilloscopes have a warning light or message when the vernier is not in its detent position.

The input coupling switch is a multiple-position switch that can be set for AC, GND, or DC and sometimes includes a 50 Ω position. The GND position of the switch internally disconnects the signal from the scope and grounds the input amplifier. This position is useful if you want to set a ground reference level on the screen for measuring the dc component of a waveform. The AC and DC positions are high-impedance inputs—typically 1 MΩ shunted by 15 pF of capacitance. High-impedance inputs are useful for general probing at frequencies below about 1 MHz. At higher frequencies, the shunt capacitance can load the signal source excessively, causing measurement error. Attenuating divider probes are good for high-frequency probing because they have very high impedance (typically 10 MΩ) with very low shunt capacitance (as low as 2.5 pF).

The AC position of the coupling switch inserts a series capacitor before the input attenuator, causing dc components of the signal to be blocked. This position is useful if you want to measure a small ac signal riding on top of a large dc signal-power supply ripple, for example. The DC position is used when you want to view both the AC and DC components of a signal. This position is best when viewing digital signals, because the input *RC* circuit forms a differentiating network. The AC position can distort the digital waveform because of this differentiating circuit. The 50 Ω position places an accurate 50 Ω load to ground. This position provides the proper termination for probing in 50 Ω systems and reduces the effect of a variable load, which can occur in high-impedance termination. The effect of source loading must be taken into account when using a 50 Ω input. It is important not to overload the 50 Ω input, be-

cause the resistor is normally rated for only 2 W—implying a maximum of 10 V of signal can be applied to the input.

The vertical POSITION control varies the dc voltage on the vertical deflection plates, allowing you to position the trace anywhere on the screen. Each channel has its own vertical POSITION control, enabling you to separate the two channels on the screen. You can use vertical POSITION when the coupling switch is in the GND position to set an arbitrary level on the screen as ground reference.

There are two types of dual-channel oscilloscope: dual beam and dual trace. A dual-beam oscilloscope has two independent beams in the CRT and independent vertical deflection systems, allowing both signals to be viewed at the same time. A dual-trace oscilloscope has only one beam and one deflection system; it uses electronic switching to show the two signals. Dual-beam oscilloscopes are generally restricted to high-performance research instruments and are much more expensive than dual-trace oscilloscopes. The block diagram in Figure OG–1 is for a typical dual-trace oscilloscope.

A dual-trace oscilloscope has user controls labeled CHOP or ALTERNATE to switch the beam between the channels so that the signals appear to occur simultaneously. The CHOP mode rapidly switches the beam between the two channels at a fixed high speed rate, so the two channels appear to be displayed at the same time. The ALTERNATE mode first completes the sweep for one of the channels and then displays the other channel on the next (or alternate) sweep. When viewing slow signals, the CHOP mode is best because it reduces the flicker that would otherwise be observed. High-speed signals can usually be observed best in ALTERNATE mode to avoid seeing the chop frequency.

Another feature on most dual-trace oscilloscopes is the ability to show the algebraic sum and difference of the two channels. For most measurements, you should have the vertical sensitivity (VOLTS/DIV) on the same setting for both channels. You can use the algebraic sum if you want to compare the balance on push-pull amplifiers, for example. Each amplifier should have identical out-of-phase signals. When the signals are added, the resulting display should be a straight line, indicating balance. You can use the algebraic difference when you want to measure the waveform across an ungrounded component. The probes are connected across the ungrounded component with probe ground connected to circuit ground. Again, the vertical sensitivity (VOLTS/DIV) setting should be the same for each channel. The display will show the algebraic difference in the two signals. The algebraic difference mode also allows you to cancel any unwanted signal that is equal in amplitude and phase and is common to both channels.

Dual-trace oscilloscopes also have an X-Y mode, which causes one of the channels to be graphed on the X-axis and the other channel to be graphed on the Y-axis. This is necessary if you want to change the oscilloscope baseline to represent a quantity other than time. Applications include viewing a transfer characteristic (output voltage as a function of input voltage), swept frequency measurements, or showing Lissajous figures for phase measurements. Lissajous figures are patterns formed when sinusoidal waves drive both channels.

Horizontal Controls The horizontal controls include the SEC/DIV control and its vernier, the horizontal magnifier, and the horizontal POSITION control. In addition, the horizontal section may include delayed sweep controls. The SEC/DIV control sets the sweep speed, which controls how fast the electron beam is moved across the screen. The control has a number of calibrated positions divided into steps of 1–2–5 multiples, which allow you to set the exact time interval at which you view the input signal. For example, if the graticule has 10 horizontal divisions and the SEC/DIV control is set to 1.0 ms/div, then the screen will show a total time of 10 ms. The SEC/DIV control usually has a concentric vernier control that allows you to adjust the sweep speed continuously between the calibrated steps. This control must be in the detent position in order to make calibrated time measurements. Many scopes are also equipped with a horizontal magnifier that affects the time base. The magnifier increases the sweep time by the magnification factor, giving you increased resolution of signal details. Any portion of the original sweep can be viewed using the horizontal POSITION control in conjunction with the magnifier. This control actually speeds the sweep time by the magnification factor and therefore affects the calibration of the time base set on the SEC/DIV control. For example, if you are using a 10× magnifier, the SEC/DIV dial setting must be divided by 10.

Trigger Controls The trigger section is the source of most difficulties when learning to operate an oscilloscope. These controls determine the proper time for the sweep to begin in order to produce a stable display. The trigger controls include the MODE switch, SOURCE switch, trigger LEVEL, SLOPE, COUPLING, and variable HOLDOFF controls. In addition, the trigger section includes a connector for applying an EXTERNAL trigger to start the sweep. Trigger controls may also include HIGH or LOW FREQUENCY REJECT switches and BANDWIDTH LIMITING.

The MODE switch is a multiple-position switch that selects either AUTO or NORMAL (sometimes called TRIGGERED) and may have other positions, such as TV or SINGLE sweep. In the AUTO position, the trigger generator selects an internal oscillator that will trigger the sweep generator as long as no other trigger is available. This mode ensures that a sweep will occur even in the absence of a signal, because the trigger circuits will "free run" in this mode. This allows you to obtain a baseline for adjusting the ground reference level or for adjusting the display controls. In the NORMAL or TRIGGERED mode, a trigger is generated from one of three sources selected by the SOURCE switch: the INTERNAL signal, an EXTERNAL trigger source, or the AC LINE. If you are using the internal signal to obtain a trigger, the normal mode will provide a trigger only if a signal is present and other trigger conditions (level, slope) are met. This mode is more versatile than AUTO as it can provide stable triggering for very low to very high frequency signals. The TV position is used for synchronizing either television fields or lines and SINGLE is used primarily for photographing the display.

The trigger LEVEL and SLOPE controls are used to select a specific point on either the rising or falling edge of the input signal for generating a trigger. The trigger SLOPE control determines which edge will generate a trigger, whereas the LEVEL control allows the user to determine the voltage level on the input signal that will start the sweep circuits.

The SOURCE switch selects the trigger source—either from the CH-1 signal, the CH-2 signal, an EXTERNAL trigger source, or the AC LINE. In the CH-1 position, a sample of the signal from channel-1 is used to start the sweep. In the EXTERNAL position, a time-related external signal is used for triggering. The external trigger can be coupled with either AC or DC COUPLING. The trigger signal can be coupled with AC COUPLING if the trigger signal is riding on a dc voltage. DC COUPLING is used if the triggers occur at a frequency of less than about 20 Hz. The LINE position causes the trigger to be derived from the ac power source. This synchronizes the sweep with signals that are related to the power line frequency.

The variable HOLDOFF control allows you to exclude otherwise valid triggers until the holdoff time has elapsed. For some signals, particularly complex waveforms or digital pulse trains, obtaining a stable trigger can be a problem. This can occur when one or more valid trigger points occurs before the signal repetition time. If every event that the trigger circuits qualified as a trigger were allowed to start a sweep, the display could appear to be unsynchronized. By adjusting the variable HOLDOFF control, the trigger point can be made to coincide with the signal-repetition point.

Oscilloscope Probes

Signals should always be coupled into an oscilloscope through a probe. A probe is used to pick off a signal and couple it to the input with a minimum loading effect on the circuit under test. Various types of probes are provided by manufacturers, but the most common type is a 10 : 1 attenuating probe that is shipped with most general-purpose oscilloscopes. These probes have a short ground lead that should be connected to a nearby circuit ground point to avoid oscillation and power line interference. The ground lead makes a mechanical connection to the test circuit and passes the signal through a flexible, shielded cable to the oscilloscope. The shielding helps protect the signal from external noise pickup.

Begin any session with the oscilloscope by checking the probe compensation on each channel. Adjust the probe for a flat-topped square wave while observing the scope's calibrator output. This is a good signal to check the focus and intensity and verify trace alignment. Check the front-panel controls for the type of measurement you are going to make. Normally, the variable controls (VOLTS/DIV and SEC/DIV) should be in the calibrated (detent) position. The vertical coupling switch is usually placed in the DC position unless the waveform you are interested in has a large dc offset. Trigger holdoff should be in the minimum position unless it is necessary to delay the trigger to obtain a stable sweep.

Digital Storage Oscilloscopes

Block Diagram

The digital storage oscilloscope (DSO) uses a fast analog-to-digital converter (ADC) on each channel (typically two or four channels) to convert the input voltage into numbers that can be stored in a memory. The digitizer samples the input at a uniform rate called the sample rate; the optimum sample rate depends on the speed of the signal. The process of digitizing the waveform has many advantages for accuracy, triggering, viewing hard to see events, and

for waveform analysis. Although the method of acquiring and displaying the waveform is quite different than analog scopes, the basic controls on the instrument are similar.

A block diagram of the basic DSO is shown in Figure OG–2. As you can see, functionally, the block diagram is like that of the analog scope. As in the analog oscilloscope, the vertical and horizontal controls include position and sensitivity that are used to set up the display for the proper scaling.

Specifications Important parameters with DSOs include the resolution, maximum digitizing rate, and the size of the acquisition memory as well as the available analysis options. The resolution is determined by the number of bits digitized by the ADC. A low resolution DSO may use only six bits (one part in 64). A typical DSO may use 8 bits, with each channel sampled simultaneously. High-end DSOs may use 12 bits. The maximum digitizing rate is important to capture rapidly changing signals; typically the maximum rate is 1 GSample/s. The size of the memory determines the length of time the sample can be taken; it is also important in certain waveform measurement functions.

Triggering One useful feature of digital storage oscilloscopes is their ability to capture waveforms either before or after the trigger event. Any segment of the waveform, either before or after the trigger event, can be captured for analysis. **Pretrigger capture** refers to acquisition of data that occurs *before* a trigger event. This is possible because the data is digitized continuously, and a trigger event can be selected to stop the data collection at some point in the sample window. With pretrigger capture, the scope can be triggered on the fault condition, and the signals that preceded the fault condition can be observed. For example, troubleshooting an occasional glitch in a system is one of the most difficult troubleshooting jobs; by employing pretrigger capture, trouble leading to the fault can be analyzed. A similar application of pretrigger capture is in material failure studies where the events leading to failure are most interesting, but the failure itself causes the scope triggering.

Besides pretrigger capture, posttriggering can also be set to capture data that occurs some time after a trigger event. The record that is acquired can begin after the trigger event by some amount of time or by a specific number of events as determined by a counter. A low-level response to a strong stimulus signal is an example of when posttriggering is useful.

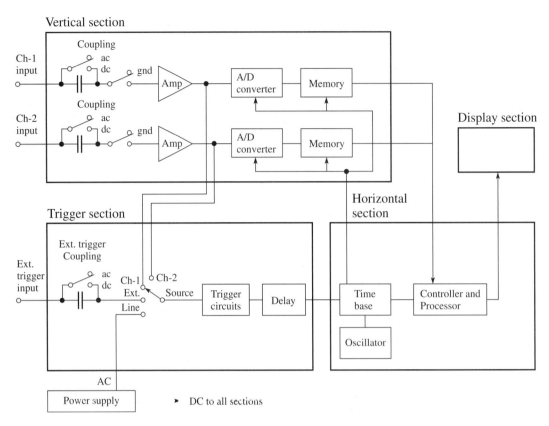

FIGURE OG–2
Block diagram of a basic digital storage oscilloscope.

A Specific DSO Because of the large number of functions that can be accomplished by even basic DSOs, manufacturers have largely replaced the plethora of controls with menu options, similar to computer menus and detailed displays that show the controls as well as measurement parameters. CRTs have been replaced by liquid crystal displays, similar to those on laptop computers. As an example, the display for a Tektronix TDS220 digital storage oscilloscope is shown in Figure OG–3. Although this is a basic scope, the information available to the user right at the display is impressive.

The numbers on the display in Figure OG–3 refer to the following parameters:

1. Icon display shows acquisition mode.

    ∿⊓∿ Sample mode

    ∿⊓⊦ Peak detect mode

    ⎍⎍ Average mode

2. Trigger status shows if there is an adequate trigger source or if the acquisition is stopped.

3. Marker shows horizontal trigger position. This also indicates the horizontal position since the Horizontal Position control actually moves the trigger position horizontally.
4. Trigger position display shows the difference (in time) between the center graticule and the trigger position. Center screen equals zero.
5. Marker shows trigger level.
6. Readout shows numeric value of the trigger level.
7. Icon shows selected trigger slope for edge triggering.
8. Readout shows trigger source used for triggering.
9. Readout shows window zone timebase setting.
10. Readout shows main timebase setting.
11. Readout shows channels 1 and 2 vertical scale factors.
12. Display area shows on-line messages momentarily.
13. On-screen markers show the ground reference points of the displayed waveforms. No marker indicates the channel is not displayed.

10

The display area for a Tektronix TDS220
oscilloscope (courtesy of Tektronix, Inc.).

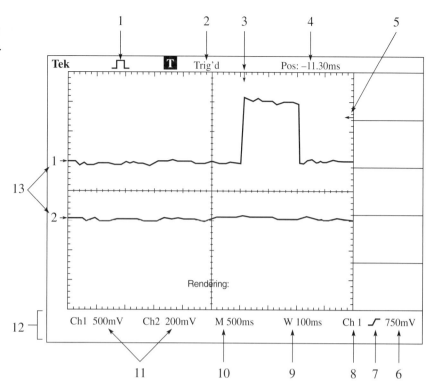

A front view of the TDS220 is shown in Figure
OG–4. Operation is similar to that of an analog
scope except more of the functions are menu controlled; in the TDS220, 12 different menus are accessed to select various controls and options. For
example, the MEASURE function brings up a menu
that the user can select from five automated measurements including voltage, frequency, period, and
averaging.

FIGURE OG–4
The Tektronix TDS220 oscilloscope.
(Copyright ©Tektronix, Inc. Reproduced
with permission.)

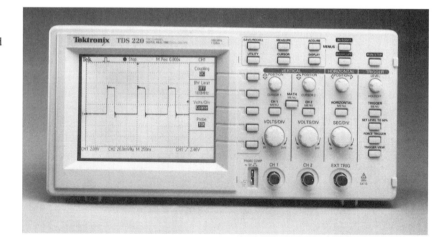

Project Board Familiarization

Materials Needed

☐ Project board
☐ Interface cables for selected project board
☐ Altera or Xilinx VHDL development tools to support your specific project board PLD
☐ PC running Windows 98, NT, or XP. Other operating systems may be problematic.

Caution! Many board features are tied to a voltage. It is important that you do not assign an output on the PLD to an on-board input feature; otherwise you can damage your board. Pin assignments should be double-checked before connecting voltage to the PLD.

Because each board is different, you will need to look for your specific board on all referenced figures and tables. The organization of figures and tables includes the board name at the end of each version of the same table. Be sure to look for this name when using this guide.

---

1. Project Board Overview

This manual supports five project boards; key features of each are shown in Figure PB–1. You will need to refer only to the specific board you are using throughout this section. Each project board has certain common characteristics. The project boards include a variety of inputs including pushbutton switches, DIP switches, and toggle switches. In addition, each board has a connector to interface it to a personal computer (PC) for easy programming. The project boards also include outputs such as an array of light-emitting diodes and seven-segment displays, which are assigned within the program to represent certain outputs. Unassigned LEDs and seven-segment displays should always be ignored, as they may show spurious results from earlier programs. This guide provides summary information for quick reference of the unique features for each board; detailed specifications are provided by the manufacturer in the user manual.

All boards use an erasable CPLD (Complex Programmable Logic Device). CPLDs are large versions of PLDs (Programmable Logic Devices). CPLDs can be programmed with VHDL to implement the logic that formerly was done with fixed-function integrated circuits. The CPLDs are not erased when power is removed and can be disconnected from the PC once programmed for operation.

Details of each of the boards that are supported by this lab manual are included in this section. In addition, installation and checkout of the boards is discussed. These boards are as follows:

1. PLDT-1
2. PLDT-2
3. PLDT-3
4. Altera University Program board (referred to as the Altera project board)
5. DeVry University eSOC board (referred to as the DeVry eSOC)

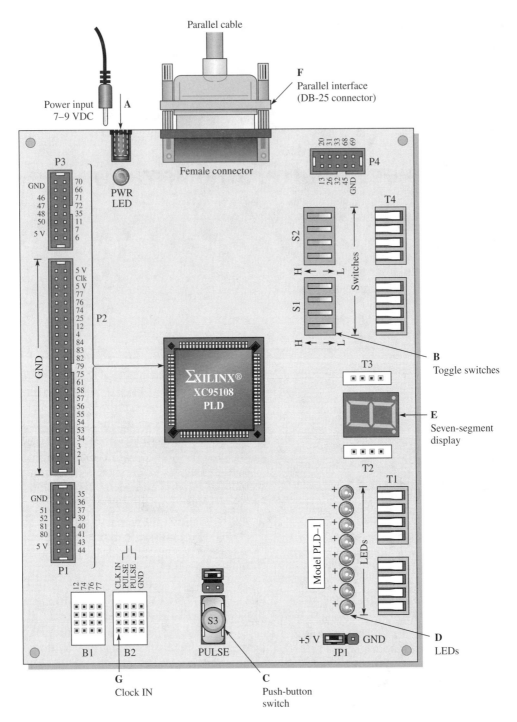

FIGURE PB–1
PLDT-1

14

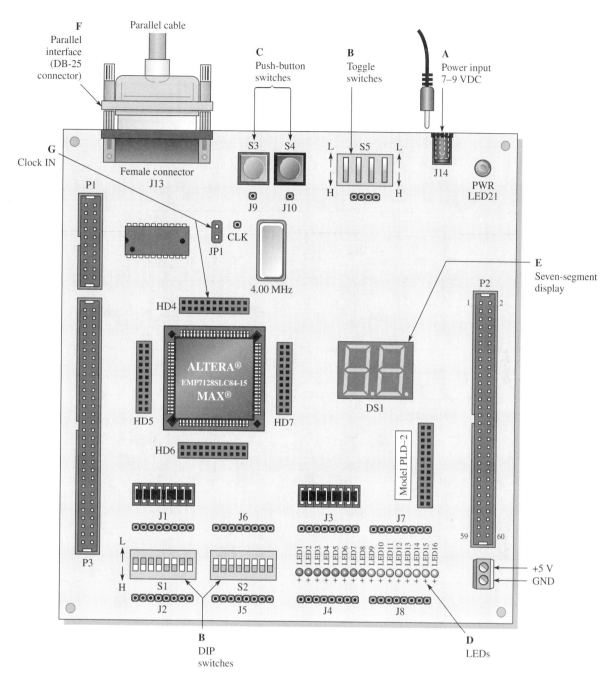

F
Parallel
interface
(DB-25
connector)

Parallel cable

C
Push-button
switches

B
Toggle
switches

A
Power input
7–9 VDC

G
Clock IN

Female connector
J13

S3   S4

J9   J10

L ↕ H   S5   L ↕ H

J14

PWR
LED21

P1

CLK
JP1

4.00 MHz

HD4

E
Seven-segment
display

P2
1   2

ALTERA®
EMP7128SLC84-15
MAX®

HD5   HD7

HD6

DS1

Model PLD–2

J1   J6   J3   J7

L ↕ H

S1   S2

P3

J2   J5

LED1 LED2 LED3 LED4 LED5 LED6 LED7 LED8 LED9 LED10 LED11 LED12 LED13 LED14 LED15 LED16

J4   J8

59   60

+5 V
GND

B
DIP
switches

D
LEDs

FIGURE PB–1
PLDT-2

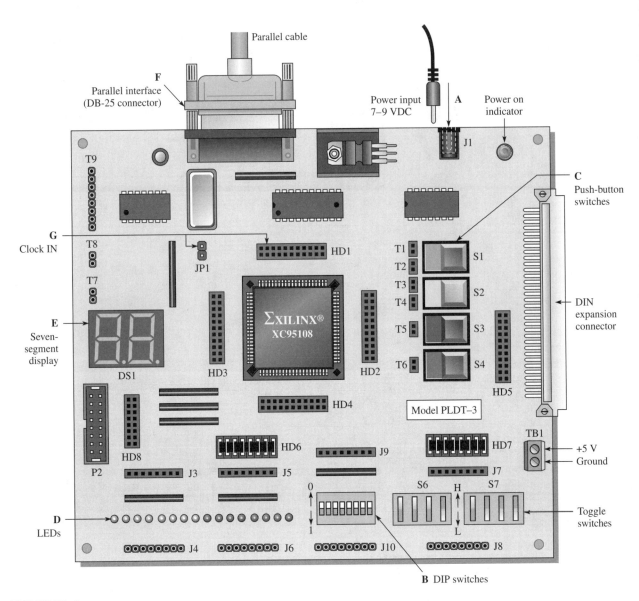

Parallel cable

F
Parallel interface
(DB-25 connector)

Power input
7–9 VDC

A

Power on
indicator

J1

T9

G
Clock IN

T8

JP1

HD1

T7

E
Seven-
segment
display

DS1

HD3

ΣXILINX®
XC95108

HD2

C
Push-button
switches

T1
T2
T3
T4
T5
T6

S1

S2

S3

S4

DIN
expansion
connector

HD5

Model PLDT–3

HD4

P2

HD8

HD6

J9

J3

J5

HD7

J7

TB1

+5 V
Ground

0

1

S6

H

L

S7

D
LEDs

J4

J6

J10

J8

Toggle
switches

B DIP switches

FIGURE PB–1
PLDT-3

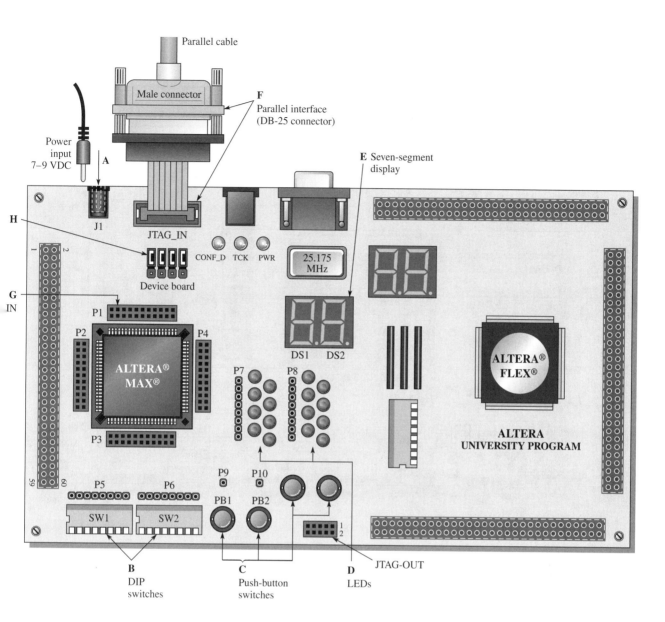

Parallel cable

Male connector

F Parallel interface (DB-25 connector)

Power input 7–9 VDC

A

E Seven-segment display

H

J1

JTAG_IN

CONF_D   TCK   PWR

25.175 MHz

Device board

G
IN

P1

P2

ALTERA® MAX®

P4

DS1   DS2

P7   P8

P3

ALTERA® FLEX®

ALTERA UNIVERSITY PROGRAM

P9   P10

P5   P6

PB1   PB2

SW1   SW2

1
2

JTAG-OUT

B
DIP switches

C
Push-button switches

D
LEDs

FIGURE PB–1

Altera Project Board. The FLEX side of this board is not used in this manual.

17

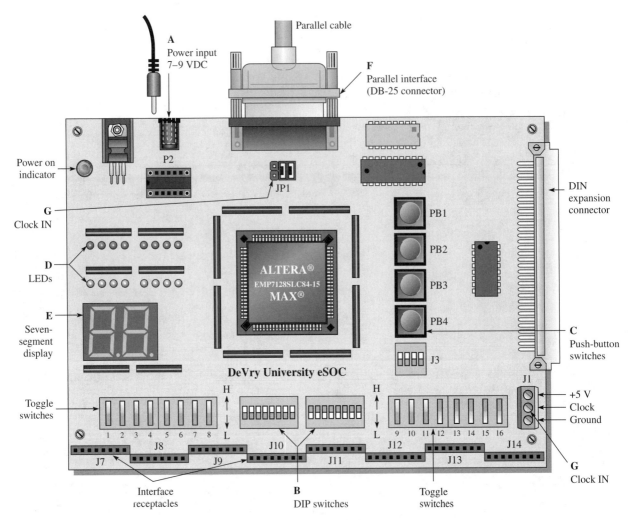

Parallel cable

A
Power input
7–9 VDC

F
Parallel interface
(DB-25 connector)

Power on
indicator

P2

JP1

G
Clock IN

DIN
expansion
connector

D
LEDs

PB1

PB2

PB3

PB4

E
Seven-
segment
display

ALTERA®
EMP7128SLC84-15
MAX®

J3

C
Push-button
switches

DeVry University eSOC

Toggle
switches

H
↑
↓
L

H
↑
↓
L

J1

+5 V
Clock
Ground

1 2 3 4 5 6 7 8

J8

J10

J11

9 10 11 12 13 14 15 16

J12

J14

G
Clock IN

J7

J9

J13

Interface
receptacles

B
DIP switches

Toggle
switches

FIGURE PB–1
DeVry eSOC

18

2. The Project Board Power Supply

Power to the project board is supplied by a 9-volt dc external power supply. Note that the center pin of the power supply connector is positive for all listed project boards. The 9-volt dc external power supply connects to the project board. See Figure PB–1 item A for project board input power location. It is critical that power supplied to the board not exceed the manufacturer's recommended voltage (+9 V), so it is a good idea to test the power supply input before connecting it to the board.

Except for the Altera project board, power and ground can be taken from each board on a specially designated connector to operate a low-current load. On the Altera project board, +5 V is available on pin 4 and ground is available on pin 2 of the **JTAG out** connector. Figure PB–1 shows the location that power and ground can be taken from the various boards. External power is required only in Experiments 14 and 15.

3. Switch Inputs

3a. Toggle/Dip Switches

Switch modules are supplied for applications requiring toggle and DIP switch inputs. See Table PB–1 for PLD pin access to the individual toggle switches. Figure PB–1 shows the board layout. See reference item B on the board layout for specific project toggle/DIP switch locations.

NOTE: Switch S2 on the PLDT-2 and switches SW1 and SW2 on the Altera project board can be accessed by using a jumper wire between the selected switch input and the desired PLD input pin.

TABLE PB–1 PLDT-1
Toggle switches S1 and S2.

Switch	PLD Pin
1	6
2	7
3	11
4	5
5	72
6	71
7	66
8	70

TABLE PB–1 PLDT-2
DIP switch S1.

Switch S1	PLD Pin
1	34
2	33
3	36
4	35
5	37
6	40
7	39
8	41

TABLE PB–1 PLDT-3
Toggle switches S6 and S7.

Switch	PLD Pin
S6-1	11
S6-2	7
S6-3	6
S6-4	5
S7-5	4
S7-6	3
S7-7	2
S7-8	1

TABLE PB–1 Altera Project Board
DIP switches SW1 and SW2.

Switches provide logic signal levels at P5 and P6.
SW1 ⟶ P5
SW2 ⟶ P6

TABLE PB–1 DeVRY eSOC

Selector Switch	J4 Status	PLD Pin	Selector Switch	J5 Status	PLD Pin
1	ON	50	9	ON	60
2	ON	51	10	ON	61
3	ON	52	11	ON	62
4	ON	53	12	ON	63
5	ON	54	13	ON	64
6	ON	55	14	ON	65
7	ON	56	15	ON	66
8	ON	57	16	ON	67

NOTE: Set selected switches on J4 and J5 to OFF for external access to listed PLD.

TABLE PB–2 PLDT-1
Push-button switch S3.

JP2 Jumper Setting	PLD Pin 10 Pulse Edge
1	falling
2	rising

TABLE PB–2 PLDT-2
Push-button switches S3 and S4.

Access to push-button switches S3 and S4 is J9 and J10.
S3 ⟶ J9
S4 ⟶ J10

TABLE PB–2 PLDT-3
Push-button switches S1 through S4.

S1 ⟶ T1 ↓ T2 ↑
S2 ⟶ T3 ↓ T4 ↑
S3 ⟶ T5 ↓
S4 ⟶ T6 ↑

TABLE PB–2 Altera Project Board
Push-button switches PB1 and PB2.

PB1 ⟶ P9
PB2 ⟶ P10

TABLE PB–2 DeVRY eSOC

Push Button	J3 Switch	PLD Pin
PB1	1	70
PB2	2	73
PB3	3	74
PB4	4	75

NOTE: Set selected switches on J3 to OFF for external access to listed PLD pins.

3b. Push-button switches

For applications requiring manual input pulses, push-button switches are provided on all boards. The number of switches, nomenclature, and specific operation is different for each board. Only the PLDT-1 and the DeVry eSoc boards provide direct access to the PLD. Other boards require a jumper from the push-button contact switch to a header block. Table PB–2 summarizes switch access. See the board layout in Figure PB–1, reference item C, for the location of push-button switches.

4. Timing Inputs

4a. Internal Clock Oscillator

A crystal oscillator is provided on the boards for high-speed clock applications. A 4 MHz clock is available through pin 9 of the Xilinx PLD for the PLDT-1 and PLDT-3 project boards. A 4 MHz oscillator is available to the Altera MAX PLD at pin 83 for the PLDT-2 and DeVry eSOC boards. The Altera project board uses a 25.175 MHz clock also located on PLD pin 83.

4b. Pulse Generator (CLK IN)

A TTL compatible pulse generator (0 to 5 V max) can be connected to the PLD. The photographs on the back cover show a typical pulse generator connection for each project board. The procedure for connecting the pulse generator is as follows:

- PLDT-1: The TTL level pulse generator can be brought in at **CLK IN** on input **B2** with PLD access at pin 67. (See reference G on Figure PB–1 for the PLDT-1 board).
- PLDT-2: Remove jumper **JP1** to allow the TTL level pulse generator to be supplied at PLD pin 83 on HD4. (See reference G on Figure PB–1 for the PLDT-2 board).
- PLDT-3: Remove jumper **JP1** to allow the TTL level pulse generator to be supplied at PLD pin 9 on HD1. (See reference G on Figure PB–1 for the PLDT-3 board).
- Altera project board: A TTL level pulse generator can be applied directly to PLD pin 9 on P1. (See reference G on Figure PB–1 for the Altera project board).
- DeVry eSOC: Remove jumper 1 at **JP1** to allow a TTL level pulse generator to be supplied at PLD clock input at J1. (See reference G on Figure PB–1 for the DeVry eSOC).

5. Output Indicators

LEDs and seven-segment displays are provided as logic indicators. There are two conventions used to define if an LED or seven-segment display is ON or OFF. Some boards use an active-HIGH convention for outputs; that is, LEDs and seven-segment displays are turned on with a logic 1. Boards with active-HIGH outputs are the PLDT-1, PLDT-2, and PLDT-3 boards and the Altera project board. All programs written out in this manual are shown with this active-HIGH convention. These programs are also given exactly as listed on the CD packaged with this manual in the folder labeled *Active High Outputs*. You may use programs from this folder to save typing time entering programs into the text editor.

Another convention is to use an active-LOW convention for outputs where LEDs and seven-segment displays are turned on with a logic 0. The DeVry board is in this category. If you are using an active-LOW board (DeVry), a small program change is necessary to make program outputs correspond to the active-HIGH convention. The changes have all been made in the CD version of programs packaged with this manual in the folder labeled *Active Low Outputs*. If your board is in this category, use programs on the CD from this folder, and your results will be the same as the programs listed in the manual. You will see a small difference in the listings from those given in the manual to reverse the output logic.

5a. LEDs

LEDs are used as logic indicators on all boards. If you have loaded the program from the proper folder (*Active High* or *Active Low*), you will be able to read LEDs that are ON as a logic 1 in all cases and LEDs that are OFF as a logic 0 in all cases.

In the experiments, only the LEDs that have pin access to the PLD are used except in the case of the Altera project board. The Altera project board requires a jumper from the appropriate output pin on the PLD header block to a pin on P7 or P8.

The LEDs and their PLD pin access are listed in Table PB–3. See the appropriate board drawing in Figure PB–1, reference item D, for the locations of LEDs.

5b. Seven-Segment Displays

Seven-segment displays are used to indicate the numbers 0–9 and certain other characters. If you have

TABLE PB–3 PLDT-1

LED	PLD Pin
1	44
2	43
3	41
4	40
5	39
6	37
7	36
8	35

TABLE PB–3 PLDT-2

LED	PLD Pin
1	44
2	45
3	46
4	48
5	49
6	50
7	51
8	52

TABLE PB–3 PLDT-3

LED	PLD Pin
1	35
2	36
3	37
4	39
5	40
6	41
7	43
8	44

TABLE PB–3 Altera Project Board

LEDs are lit by providing a logic HIGH at P7 and P8. There is no direct access to the PLD pins.

LED 1–8 ⟶ P7

LED 9–16 ⟶ P8

TABLE PB–3 DeVRY eSOC

LED	PLD Pin	LED	PLD Pin
1	4	9	16
2	5	10	17
3	8	11	18
4	9	12	20
5	10	13	21
6	11	14	22
7	12	15	24
8	15	16	25

TABLE PB–4 PLDT-1
7-segment display.

Segment	Pin
A	15
B	18
C	23
D	21
E	19
F	14
G	17
DP	24

TABLE PB–4 PLDT-2
7-segment display.

Segment	DS1 Pin L	DS1 Pin R
A	58	69
B	60	70
C	61	73
D	63	74
E	64	76
F	65	75
G	67	77
DP	68	79

TABLE PB–4 PLDT-3
7-segment display.

Segment	DS1 Pin L	DS1 Pin R
A	57	15
B	58	18
C	61	23
D	62	21
E	63	19
F	65	14
G	66	17
DP	67	24

TABLE PB–4 Altera Project Board
7-segment display.

Segment	Max Digit Pin L	Max Digit Pin R
A	58	69
B	60	70
C	61	73
D	63	74
E	64	76
F	65	75
G	67	77
DP	68	79

TABLE PB–4 DeVRY eSOC
7-segment display.

Segment	7-seg Pin L	7-seg Pin R
A	31	45
B	30	44
C	29	41
D	28	37
E	27	36
F	34	48
G	33	40
DP	35	49

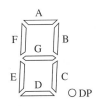

FIGURE PB–2
Seven-segment display.

loaded the program from the proper folder (*Active High* or *Active Low*), you will be able to read seven-segment displays correctly. Figure PB–2 shows the segment assignments. All project boards except the PLDT-1 board have dual seven-segment displays; the PLDT-1 board has a single display. See Table PB–4 for PLD pin access for each of the seven segments (a–g) and the decimal point (dp). See Figure PB–1, reference item E, for location of project board seven segment display(s).

6. External Board Interface

PLD pin access as well as +5V DC power and ground are available through ribbon connectors located on the project boards. Only two of the experiments in this manual use external signals. Some important information is listed here for each board about the external interface and related matters.

- PLDT-1: Only one connector is required in the experiments for this board. The only pin assignments that you will use are given in Table PB–5. Other pins and connectors are listed in the user manual.
- PLDT-2: Header blocks are available on the board for connecting external signals to the PLD via jumper wires, so the External Board Interface connector is not needed. Pin assignments are listed in the user manual and not repeated here.
- PLDT-3: Header blocks are available on the board for connecting external signals to the PLD via jumper wires, so the External Board Interface connector is not needed. Pin assignments are listed in the user manual and not repeated here.
- Altera project board: Header blocks are available on the board for connecting external signals to the PLD via jumper wires, so the External Board Interface connector is not needed. Pin assignments are listed in the user manual and not repeated here.

TABLE PB–5 PLDT-1
Connector P2.

P2 Pin	PLD Pin
17	57
19	58
21	61
23	75

TABLE PB–5 DeVRY eSOC
Edge connectors.

Connector	PLD Pin
J11-1	50
J11-2	51
J11-3	52
J11-4	54
J11-5	55
J11-6	56
J11-7	57
J11-8	58
J12-1	60
J12-2	61
J12-3	63
J12-4	64
J12-5	65
J12-6	67
J12-7	68
J12-8	69

The Altera project board does *not* have ribbon connectors installed at the factory. It has header connectors P1 through P4 located next to the Altera MAX device.

- DeVry eSOC: Only one connector is required in the experiments for this board. The only pin assignments that you will use are given in Table PB-5. Other pins and connectors are listed in the user manual. The 16 DIP switches in J4 and J5 correspond to the 16 toggle switches S1–S16, reading left to right on both. For external PLD access on the edge connectors J11 and J12, corresponding DIP switches should be moved to the OFF position. The toggle switch will then be removed from the circuit.

7. Oscilloscope

You will need to connect an oscilloscope to the boards for several of the experiments. Generally, you will want to look at the input signal and one (or more) output signals. The photographs on the back cover show a typical oscilloscope hookup for each project board.

> *Caution! Make sure all grounds are connected together to the common board ground. A "dangling" scope probe ground can damage a board. Connect the scope through a small jumper wire to header blocks or other large pins; do not probe directly on the PLD pins. The tiny pins on the PLD can easily be shorted by a scope probe, damaging the board.*

8. Connecting the Project Board to the PC

Each board has a parallel cable supplied by the manufacturer.

Connect the parallel cable to the parallel port of a personal computer and to connector J2 on the project board. See Figure PB–1 item F for location of parallel connector J2 on your particular project board.

Connect the 7–9 volt dc external power supply to the appropriate connector. See Figure PB–1, item A, for location of power connector. It is a good idea to verify that the dc power supply meets the manufacturer's specification prior to connecting it for the first time. If the voltage is too high, the board may be damaged by excessive heat. After checking the voltage, apply power to the board and to the personal computer.

> **Altera Project Board Users Only**
>
> *The Altera project board has two programmable devices; this lab manual uses only the EMP7128SLC84-7. On-board jumpers must be set to enable the Altera MAX+PLUS II software to access this area of the project board. Refer to item H in Figure PB–1, Altera project board, on page 17. The jumpers are located below the JTAG_IN connector.*
>
> *Connect the ByteBlaster parallel port download cable to the Altera project board at the JTAG_IN connector. See Figure PB–1, Item F.*

VHDL Software Familiarization

This section includes two tutorials that introduce Xilinx and Altera software. The first tutorial is for the Xilinx WebPACK Project Navigator. The second tutorial is for the Altera MAX+Plus II PLD Programming tools. The Xilinx WebPACK Project Navigator supports the PLDT-1 and PLDT-3 project boards. The Altera MAX+PLUS II supports the PLDT-2, the Altera project board, and the DeVry eSOC project board. Choose the appropriate tutorial (Xilinx or Altera) for your board. In the tutorial, you will write a simple VHDL program, and then you will download it to the project board. Finally you will test the program.

The Xilinx and Altera software packages are considered to be development tools. They are available through Xilinx and Altera at their respective websites. The Xilinx website address is http:\\www.xilinx.com. The Altera website is http:\\www.altera.com. You will need to obtain a student software license for your computer from the Xilinx or Altera website to operate the software.

Before doing one of the tutorials, you will need to connect the project board to a personal computer as described in *Project Board Familiarization* in section 8 "Connecting the Project Board to the PC." You will also need to load the appropriate software on your PC.

Important! PLD and pin numbers shown in the tutorials that follow may differ depending on the specific board you are using.

Xilinx Software Tutorial

Programming the project board using Xilinx WebPACK Project Navigator

The purpose of this tutorial is to cause toggle switch S1 to control LED1 on the project board.

Step 1. Click **Start** from the MS Windows Desktop.

Step 2. Select **Programs** from the MS Windows Start menu.

Step 3. Select **Xilinx Webpack** from the Programs menu.

Step 4. Select **WebPack Project Navigator** from the Xilinx WebPACK option. The project navigator window will open as shown in Figure SF-X–1. From this window, all VHDL programs will be developed, compiled, and downloaded to the project board.

Step 5. From the **File** menu, select **New Project.** Enter the project name *Example1* under Project Name. Under Project Device Options, select the **XC9500 CPLDs** Device Family, and select the **XC95108 PC84** device used by the Xilinx PLD from Device. Select **XST VHDL** for the Design Flow. With the data entered, your menu screen should look similar to Figure SF-X–2.

Step 6. Select **OK** from the New Project window when all data is entered. Following this, the window shown in Figure SF-X–3

FIGURE SF-X–1

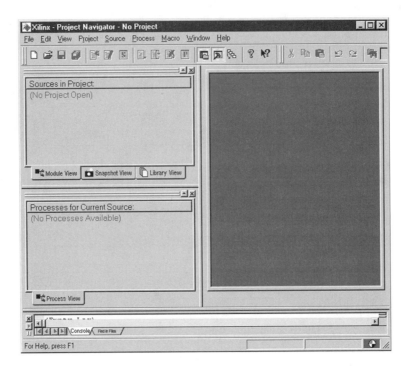

FIGURE SF-X–2

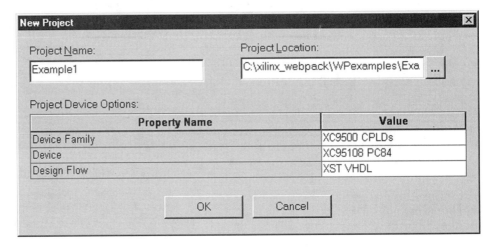

appears. Notice that the chip and development language (VHDL) appear in the "Sources in Project" selection box. Click to highlight the XC95108 PC84-XST VHDL selection from the Sources in Project window. Once highlighted, select **New Source** from Project on the project navigator menu bar.

Step 7. A window labeled **New** will open automatically as shown in Figure SF-X–4. Enter *Example1* in the File Name text box and highlight **VHDL Module**. Check the **Add to project** check box and click **Next.**

Step 8. In this Example1 program, there will be one input and one output. Name the input port "Switch1" and set the direction to "in". Name the output port LED1 and set the direction to "out". Do not set the MSB or LSB. Figure SF-X–5 shows the named input and output ports.

Step 9. Click Next from the Define VHDL Source window. The VHDL compiler will use this

26

FIGURE SF-X–3

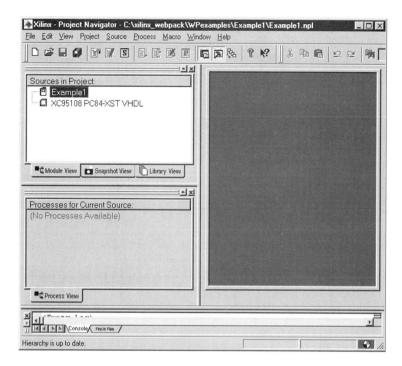

FIGURE SF-X–4

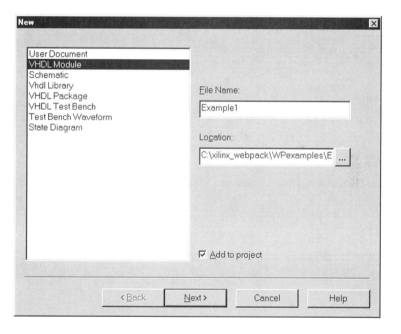

information to create a skeleton of the VHDL application program for you automatically. Figure SF-X–6 shows the information about the VHDL application before generating the program skeleton. This program can later be modified in the text editor as desired.

Step 10. Select Finish from the New Source Information window to cause the Xilinx VHDL compiler to create the VHDL program skeleton for the Example1 program. Figure SF-X–7 shows the project manager and the skeleton program.

Step 11. Enter the Example1 program in the program navigator window. The skeleton program can be modified as needed. Figure SF-X–8 shows the complete program for this sample application. Notice

27

FIGURE SF-X–5

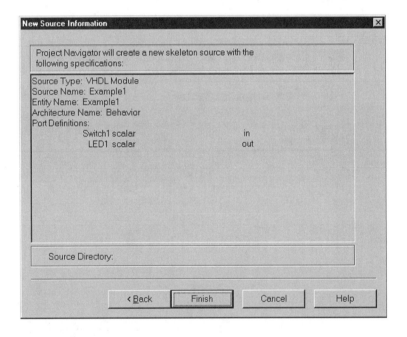

that two unused library definitions have been removed and an assignment line has been added.

Step 12. Assign Pins to the PLD. From the **Processes for Current Source** selection box expand **Design Entry Utilities** and **User Constraints**. Then select **Assign Pins** as shown in Figure SF-X–9. If you made a typing error, you will need to correct it and right click the **Assign pins** to select **Rerun**.

Figure SF-X–10 shows the window that will appear with a graphic representation of the PLD and a list of inputs and outputs that apply to the application.

Expand the **Input** and **Output** folders. PLD pins will be assigned by clicking and dragging the input and output identifiers label to the PLD graphic pins and then clicking on the pin that you wish to assign the label. Assign the input and

FIGURE SF-X–7

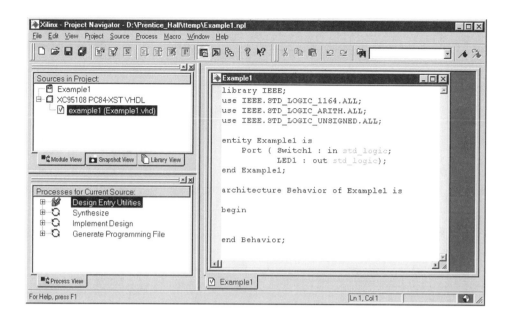

FIGURE SF-X–8

```
Example1                                    _ □ ×
library IEEE;
use IEEE.STD_LOGIC_1164.ALL;

entity Example1 is
     Port ( Switch1 : in std_logic;
            LED1 : out std_logic);
end Example1;

architecture Behavior of Example1 is
begin
    LED1 <= Switch1;
end Behavior;
```

FIGURE SF-X–9

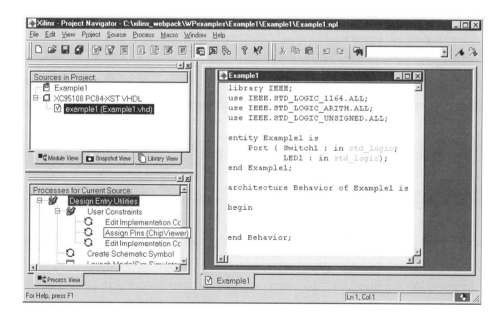

29

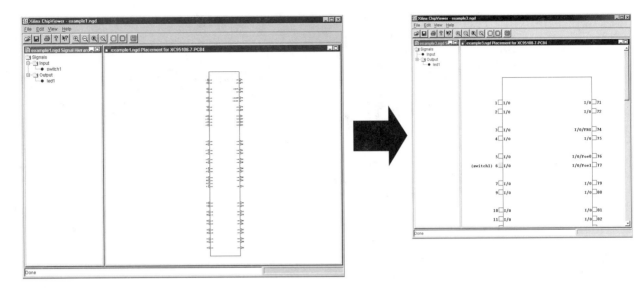

FIGURE SF-X–10
PIN numbers may be different from those shown.

output pins for your particular board as follows:

1. **PLDT-1:** Assign Switch1 to PLD pin 6. Assign LED1 to PLD pin 44.
2. **PLDT-3:** Assign Switch1 to PLD pin 11. Assign LED1 to PLD pin 35.

Select **Zoom** from **View** to enlarge the graphic if needed. Refer to *Project Board Familiarization* for project board access to switches and LEDs. Figure SF-X–11 shows the completed pin assignments for this programming project.

From **File** select **Save** to save the program pin assignments. From **File** select **Exit** to exit the pin assignment window.

Step 13. Compile the VHDL project. From the **Process for Current Source** window, click **Synthesize.** (Note: You may need to respond to a **Reset** prompt by selecting **Reset**).

Next double-click **Implement Design,** followed by **Generate Programming File.** Expand Generate Programming File to reveal **Configure Device (IMPACT)** and double-click it. See Figure SF-X–12.

Step 14. Right click on the PLD icon that appears in the IMPACT window (see Figure SF-

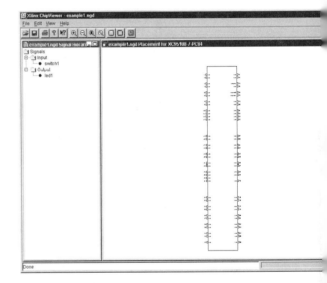

FIGURE SF-X–11

X–13) and select **Program.** Accept defaults by clicking **OK** in the **Program Options** window. See Figure SF-X–14.

Figure SF-X–15 shows the response to a successful PLD load after the loading process has completed. Congratulations, you have just created and implemented your first VHDL application. Move toggle switch 1 and observe LED1 to confirm that your program works.

FIGURE SF-X–12

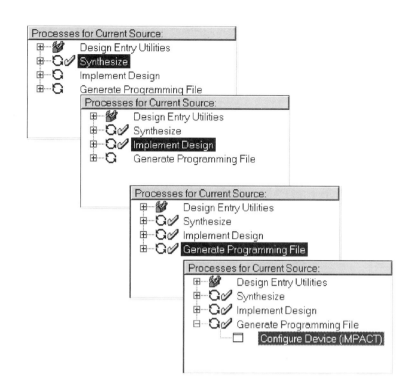

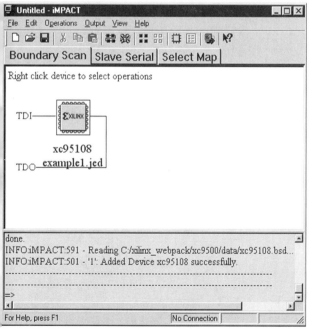

FIGURE SF-X–13

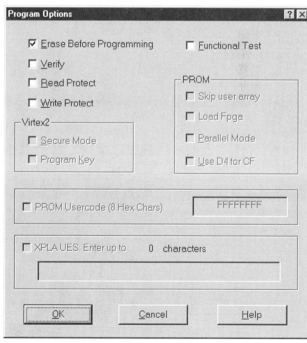

FIGURE SF-X–14

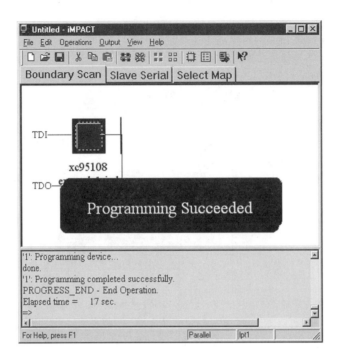

Altera Software Tutorial

Programming the project board using Altera MAX+Plus II Manager

The purpose of this tutorial is to cause toggle switch S1 to control LED1 on the project board.

Step 1. Click **Start** from the MS Windows Desktop.

Step 2. Select **Programs** from the MS Windows Start menu.

Step 3. Select **Max+plus II 10.X BASELINE** from the Programs menu.

Step 4. Select **Max+plus II 10.X BASELINE** from the Max+plus II 10.X BASELINE menu. The Max+plus II main menu will open as shown in Figure SF-A–1. From this window, all VHDL programs will be developed, compiled, and downloaded to the project board.

Step 5. From main menu, select **File** then **New**. The New menu appears as shown in Figure SF-A–2.

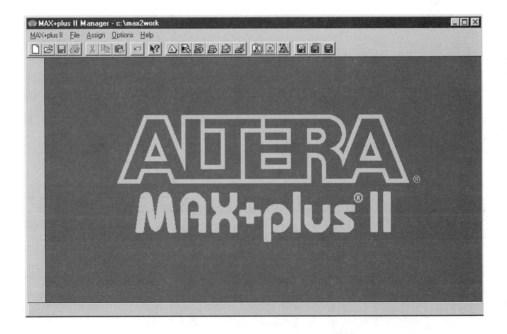

FIGURE SF-A–2

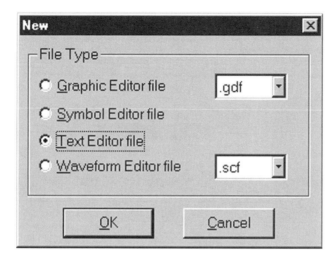

FIGURE SF-A–3

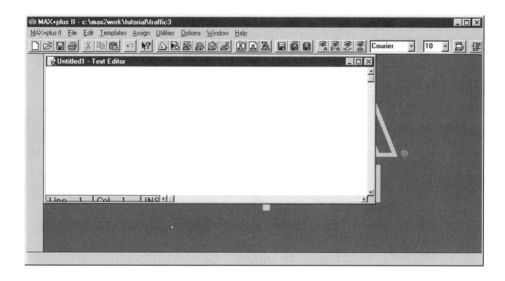

Step 6. Select **Text Editor file** from the New menu and select **O**K. A new Text Editor window will appear with the title **Untitled <Num> - Text Editor** as shown in Figure SF-A–3. This is the program window where the VHDL program will be written.

Step 7. Save the Text Editor. Select **File** then **Save** from the main menu. The Altera editor will highlight VHDL keywords, comments, and other program development features to aid in the creation of VHDL code when saved as a file with the **.vhd** extention.

From the **Save As** menu shown in Figure SF-A–4, enter the file name *Example1* in the **File Name** input box. From the **Directories** selection box, select the tutorial subdirectory from the max2work directory. Select **.vhd** from **Automatic Extention** dropdown list and click **O**K.

Once saved, the Altera development tool will recognize the file as a VHDL program. In the text editor window, the title bar will display the name of the saved program as shown in Figure SF-A–5.

Step 8. Enter the program shown in Figure SF-A–6 in the text editor window. This is the complete program for *Example1*.

With the **Text Editor** window highlighted, open the **File** menu, select Project, and select **Set Project to Current File.**

Step 9. From the main menu, select **Device** from **Assign.** Select the MAX7000S family from **Device Family,** then uncheck the **Show Only Fastest Speed Grades** check box. Next, select EMP7128SLC84-15 or EMP7128SLC84-7 as shown in Figure SF-A–7 from the **De**v**ices** window for your particular project board and click **O**K.

33

FIGURE SF-A–4

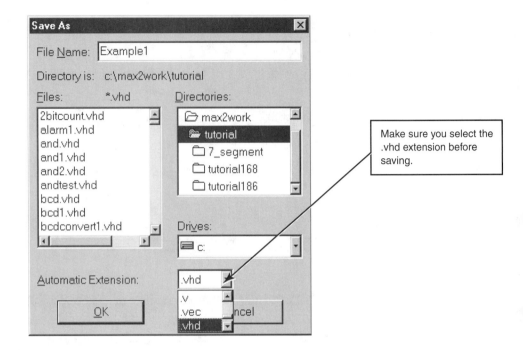

Make sure you select the .vhd extension before saving.

FIGURE SF-A–5

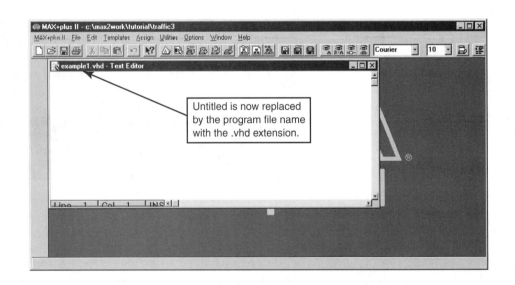

Untitled is now replaced by the program file name with the .vhd extension.

FIGURE SF-A–6

```
example1.vhd - Text Editor

Library IEEE;
use IEEE.STD_LOGIC_1164.ALL;

entity Example1 is
    port ( Switch1 : in std_logic;
           LED1 : out std_logic);

end entity Example1;

architecture Behavior of Example1 is
begin
    LED1 <= Switch1;
end architecture Behavior;

Line  10  Col  16  INS
```

34

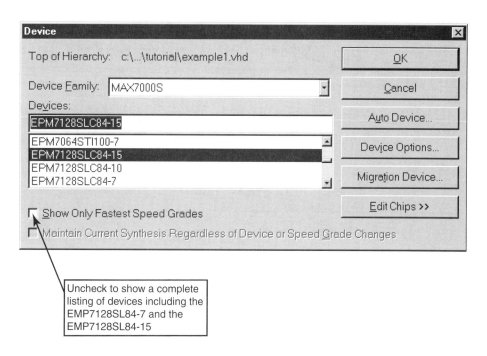

Uncheck to show a complete
listing of devices including the
EMP7128SL84-7 and the
EMP7128SL84-15

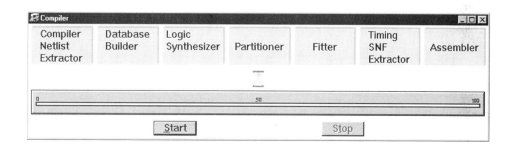

Step 10. Compile the VHDL project. Select **Compiler** from the MAX+plus II menu. By compiling the program at this time, part of the input and output identifier information is automatically entered for Step 11. You will compile the program again after the pin assignments are made. The Altera Compiler window will appear as shown in Figure SF-A-8.

Click **Start** from the Compiler window. Save all changes when prompted. When the program has completed the compile process, a completion window will appear, indicating that the process has completed. If you have errors, you will need to correct them and repeat the compilation. Figure SF-A–9 shows the Altera compiler completion notice. Click the **OK** button.

Step 11. Select **Pin/Location/Chip...** from **Assign** on main menu. Remove any old pin assignments by highlighting them in the Existing Pin/Location/Chip Assignments box and clicking **Delete.** For identifiers Switch1 and LED1, enter the name in the **Node Name** input box. Assign PLD pins for your particular project board as follows:

1. **PLDT-2:** Type the identifier *Switch1* in the space labeled Node Name, check the **Pin** radio button, and select pin 33. Type the identifier *LED1* and select pin 44. Click **Add** for each pin assignment and verify that each entry appears in the **Existing Pin/Location/Chip Assignments** window. Figure SF-A–10 illustrates the process. When you have assigned all pins, select **O**K.

FIGURE SF-A-9

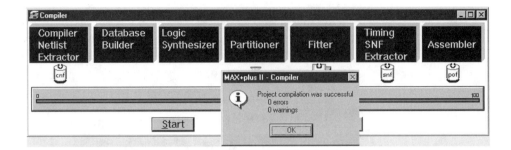

FIGURE SF-A-10

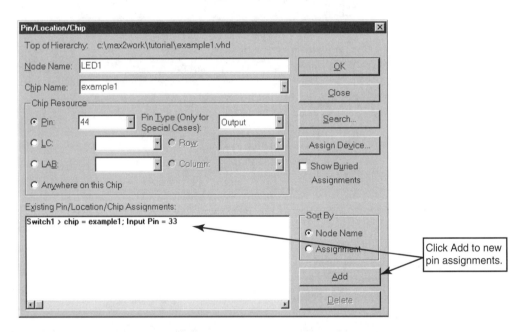

Click Add to new pin assignments.

FIGURE SF-A-11

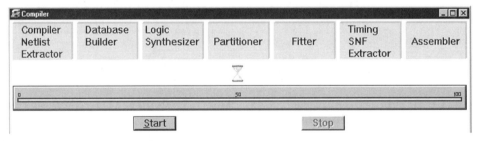

2. **Altera project board:** Type the identifier *Switch 1* in the space labeled Node Name, check the **Pin** radio button, and select pin 33. Type the identifier *LED1* and select pin 34. Click **Add** for each pin assignment and verify that each entry appears in the **Existing Pin/Location/Chip Assignments** window. Figure SF-A-10 illustrates the process. When you have assigned all pins, select **O**K.

3. **DeVry eSOC:** Type the identifier *Switch1* in the space labeled Node Name, check the **Pin** radio button, and select pin 33. Type the identifier *LED1* and select pin 44. Click **Add** for each pin assignment

and verify that each entry appears in the **Existing Pin/Location/Chip Assignments** window. Figure SF-A-10 illustrates the process. When you have assigned all pins, select **O**K.

Step 12. Compile the VHDL project. From the MAX+plus II main menu, select **Compiler.** The Altera Compiler window will appear as shown in Figure SF-A-11.

Click **Start** from the Compiler window. When the program has completed the compile process, a completion window will appear, indicating that the process has completed. Figure SF-A-12 shows the Altera compile completion notice. Click **O**K.

FIGURE SF-A–12

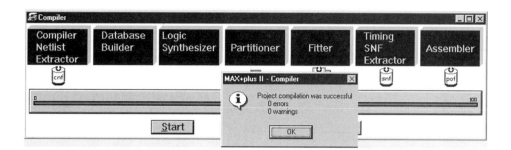

FIGURE SF-A–13

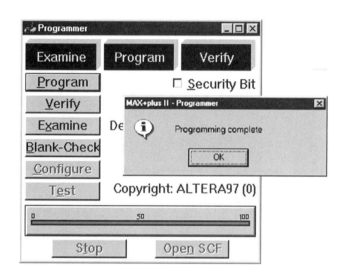

FIGURE SF-A–14

Step 13. Download the project. Select **Program-mer** from MAX+plus II from the main menu. The programmer menu will appear as shown in Figure SF-A–13.

Click **Program.** The Programmer menu will download your Example1 program to the project board and display the **Programming complete** information box as shown in Figure SF-A–14.

Step 14. Program Testing. Change the position of switch 1 located on S1 of the project board and verify that LED1 follows the switch position selection.

Altera Project Board Users Only

Refer to Tables PB–1 and PB–3 from *Project Board Familiarization* to connect the DIP switch and LED on the project board to the on-board PLD. See Figure SF-A–15.

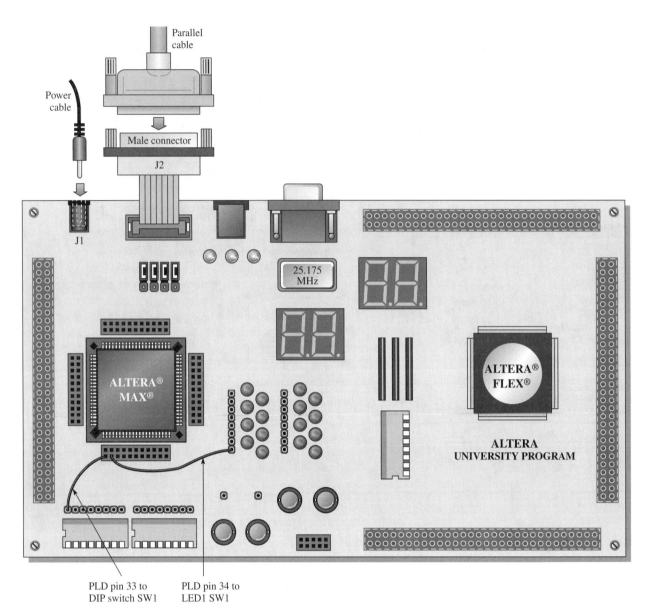

Parallel
cable

Power
cable

Male connector

J2

J1

25.175
MHz

ALTERA®
MAX®

ALTERA®
FLEX®

ALTERA
UNIVERSITY PROGRAM

PLD pin 33 to
DIP switch SW1

PLD pin 34 to
LED1 SW1

FIGURE SF-A–15

1

Laboratory Instrument Familiarization

Objectives

After completing this experiment, you will be able to
- ☐ Use a digital multimeter (DMM) to measure a specified dc voltage from the power supply.
- ☐ Use an oscilloscope to measure circuit voltages and frequencies.
- ☐ Set up the function generator to obtain a transistor-transistor logic (TTL) compatible pulse of a specified frequency. Measure the pulse amplitude and the frequency with an oscilloscope.
- ☐ Construct a digital oscillator circuit on a laboratory protoboard and measure various parameters with the oscilloscope.

Reference Reading

Floyd, *Digital Fundamentals with VHDL*, Chapter 1, "Introductory Digital Concepts"

Materials Needed

Light-emitting diode (LED)
Resistors: one 330 Ω, one 1.0 kΩ, one 2.7 kΩ
Capacitors: one 0.1 μF, one 100 μF
One 555 timer

For Further Investigation:
Current tracer (H-P 547A or equivalent)
Logic pulser (H-P 546A or equivalent)
One 100 Ω resistor

Summary of Theory

Laboratory equipment needed for most electronics work includes a DMM, a power supply, a function generator, and a dual-trace analog or digital oscilloscope. This experiment is an introduction to these instruments and to protoboards that are commonly used to wire laboratory experiments. Since each laboratory will have instruments from different manufacturers and different models, you should familiarize yourself with your particular lab station using the manufacturer's operating instructions or information provided by your instructor. There is a wide variety of instruments used in electronics labs; however, the directions in this experiment are general enough that you should be able to follow them for whatever instruments you are using.

The Power Supply

All active electronic devices, such as the integrated circuits used in digital electronics, require a stable source of dc voltage to function properly. The power supply provides the proper level of dc voltage. It is very important that the correct voltage be set before connecting it to the ICs on your board or permanent damage can result. The power supply at your bench may have more than one output and normally will have a built-in meter to help you set the voltage. For nearly all of the circuits in this manual, the power supply should be set to $+5.0$ V. When testing a faulty circuit, one of the first checks is to verify that the supply voltage is correct and that there is no ac component to the power supply output.

The Digital Multimeter

The DMM is a multipurpose measuring instrument that combines in one instrument the characteristics of a dc and ac voltmeter, a dc and ac ammeter, and an ohmmeter. The DMM indicates the measured quantity as a digital number, avoiding the necessity to interpret the scales as was necessary on older instruments.

Because the DMM is a multipurpose instrument, it is necessary to determine which controls select the desired function. In addition, current measurements (and often high-range voltage measurements) usually require a separate set of lead connections to the meter. After you have selected the function, you may need to select the appropriate range to make the measurement. Digital multimeters can be autoranging, meaning that the instrument automatically selects the correct scale and sets the decimal place, or they can be manual ranging, meaning that the user must select the correct scale.

The voltmeter function of a DMM can measure either ac or dc volts. For digital work, the dc volts function is always used to verify the dc supply voltage is correct and to check steady-state logic levels. If you are checking a power supply, you can verify that there is no ac component in the supply voltage by selecting the ac function. With ac voltage selected, the reading of a power supply should be very close to zero. Except for a test like this, the ac voltage function is not used in digital work.

The ohmmeter function of a DMM is used only in circuits that are not powered. When measuring resistance, the power supply should be disconnected from the circuit to avoid measuring back through the power supply. An ohmmeter works by inserting a small test voltage into a circuit and measuring the resulting current flow. Consequently, if any voltage is present, the reading will be in error. The meter will show the resistance of all possible paths between the probes. If you want to know the resistance of a single component, you must isolate that component from the remainder of the circuit by disconnecting one end. In addition, body resistance can affect the reading if you are holding the conducting portion of both probes in your fingers. This procedure should be avoided, particularly with high resistances.

The Function Generator

The function generator is used to produce signals required for testing various kinds of circuits. For digital circuits, a periodic rectangular pulse is the basic signal used for testing logic circuits. It is important that the proper voltage level be set up before connecting the function generator to the circuit or else damage may occur. Function generators normally have controls for adjusting the peak amplitude of a signal and may also have a means of adjusting the 0 volt level. Most function generators have a separate pulse output for use in logic circuits. If you have a TTL compatible output, it will be the one used for the experiments in this manual.

A periodic rectangular pulse is a signal that rises from one level to another level, remains at the second level for a time called the pulse width, (t_w), and then returns to the original level. Important parameters for these pulses are illustrated in Figure 1–1. For digital testing, it is useful to use a duty cycle that is *not* near 50% so that an inverted signal can be readily detected on an oscilloscope.

In addition to amplitude and dc offset controls, function generators have switches that select the range of the output frequency. A vernier control may be present for fine frequency adjustments.

The Oscilloscope

The oscilloscope is the most important test instrument for testing circuits, and you should become completely familiar with its operation. It is a versa-

FIGURE 1–1

Definitions for a periodic pulse train.

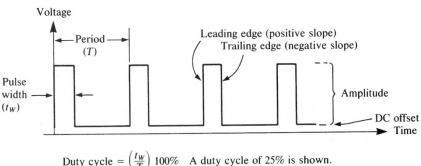

Duty cycle = $\left(\frac{t_W}{T}\right)$ 100%   A duty cycle of 25% is shown.

tile test instrument, letting you see a graph of the voltage as a function of time in a circuit and compare waves. Because an oscilloscope allows you to measure various parameters, it is considered to be an instrument capable of parametric measurements important in both digital and analog work. Nearly all complex digital circuits have specific timing requirements that can be readily measured with a two-channel oscilloscope.

There are two basic types of oscilloscopes: analog and digital. Because of its versatility, accuracy, and ability to do automated measurements, digital scopes are the choice of many technicians today. Both types of scopes have four main control groups: display controls, vertical and horizontal controls, and trigger controls. If you are not familiar with these controls, or the operation of the oscilloscope in general, you should read the Oscilloscope Guide starting on page 5. Both analog and digital scopes are covered in this summary. In addition, you may want to review the operator's manual that came with the oscilloscope at your lab station.

Logic Pulser and Current Tracer

The logic pulser and current tracer are simple digital test instruments that are useful for finding certain difficult faults, such as a short between V_{CC} and ground. A problem like this can be very difficult to find in a large circuit because the short could be located in many possible places. The current tracer responds to pulsing current by detecting the changing magnetic field. A handheld logic pulser can provide very short duration, nondestructive pulses into the shorted circuit. The current tracer, used in conjunction with the pulser or other pulsating source, allows you to follow the current path, leading you directly to the short. This method of troubleshooting is also useful for "stuck" nodes in a circuit (points that have more than one path for current). The sensitivity of the current tracer can be varied over a large range to allow you to trace various types of faults.

Logic Probe

Another handheld instrument that is useful for tracing simple logic circuits is the logic probe. The logic probe can be used to determine the logic level of a point in a circuit or to determine whether there is pulse activity at the point by LED (light-emitting diode) displays. Although it is used primarily for simple circuits because it cannot show important time relationships between digital signals, a good probe can indicate activity on the line, even if it is short pulses. A simple logic probe can determine if logic levels are HIGH, LOW, or INVALID.

Logic Analyzer

One of the most powerful and widely used instruments for digital troubleshooting is the logic analyzer. The logic analyzer is an instrument that originally was designed to make functional (as opposed to parametric) measurements in logic circuits. It is useful for observing the time relationship between a number of digital signals at the same time, allowing the technician to see a variety of errors, including "stuck" nodes, very short noise spikes, intermittent problems, and timing errors. Newer analyzers can include multiple channels of a digital storage oscilloscope (DSO) as well as logic channels. An example of a two-function analyzer that can be equipped with multiple channels of DSO and as many as 680 logic analyzer channels is the Tektronix TLA700 series shown in Figure 1–2. Not all electronic laboratories are equipped with a logic analyzer, even a simple one, and one is not necessary for the experiments in this manual. Further information on logic analyzers is given on various Web sites on the Internet (see *www.Tektronix.com* for example).

Protoboards

Protoboards are a convenient way to construct circuits for testing and experimenting. While there are some variations in the arrangement of the hole

FIGURE 1–2

Tektronix logic analyzers. (Copyright © Tektronix, Inc. Reproduced with permission.)

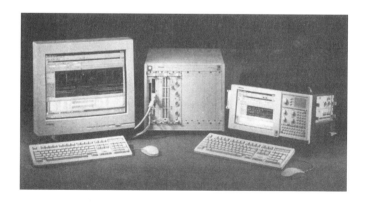

patterns, most protoboards are similar to the one shown in Figure 1–3, which is modeled after the Radio Shack board 276-174. Notice that the top and bottom horizontal rows are connected as a continuous row. Vertical groups of five holes are connected together; the vertical group above the center strip is not connected to the vertical group below the center strip. The holes are 0.1 inch apart, which is the same spacing as the pins on an integrated circuit DIP (dual in-line pins). Integrated circuits (ICs) are inserted to straddle the center; in this manner, wires can be connected to the pins of the IC by connecting them to the same vertical group as the desired pin.

Pin Numbering

Integrated circuits come in various "packages" as explained in the text. In this manual, you will be using all "DIP chips". To determine the pin numbers, you need to locate pin 1 by looking for a notch or dot on one end (see Figure 1–3). Pin 1 is adjacent to this notch as shown. The numbering for a DIP chip always is counterclockwise from pin 1.

Pre-lab Questions

1. What precautions are necessary when measuring resistance in a circuit?
2. The Oscilloscope Guide (on p. 7) states that it is best to couple digital signals to an oscilloscope using DC coupling. Explain why.
3. Why is it useful to use a nonsymmetrical pulse for testing digital logic?

Procedure

Measurement of DC Voltage with the DMM

1. Review the operator's manual or information supplied by your instructor for the power supply at your lab station. Generally, power supplies have a meter or meters that enable you to set the output voltage and monitor the current. Set the voltage based on the power supply meter to +5.0 V and record the reading in Table 1–1 (in the Report section).

2. The +5.0 V is the voltage you will use for nearly all of the experiments in this manual. For most digital circuits it must be within 0.2 V. To check that you have correctly set up the supply, measure the voltage with the DMM. Record the reading of the DMM in Table 1–1.

Measurement of DC Voltage with the Oscilloscope

3. In this step, you will confirm the dc voltage from the power supply using the oscilloscope. Set the SEC/DIV control of your oscilloscope to a convenient value (a value near 0.2 ms/div is suggested, to give a steady line on the display). Set the trigger controls to AUTO and INT (internal trigger) to assure a sweep is on the display. Select channel 1 as the input channel, and connect a scope probe to the vertical input. Put the input coupling control on GND to disconnect the input signal and find the ground position on the oscilloscope (digital scopes may have a marker for the GND

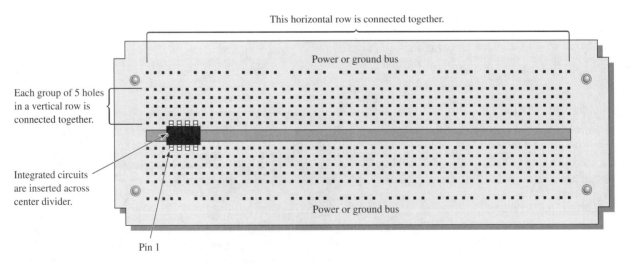

This horizontal row is connected together.

Power or ground bus

Each group of 5 holes in a vertical row is connected together.

Integrated circuits are inserted across center divider.

Power or ground bus

Pin 1

FIGURE 1–3
Protoboard. An 8-pin integrated circuit is shown inserted into the board.

level, as illustrated in Figure OG–3, p. 11). Adjust the beam for a sharp, horizontal line across the scope face.

4. Since you will be measuring a positive voltage, position the ground on a convenient graticule line near the bottom of the display using the vertical POSITION control. If you are using an analog scope, check that the vertical VOLTS/DIV variable knobs are in their calibrated positions. A digital scope, such as the Tektronix TDS220, is always calibrated, and there is no vernier control.

5. Move the channel 1 input coupling control from the GND position to the dc position. For almost all digital work, the input coupling control should be in the DC position. Clip the ground lead of the scope probe to the ground of the power supply and touch the probe itself to the power supply output. The line on the face of the oscilloscope should jump up 5 divisions. You can determine the dc voltage by multiplying the vertical sensitivity (1.0 V/div) by the number of divisions observed between ground and this line (5 divisions). Record the measured voltage (to the nearest 0.1 V) in Table 1–1.

Measurement of Pulses with the Oscilloscope

6. Now you will set up the function generator or pulse generator for a logic pulse and measure some characteristics of the pulse using the oscilloscope. Review the operator's manual or information supplied by your instructor for the function generator at your lab station. Select the pulse function and set the frequency for 1.0 kHz. (If you do not have a pulse function, a square wave may be substituted.)

7. Set up and measure the pulse amplitude of the function generator. The vertical sensitivity (VOLTS/DIV) control of the oscilloscope should be set for 1.0 V/div and the SEC/DIV should be left at 0.2 ms/div. Check that both controls are in their cali-

brated positions. Check the ground level on the oscilloscope as you did in Step 3 and set it for a convenient graticule near the bottom of the scope face. Switch the scope back to dc coupling and clip the ground lead of the scope probe to a ground on the generator. Touch the probe to the function generator's pulse output. If the generator has a variable amplitude control, adjust it for a 4.0 V pulse (4 divisions of deflection). Some generators have a separate control to adjust the dc level of the pulse; others do not. If your generator has a dc offset control, adjust the ground level of the pulse for zero volts.

8. You should obtain a stable display that allows you to measure both the time information and the voltage parameters of the waveform. (If the waveform is not stable, check triggering controls.) In Plot 1 of your report, sketch the observed waveform on the scope display. It is a good idea, whenever you sketch a waveform from a scope, to record the VOLTS/DIV and SEC/DIV settings of controls next to the sketch and to show the ground level. Measure the pulse width (t_w), period, and amplitude of the waveform and record these values in Table 1–2. The amplitude is defined in Figure 1–1 and is measured in volts.

9. Connect the LED and series-limiting resistor, R_1, to the pulse generator as shown in Figure 1–4. Note that the LED is a polarized component and must be connected in the correct direction to work. The schematic and an example of protoboard wiring is shown. Measure the signal across the LED with the oscilloscope and show it in Plot 2 of your report. Label the scope settings as in step 8 and show the ground level.

10. Sometimes it is useful to use an oscilloscope to measure the voltage across an ungrounded component. The current-limiting resistor, R_1, in Figure 1–4 is an ungrounded component. To measure

FIGURE 1–4
Circuit for Step 9.

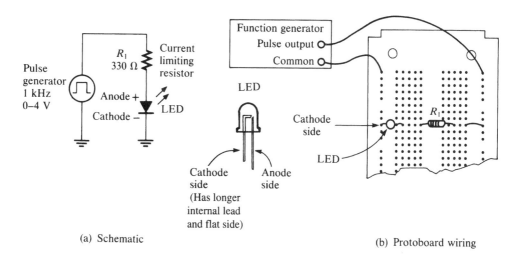

(a) Schematic

(b) Protoboard wiring

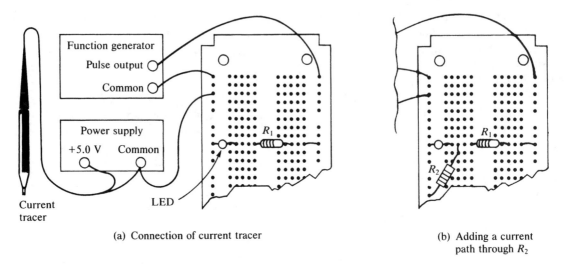

(a) Connection of current tracer

(b) Adding a current
path through R_2

FIGURE 1–5
Measuring an ungrounded component. Both channels must be calibrated and have the same vertical sensitivity settings. On the TDS220, the difference between the two channels is on the MATH functions menu.

the voltage across it, connect both channels of your oscilloscope as shown in Figure 1–5. Make sure that both channels are calibrated and that the vertical sensitivity (VOLTS/DIV) is 1 V/div for each channel. If you are using a newer scope, the difference operation (Channel 1 – Channel 2) is likely to be shown as a menu item. On older scopes, the difference measurement is done by inverting channel 2 and selecting the ADD function. Consult the operator's manual if you are not sure. Measure the signal across R_1 and show the result on Plot 3. As a check, the sum of the voltages across the LED and resistor should be equal to the voltage of the generator.

Constructing and Measuring Parameters in a Digital Circuit

11. In this step, you will construct a small digital oscillator. This oscillator generates pulses that could be used to drive other digital circuits. The basic integrated circuit for the oscillator is the 555 timer, which will be covered in detail later. The schematic and sample protoboard wiring is shown in Figure 1–6. Construct the circuit as shown.

12. Using your oscilloscope, observe the signal on pin 3. Sketch the observed signal in Plot 4. Be sure to label the plot with the scope settings (VOLTS/DIV and SEC/DIV). Measure the parameters listed in the first four rows of Table 1–3. The frequency is computed from the period measurement ($f = 1/T$).

13. Replace C_1 with a 100 μF capacitor. The light should blink at a relatively slow rate. A slow

frequency like this is useful for visual tests of a circuit or for simulating the opening and closing of a manual switch. Measure the period and frequency of the oscillator with the 100 μF capacitor. This signal, with a low frequency like this, may give you difficulty if you are using an analog scope. You will need to use NORMAL triggering instead of auto triggering and you may need to adjust the trigger LEVEL control to obtain a stable display. Record your measured values in Table 1–3.

For Further Investigation

Using the Current Tracer

If you have a current tracer available, you can test the paths for current in a circuit such as the one you constructed in step 9. The current tracer can detect the path of pulsing current, which you can follow. The current tracer detects fast current pulses by sensing the changing magnetic field associated with them. It cannot detect dc. Set the generator to a 1.0 kHz TTL level pulse for this test.

Power the current tracer using a +5.0 V power supply. You will need to provide a common ground for the pulse generator and the power supply, as shown in Figure 1–7(a). (Note that the current tracer has a red wire in one of the leads, which should be connected to the +5.0 V source, and a black wire in the other lead, which should be connected to the common.) The sensitivity of the tracer is adjusted with a variable control near the tip of the current tracer. The current tracer must be held perpendicu-

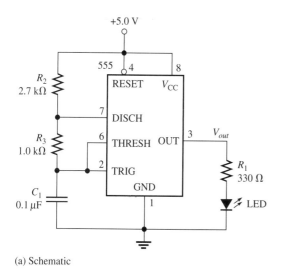

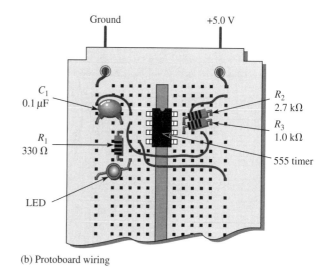

(a) Schematic

(b) Protoboard wiring

FIGURE 1–6
Digital oscillator.

larly with respect to the conductor in which you are sensing current. In addition, the small mark on the probe tip must be aligned with the current path to obtain maximum sensitivity.

Begin by holding the current tracer above R_1. Rotate the current tracer so that the tip is aligned with the path of current. Adjust the sensitivity to about half-brightness. You should now be able to trace the current path through R_1, the LED, and along the protoboard. Practice tracing the path of current. Simulate a low-impedance fault by installing a 100 Ω resistor (call this R_2 for this experiment) in parallel with the LED, as shown in Figure 1–7(b). Test the circuit with the current tracer to de-

termine the path for current. Does most of the current go through R_2 or through the LED?

Using the Current Tracer and Logic Pulser

Circuit boards typically have many connections where a potential short can occur. If a short occurs between the power supply and ground due to a solder splash or other reason, it can be difficult to find. A logic pulser, used in conjunction with a current tracer, can locate the fault without the need for applying power to the circuit. The logic pulser applies very fast pulses to a circuit under test. A flashing LED in the tip indicates the output mode, which can

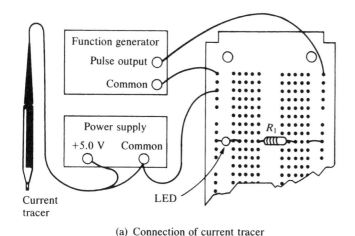

(a) Connection of current tracer

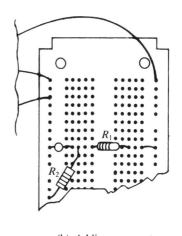

(b) Adding a current path through R_2

FIGURE 1–7

45

FIGURE 1–8
Stimulating the circuit with a logic pulser.

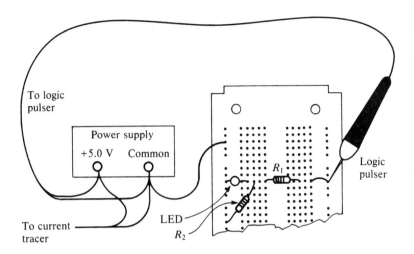

be set to various pulse streams or to a continuous series of pulses. The pulser can be used in an operating circuit without damaging it because the energy supplied to the circuit is limited.

Start with the logic pulser by setting it for continuous pulses. Remove the pulse generator from the test circuit and touch the logic pulser to the test circuit, as shown in Figure 1–8. You can hold the current tracer at a 90-degree angle and against the tip of the logic pulser in order to set the sensitivity of the current tracer. You should now be able to follow the path for current as you did before.

Now simulate a direct short fault across the circuit by connecting a wire as shown in Figure 1–9. You may need to adjust the sensitivity of the current tracer. Use the logic pulser and current tracer to follow the path of current. Can you detect current in R_1? Describe in your report the current path in the wire and in the protoboard.

FIGURE 1–9
Simulating a short circuit. The logic pulser forces current through the short; this current can be detected with the current tracer.

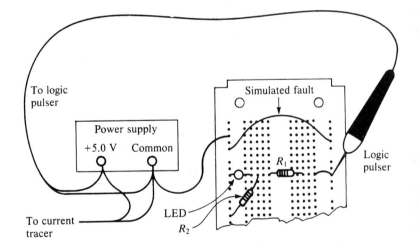

46

Report for Experiment 1

Name: _____ Date: _____ Class: _____

Data and Observations:

TABLE 1–1

Voltage Setting 5 5.0 V	Voltage Reading
Power supply meter	
DMM	
Oscilloscope	

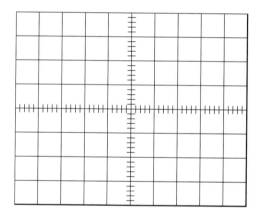

Plot 1   Generator waveform

TABLE 1–2

Function Generator Parameters (at 1.0 kHz)	Measured Values
Pulse width	
Period	
Amplitude	

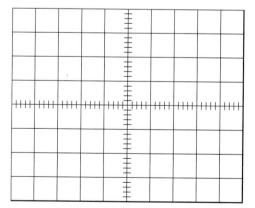

Plot 2   Voltage across LED

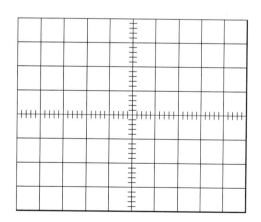

Plot 3   Voltage across R_1

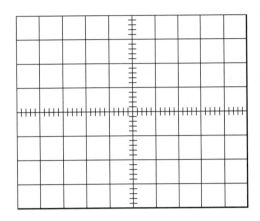

Plot 4   Digital oscillator output (pin 3)

Results and Conclusion:

Further Investigation Results:

TABLE 1–3

Step	Digital Oscillator Parameters	Measured Values
12	Period	
	Duty cycle	
	Amplitude	
	Frequency	
13	Period	
	Frequency	

Review Questions

1. Explain how to measure voltage across an ungrounded component with a two-channel oscilloscope.

2. In Step 11, you constructed a digital oscillator. Assume each of the following faults were in the circuit (each fault is independent of the others). Explain what symptom you would expect to observe with an oscilloscope.

   a. The LED is inserted in reverse.

   b. The value of C_1 is larger than it should be.

   c. The power and ground connections on the power supply were accidentally reversed. (Don't test this one!)

   d. R_1 is open.

3. Compare the advantage and disadvantage of making a dc voltage measurement with a DMM and a scope.

2

Constructing a Logic Probe

Objectives

After completing this experiment, you will be able to
- [ ] Construct a simple logic probe using a 7404 inverter.
- [ ] Use this logic probe to test another circuit.
- [ ] Troubleshoot a simulated failure in the test circuit.
- [ ] Measure logic levels with the digital multimeter (DMM) and the oscilloscope, and compare them with valid input logic levels.

Reference Reading

Floyd, *Digital Fundamentals with VHDL*, Chapter 1, "Introductory Digital Concepts"

Materials Needed

7404 hex inverter
Two LEDs (light-emitting diodes)
Two signal diodes (1N914 or equivalent)
Resistors: three 330 Ω, one 2.0 kΩ
1 kΩ potentiometer

Summary of Theory

Digital circuits have two discrete voltage levels to represent the binary digits (*bits*) 1 and 0. All digital circuits are switching circuits that use high-speed transistors to represent either an ON condition or an OFF condition. Various types of logic, representing different technologies, are available to the logic designer. The choice of a particular family is determined by factors such as speed, cost, availability, noise immunity, and so forth. The key requirement within each family is compatibility; that is, there must be consistency within the logic levels and power supplies of various integrated circuits made by different manufacturers. The fixed-function experiments in this lab book use primarily transistor-transistor logic, or TTL. The input logic levels for TTL are illustrated in Figure 2–1.

For any integrated circuit (IC) to function properly, power and ground must be connected. The connection diagram for the IC shows these connections, although in practice the power and ground connections are frequently omitted from diagrams of logic circuits. Figure 2–2 shows the connection diagram for a 7404 hex inverter, which will be used in this experiment. Pins are numbered counterclockwise from the top, starting with a notch or circle at the top or next to pin 1; see Figure 2–3.

The circuit in this experiment is a simple logic probe. Logic probes are useful for detecting the presence of a HIGH or a LOW logic level in a circuit. The logic probe in this experiment is a simple one designed only to illustrate the use of this tool and the wiring of integrated circuits. The simple probe shown in Figure 2–4 works as follows: If the probe is not connected, the top inverter is pulled HIGH (through the 2.0 kΩ resistor) and the bottom inverter

FIGURE 2–1
TTL logic levels.

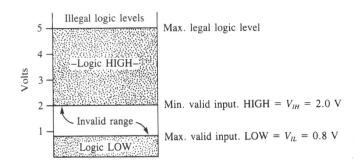

is pulled LOW (through the 330 Ω resistor). As a result, both outputs are HIGH and neither LED is on. (A LOW is required to turn on either LED). If the probe input is connected to a voltage above approximately 2.0 V, the voltage at the input of the lower inverter is interpreted as a logic HIGH through diode D_2. As a result, the output of the lower inverter goes LOW, and the lower LED, representing a HIGH input, turns on. If the probe input is connected to a voltage below approximately 0.8 V, the upper input inverter is pulled below the logic threshold for a LOW, and the output inverter is LOW. Then the upper LED, which represents a logic LOW input turns on. A more sophisticated probe could detect pulses, has a much higher input impedance, and is useful for logic families other than TTL; however, this probe will allow you to troubleshoot basic gates.

Pre-lab Questions

1. How are pins numbered on a 7404?
2. What is the range of voltages considered to be invalid on a TTL IC?

Procedure

A Simple Logic Probe

1. Using the pin numbers shown, construct the simple logic probe circuit shown in Figure 2–4. Pin numbers are included on the drawing but frequently are omitted from logic drawings. Note that the LEDs and the signal diodes are polarized; that is, they must be connected in the correct direction. The arrow on electronic components always points in the direction of *conventional* current flow, defined as from plus to minus. Signal diodes are marked on the cathode side with a line. The LEDs generally have a flat spot on the cathode side or are the longer element inside the diode. As a guide, Figure 2–5(a) shows an example of the wiring of the logic probe.

2. Test your circuit by connecting the probe to +5.0 V and then to ground. One of the LEDs should light to indicate a HIGH, the other, a LOW. When the probe is not connected, neither LED should be on. If the circuit does not work, double-check your wiring and the direction of the diodes.

FIGURE 2–2
Connection diagram from a manufacturer's logic data book.

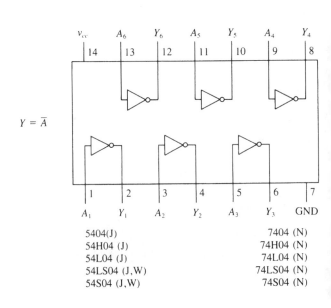

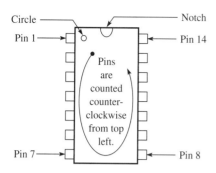

FIGURE 2–3
Numbering of pins.

In the figure: Circle — Pin 1 — Notch — Pin 14 — Pin 7 — Pin 8. Pins are counted counter-clockwise from top left.

3. You can test the HIGH and LOW threshold voltages of your logic probe with the circuit shown in Figure 2–5(b). Connect the logic probe to a 1 kΩ variable resistor, as shown. Vary the resistor and find the HIGH and LOW thresholds. Use a DMM to measure the threshold voltages. Record the thresholds in the report.

4. In the last step, you should have observed that the thresholds for the logic probe are very close to the TTL specifications given in Figure 2–1. If so, you can now use the probe to test the logic for logic gates including various inverter circuits. Remember that there are six independent inverters in a 7404 (but they share a common power supply). Begin by testing the inverter that is between pins 3 and 4 (this is inverter 2). Connect your logic probe to the output (pin 4) and observe the output logic when the input is LOW (use ground), OPEN, and is HIGH (use +5 V). Record your observations for these three cases in Table 2–1 of the report. An open input will have an invalid logic level; however, the output will be a *valid* logic level (an open input is not desirable because of potential noise problems).

5. Connect two inverters in series (cascade) as shown in Figure 2–6(a). Move the logic probe to the output of the second inverter (pin 6). Check the logic when the input is connected to a logic LOW, OPEN, and HIGH as before. Record your observations for these three cases in Table 2–1.

6. Connect the two inverters as cross-coupled inverters as shown in Figure 2–6(b). This is a basic latch circuit, the most basic form of memory. This arrangement is not the best way to implement a latch but serves to illustrate the concept (you will study latch circuits in more detail later). This latch works as follows: the input signal is first inverted by the top inverter. The original logic is inverted a second time by the lower inverter which restores the logic back to the original input logic level (similar to your observation in step 5). This is a "feedback" signal which forms the latch. If the input is now removed, the feedback signal keeps the input from changing and the circuit remains stable. You will test this in the next step.

7. Connect the logic probe to pin 4 (the output) of the latch circuit. Then momentarily touch V_{in} (pin 3) to ground. Observe the output logic and record it (HIGH, LOW, or INVALID) in Table 2–2 of the report.

8. Touch the input to +5.0 V, test the output again, and record the logic in Table 2–2.

9. Place a fault in the circuit of Figure 2–6(b) by removing the wire that is connected to pin 5, the input of the lower inverter. Now momentarily touch the input, pin 3, to ground. Test the logic levels at each point in the circuit and record them in Table 2–2.

10. An open circuit on the input of TTL logic has an invalid logic level. Even though it is invalid, it acts as a logic HIGH at the input to the gate. (However, open circuits should never be used as a means of connecting an input to a constant HIGH.) In this step, repeat Step 9 but use a DMM to measure the actual voltages at each pin. Record the data in Table 2–2.

FIGURE 2–4
Simple logic probe.

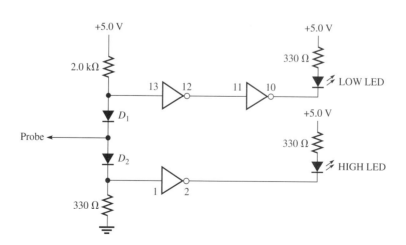

53

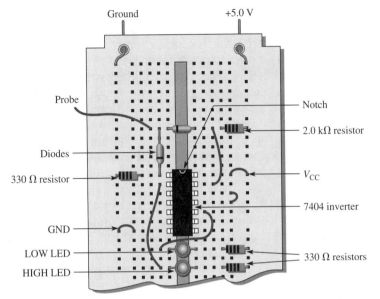

(a) Wiring of a logic probe

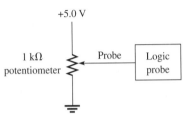

(b) Test circuit to determine logic thresholds

FIGURE 2–5

11. In order to gain practice with the oscilloscope, repeat the measurements of Step 9 using the oscilloscope. You may want to review the procedure for making dc voltage measurements with the oscilloscope in the Oscilloscope Guide. Record the measured voltages in Table 2–2.

For Further Investigation

In this investigation, you will check the logic inverter with a pulse waveform. Set up the pulse generator with a 1 kHz TTL compatible pulse. Set up the series inverters shown in Figure 2–6(a). Then compare the waveforms on the input and on the output of the circuit. Sketch the waveforms in Plot 1 provided in the Report section; be sure and label the voltage and time. Are the waveforms identical? If not, why not? Explain your observations in the space provided in the Report section.

EWB/MSM Troubleshooting

The CD packaged with this lab manual contains Electronics Workbench (.ewb) and Multisim (.msm) files. Open the file named Exp-02. Three versions of the cross-coupled inverters are on the workbench. The first one has no fault and can be used as a reference. Note that two switches are shown in order to simulate the open position of an SPDT switch. Analyze the two files containing faults. In the space provided in the report, indicate the most likely problem.

FIGURE 2–6

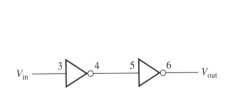

(a) Series inverters

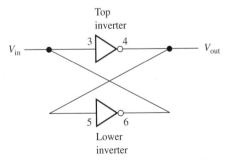

(b) Cross-coupled inverters

Report for Experiment 2

Name: _____ Date: _____ Class: _____

Data and Observations:

Step 3: Logic thresholds: HIGH _____ V LOW _____ V

TABLE 2–1

Step		Input is LOW	Output Logic Level Input is OPEN	Input is HIGH
4	One inverter			
5	Two series inverters			

TABLE 2–2

Step		Input Logic Level (pin 3)	Output Logic Level (pin 4)	Logic Level (pin 5)	Logic Level (pin 6)
7	V_{in} momentarily on ground.				
8	V_{in} momentarily on 15.0 V.				
9	Fault condition: open at pin 5.				
10	Voltages with fault (DMM):	V	V	V	V
11	Voltages with fault (scope):	V	V	V	V

Results and Conclusion:

EWB/MSM Troubleshooting:

Fault 1 Most likely problem: _____

_____

Fault 2 Most likely problem: _____

_____

Further Investigation Results:

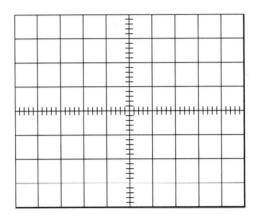

Plot 1 Input and output waveforms for two series inverters

Observations: _____

_____

Review Questions (TTL)

1. In Step 4, you tested the threshold voltages of the logic probe. What simple change to the circuit of Figure 2–4 would you suggest if you wanted to raise these thresholds a small amount?

2. Consider the logic drawing in Figure 2–7.

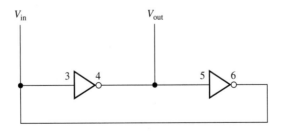

FIGURE 2–7

a. Is this the same or different than the circuit in Figure 2–6(b)? _____

b. If the conductor leading to pin 3 is open, what voltage do you expect to see at pin 3? _____

c. If the conductor leading to pin 3 is open, what voltage do you expect to see at pin 4? _____

3. Consider the circuit in Figure 2–8 with five inverters. Assume each inverter requires 10 ns for the input logic to affect the output logic (this is called *propagation delay*).

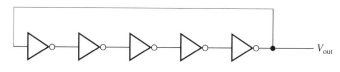

FIGURE 2–8

a. Describe V_{out}.

b. How long does it take for the input to the first inverter to affect the last inverter? _____

c. What is the frequency of the output? (Hint: The logic must change twice in one period.) _____

3

Number Systems

Objectives

After completing this experiment, you will be able to
- ☐ Convert binary or binary coded decimal (BCD) numbers to decimal.
- ☐ Implement a portion of a digital system that decodes a BCD number and displays it on a seven-segment display.
- ☐ Troubleshoot the circuit for simulated faults.
- ☐ Implement logic for a portion of a BCD number decoder in VHDL.

Reference Reading

Floyd, *Digital Fundamentals with VHDL,* Chapter 2, "Number Systems, Operations, and Codes"

Materials Needed (TTL)

Four LEDs
7447A BCD/decimal decoder
MAN72 seven-segment display
Four-position DIP switch
Resistors: eleven 330 Ω, one 1.0 kΩ

For Further Investigation:
   Additional LED
   One 330 Ω resistor

Materials Needed (VHDL)

Project Board

Summary of Theory

The number of symbols in a number system is called the *base,* or *radix,* of that system. The decimal number system uses ten counting symbols, the digits 0 through 9, to represent quantities. Thus it is a base ten system. In this system, we represent quantities larger than 9 by using positional weighting of the digits. The position, or column, that a digit occupies indicates the weight of that digit in determining the value of the number. The base 10 number system is a weighted system because each column has a value associated with it.

   Digital systems use two states to represent quantities and thus are *binary* in nature. The binary counting system has a radix of two and uses only the numbers 0 and 1. (These are often called *bits,* which is a contraction of BInary digiT). It too is a weighted counting system, with each column value worth twice the value of the column to the immediate right. Because binary numbers have only two digits, large numbers expressed in binary require a long string of 0s and 1s. Other systems, which are related to binary in a simple way, are often used to simplify these numbers. These systems include octal, hexadecimal, and BCD.

   The octal number system is a weighted number system using the digits 0 through 7. The column values in octal are worth 8 times that of the column to the immediate right. You convert from binary to octal by arranging the binary number in groups of 3 bits, starting at the binary point, and writing the octal symbol for each binary group. You can reverse the procedure to convert from octal to binary. Simply write an equivalent 3-bit binary number for each octal character.

The hexadecimal system is a weighted number system using 16 characters. The column values in hexadecimal (or simply hex) are worth 16 times that of the column to the immediate right. The characters are the numbers 0 through 9 and the first six letters of the alphabet, A through F. Letters were chosen because of their sequence, but remember that they are used to indicate numbers, not letters. You convert binary numbers to hexadecimal numbers by arranging the binary number into 4-bit groups, starting at the binary point. Then write the next symbol for each group of 4 bits. You convert hex numbers to binary by reversing the procedure. That is, write an equivalent 4-bit binary number for each hexadecimal character.

The BCD system uses four binary bits to represent each decimal digit. It is a convenient code because it allows ready conversion from base ten to a code that a machine can understand; however, it is wasteful of bits. A 4-bit binary number could represent the numbers 0 to 15, but in BCD it represents only the quantities 0 through 9. The binary representations of the numbers 10 through 15 are not used in BCD and are invalid.

A tablet control digital system from the text is shown in Figure 3–1. The circuit for this experiment represents the BCD decoder to a seven-segment display and is the upper right portion of the system. You will construct a simplified portion of the display for this system.

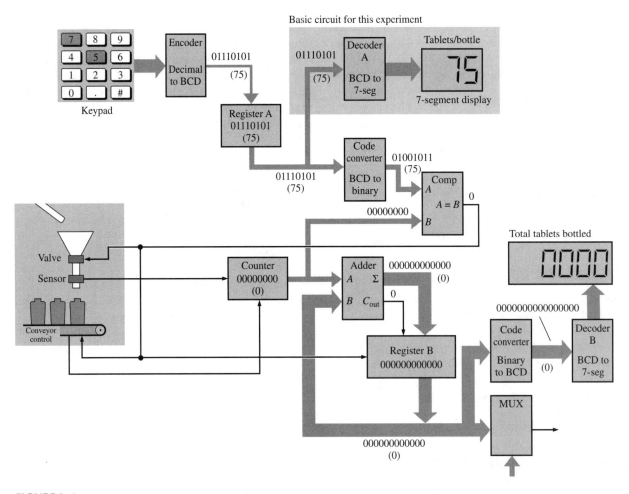

FIGURE 3–1
Tablet control digital system.

Pre-lab Questions

1. Explain the difference between binary and BCD.
2. Convert each number shown into the other bases:

Binary	Octal	Hexadecimal	Decimal	BCD
01001100	_____	_____	_____	_____
_____	304	_____	_____	_____
_____	_____	E6	_____	_____
_____	_____	_____	57	_____
_____	_____	_____	_____	01001001

TTL

Procedure

1. Take a moment to review "Circuit Wiring" in the Introduction before constructing this experiment. The pin numbers for the integrated circuits (ICs) in this and succeeding experiments are not shown; pin numbers may be found in the data sheets in the back of this lab manual or in manufacturer's data books. It is a good idea to write the pin numbers directly on the schematic before you begin wiring.

2. Begin by constructing the circuit shown in Figure 3–2. This set of switches represents a portion of register A of the digital system shown in Figure 3–1. Although it only indicates a 4-bit BCD number, the concept is the same as that shown in the digital system as the input to the decoder. After wiring the circuit, connect power and test each switch to see that it lights an LED.

3. Remove power and add the circuit shown in Figure 3–3. An example of the wiring is shown in Figure 3–4. If you have not already done so, write the pin numbers on the schematic. The pin numbers for the MAN72 display are shown in Figure 3–5. Note that the 7447A* has 16 pins, but the MAN72 has only 14 pins.

Before applying power, check that you have connected a 330 Ω current-limiting resistor between each output of the decoder and the input to the MAN72. Connect the Lamp test, BI/RBO, and RBI inputs through a 1.0 kΩ resistor to +5.0 V. This is a *pull-up resistor,* used to assure a solid logic HIGH is present at these inputs.

*Pin numbers for the 7447A decoder can be found in Appendix A.

FIGURE 3–2

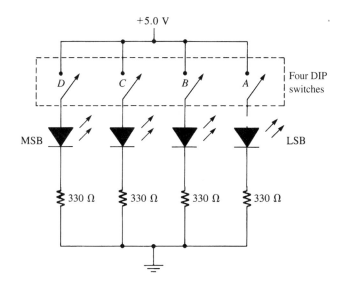

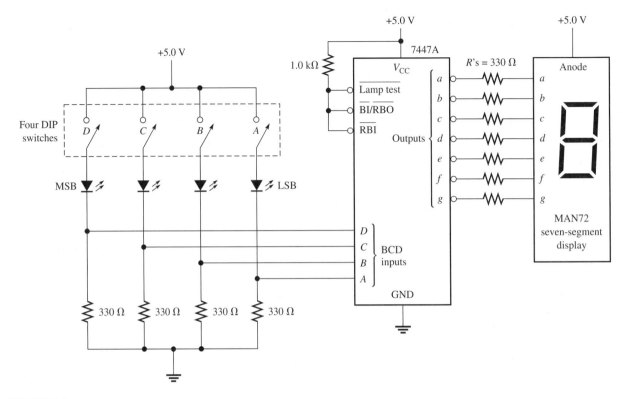

FIGURE 3–3

FIGURE 3–4

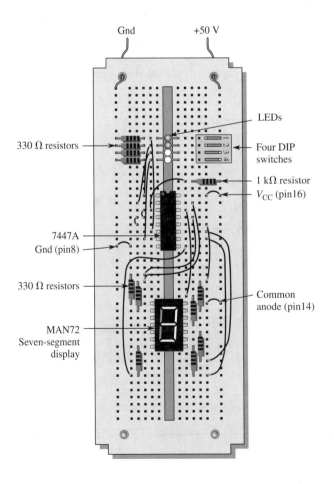

FIGURE 3–5
MAN72 seven-segment display.

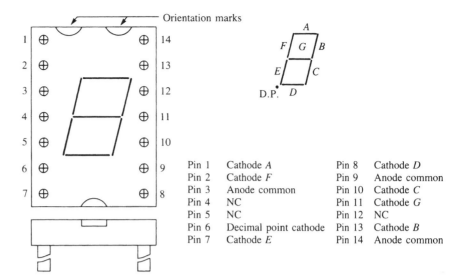

Orientation marks

Pin 1	Cathode A	Pin 8	Cathode D
Pin 2	Cathode F	Pin 9	Anode common
Pin 3	Anode common	Pin 10	Cathode C
Pin 4	NC	Pin 11	Cathode G
Pin 5	NC	Pin 12	NC
Pin 6	Decimal point cathode	Pin 13	Cathode B
Pin 7	Cathode E	Pin 14	Anode common

4. When you have completed the wiring, apply power, and test the circuit by setting each switch combination listed in Table 3–1 of the report. The last six codes are invalid BCD codes; however, you can set the switch combinations in binary and observe the display. It will show a unique display for each of the invalid codes. Complete the table by showing the appearance of the seven-segment display in the output column.

5. In this step, you will insert some simulated "troubles" in the circuit and observe the effect of these troubles on the output. The troubles are listed in Table 3–2 of the report. Insert the given trouble, and test its effect. Indicate what effect it has on the output. Assume each trouble is independent of others; that is, restore the circuit to its normal operating condition after each test.

6. The display you have built for this experiment is satisfactory only for showing a single decimal digit at a time. You could show more digits by simply replicating the circuit for as many digits as needed, although this isn't the most efficient way to make larger displays. With a larger number of digits, it is useful to blank (turn off) leading zeros in a number. Look at the function table in the manufacturer's specification sheet for the 7447A and decide what has to be applied to the $\overline{\text{Lamp test}}$, $\overline{\text{BI}}/\overline{\text{RBO}}$, and $\overline{\text{RBI}}$ inputs in order to suppress leading zeros.* Summarize the method in the space provided in the report.

* A complete discussion of these inputs can be found in Section 6–4 of the text. The data sheets are in Appendix A.

For Further Investigation

As you observed, the 7447A decoder used in this experiment is designed for BCD-to-decimal decoding; however, a slight modification of the circuit can be made to decode a binary number into octal. The largest number that we can show with a 4-bit binary input is octal 17, which requires two seven-segment displays to show both digits.

Recall that the conversion of a binary number to octal can be accomplished by grouping the binary number by threes, starting at the binary point. To display the octal numbers larger than binary 111 would normally require a second decoder and seven-segment display. For this problem, the most significant digit is either a zero or a one; therefore, we can dispense with the extra decoder and we could even use an ordinary LED to represent the most significant digit. The seven-segment display you have will still show the least significant digit. Modify the circuit in Figure 3–3 so that it correctly shows the octal numbers from 0 to 17. For example, if the switches are set to binary 1011, your circuit should light the LED representing the most significant digit and the seven-segment display should show a three.

A partial schematic is shown in the report to help you get started. Complete the schematic, showing how to connect the circuit to show octal numbers. Construct the circuit, test it, and summarize how it works.

TTL

Report for Experiment 3

Name: _____ Date: _____ Class: _____

Data and Observations:

TABLE 3–1

Inputs		Output	Inputs		Output
Binary Number	BCD Number	Seven-Segment Display	Binary Number	BCD Number	Seven-Segment Display
0 0 0 0			1 0 0 0		
0 0 0 1			1 0 0 1		
0 0 1 0			1 0 1 0	INVALID	
0 0 1 1			1 0 1 1	INVALID	
0 1 0 0			1 1 0 0	INVALID	
0 1 0 1			1 1 0 1	INVALID	
0 1 1 0			1 1 1 0	INVALID	
0 1 1 1			1 1 1 1	INVALID	

TABLE 3–2

Trouble Number	Trouble	Observations
1	LED for the C input is open.	
2	A input to 7447A is open.	
3	LAMP TEST is shorted to ground.	
4	Resistor connected to pin 15 of the 7447A is open.	

Step 6: Method for causing leading zero suppression: _____

_____

Results and Conclusion:

Further Investigation Results:

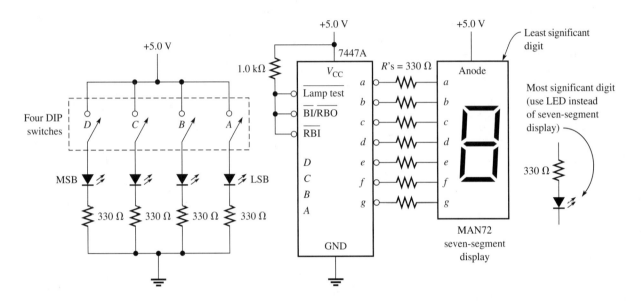

Review Questions (TTL)

1. Assume the switches in Figure 3–3 are set for a binary 1000, but the display shows a zero. What are three possible causes for this error?

2. Looking at the possible causes for an error from Question 1, how would you go about troubleshooting the problem?

3. Suppose that the BI/RBO input line was shorted to ground on the 7447A decoder and all other input lines were okay. Looking at the function table for the 7447A in Appendix A, determine the effect this would have on the display.

VHDL

Program Overview

The toggle switches located on the digital logic project board can be used to supply the logic for these experiments. Refer to the *Project Board Familiarization,* Table PB–1, for mapping information of the pins on the PLD to the toggle switches for your particular board. Table PB–3 has mapping information of the pins on the PLD to the LEDs. It is a good idea to write down the pin numbers you choose for inputs and outputs for reference later.

The VHDL section of the experiment simulates the functions of the 7447A seven-segment decoder IC except for ripple blanking and light test functions that are not used in this experiment. In addition, the outputs for the BCD invalid states will be changed from the 7447A to illustrate the flexibility of programming a PLD.

This experiment has two complete VHDL programs. All of the student programs that are in the manual are also on the CD. You may choose to type the programs into the text editor or "copy and paste" the appropriate program from the CD file.

Procedure

1. Connect the project board to a computer as described in *Project Board Familiarization* and review *VHDL Software Familiarization.* The tutorial can serve as a model for compiling and downloading programs for all of the VHDL experiments.

2. Examine Figure 3–6. The four switches represent a portion of register A of the tablet control digital system shown in Figure 3–1. For simplicity, a 4-bit BCD number is represented here with four switches for inputs and four LEDs for outputs. Enter the supplied VHDL program in Figure 3–7 into the

VHDL text editor by either typing it or copying it from the CD and pasting it into the editor. The program editor differs depending on the VHDL software you are using; see *VHDL Software Familiarization* for the instructions for your particular board.

3. The program assigns four inputs labeled *A, B, C,* and *D.* These inputs are defined in the **entity** section of the program and correspond to the TTL schematic in Figure 3–3. On your board, the inputs are represented by switches. Refer to the section entitled *Project Board Familiarization.* Pin assignments for the switches are shown in Table PB–1. Assign each of the four inputs (*A, B, C, D*) defined in the **entity** section to an on-board switch.

4. The program assigns four outputs labeled *LEDA, LEDB, LEDC,* and *LEDD.* These outputs are defined in the **entity** section of the program and correspond to the LEDs in the TTL schematic in Figure 3–3. Choose four consecutive LEDs on the board. There are 8 or 16 LEDs available, depending on the board you are using. Assign each of the outputs listed in the **entity** section to an LED on the board. Refer to the section entitled *Project Board Familiarization,* Table PB–3, for the mapping information of PLD pins to the LEDs.

5. Referring to the section entitled *VHDL Software Familiarization,* find the development software (Xilinx or Altera) for your particular project board. Then compile and download the program shown in Figure 3–7 to your project board.

6. Test the logic system by setting each switch assigned in step 3 to a HIGH and back to LOW and verify that the corresponding LED illuminates.

7. In this step, you will reprogram the PLD. Close any open VHDL project windows on the computer. The VHDL program of Figure 3–8 provides the logic to drive an on-board seven-segment display. Refer to the *Project Board Familiarization* section, Table PB–1, and assign each of the binary inputs *A0* through *A3* to an on-board switch. Then assign each of the seven-segment outputs *X0* through *X6* to the

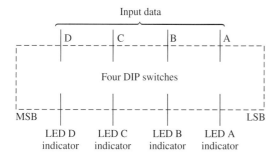

Input data

FIGURE 3–6

```
entity RegA is
    port( A, B, C, D: in bit;
           LEDA, LEDB, LEDC, LEDD: out bit);
end entity RegA;

architecture RegAExample of RegA is
begin
    LEDA <= A;
    LEDB <= B;
    LEDC <= C;
    LEDD <= D;
end architecture RegAExample;
```

FIGURE 3–7

appropriate segment of the 7-segment display on your project board. Figure 3–5 shows the segment locations on the display as given in Table PB-4.

8. Compile and download the program given in Figure 3–8 (and on the CD) to the PLD. Then test the logic system by setting the switches to each of the binary numbers listed in Table 3–3 of the report. Complete Table 3–3 by showing the appearance of the seven-segment display in the output column.

```
entity Decimal is
  port ( A: in bit_vector(0 to 3);     -- Defines array of 4 bits
         X: out bit_vector(0 to 6));   -- Defines array of 7 bits
end entity Decimal;

architecture BCDtoDecimal of Decimal is
begin
  process (A)
  begin
    case A is
          --BCD              Seven-Segment
          --Inputs           Outputs
          --ABCD             ABCDEFG
      when "0000" => X <= "1111110"; -- Displays Decimal 0
      when "0001" => X <= "0000110"; -- Displays Decimal 1
      when "0010" => X <= "1101101"; -- Displays Decimal 2
      when "0011" => X <= "1111001"; -- Displays Decimal 3
      when "0100" => X <= "0110011"; -- Displays Decimal 4
      when "0101" => X <= "1011011"; -- Displays Decimal 5
      when "0110" => X <= "1011111"; -- Displays Decimal 6
      when "0111" => X <= "1110000"; -- Displays Decimal 7
      when "1000" => X <= "1111111"; -- Displays Decimal 8
      when "1001" => X <= "1110011"; -- Displays Decimal 9
      when "1010" => X <= "1110111"; -- Displays Decimal A
      when "1011" => X <= "1111111"; -- Displays Decimal B
      when "1100" => X <= "1001110"; -- Displays Decimal C
      when "1101" => X <= "1111110"; -- Displays Decimal D
      when "1110" => X <= "1001111"; -- Displays Decimal E
      when "1111" => X <= "1000111"; -- Displays Decimal F
      when others => X <= "0000000"; -- Displays Decimal 0
    end case;
  end process;
end BCDtoDecimal;
```

CODE TIP

The program shown in Figure 3–8 uses a VHDL **case** statement. A **case** statement allows the program to execute alternate commands based on the input. The keyword **when** precedes the test case which determines the program statements to be executed. For the BCD-to-decimal converter, the seven-segment output is contained in a series of seven 1s and 0s selected by examining a series of four 1s and 0s read from the inputs.

FIGURE 3–8
Code for BCD-to-decimal decoder.

Report for Experiment 3

Name: _____ Date: _____ Class: _____

Data and Observations:

TABLE 3–3

Inputs		Output
Binary Number	BCD Number	Seven-Segment Display
0 0 0 0		
0 0 0 1		
0 0 1 0		
0 0 1 1		
0 1 0 0		
0 1 0 1		
0 1 1 0		
0 1 1 1		
1 0 0 0		
1 0 0 1		
1 0 1 0		
1 0 1 1		
1 1 0 0		
1 1 0 1		
1 1 1 0		
1 1 1 1		

Results and Conclusion:

Review Questions (VHDL)

1. You may have noticed that the number 1 and the number 6 are different than the decoded output of a 7447A. Explain the modification you would make to the program in Figure 3–8 to make these two digits look the same as the 7447A.

2. The characters after the number 9 are different in the VHDL program than in the 7447A output. Which do you think is more useful? Explain your answer.

3. What determines which code is sent to the output in the **case** block in Figure 3–8?

4

Logic Gates

Objectives

After completing this experiment, you will be able to
- ☐ Determine experimentally the truth tables for the NAND, NOR, and inverter gates.
- ☐ Use NAND and NOR gates to formulate other basic logic gates.

Reference Reading

Floyd, *Digital Fundamentals with VHDL,* Chapter 3, "Logic Gates"

Materials Needed (TTL)

7400 quad 2-input NAND gate
7402 quad 2-input NOR gate
1.0 kΩ resistor

For Further Investigation:
   7486 quad XOR gate

Materials Needed (VHDL)

Project Board

Summary of Theory

Logic deals with only two normal conditions: logic "1" or logic "0." These conditions are like the yes or no answers to a question. Either a switch is closed (1) or it isn't (0); either an event has occurred (1) or it hasn't (0); and so on. In Boolean logic, 1 and 0 represent conditions. In positive logic, 1 is represented by the term *HIGH* and 0 is represented by the term *LOW.* In positive logic, the more positive voltage is 1 and the less positive voltage is 0. Thus, for positive TTL logic, a voltage of $+2.4\,V = 1$ and a voltage of $+0.4\,V = 0$.

In some systems, this definition is reversed. With negative logic, the more positive voltage is 0 and the less positive voltage is 1. Thus, for negative TTL logic, a voltage of $+0.4\,V = 1$ and a voltage of $+2.4\,V = 0$.

Although negative logic is sometimes useful in simplifying designs, it can easily become confusing. For example, in positive logic a 2-input AND gate has a HIGH output if both input A AND input B are HIGH. But in negative logic it becomes an OR gate because if either input A OR input B is LOW, the output is LOW. Figure 4–1 illustrates this idea. The electrical signals are identical for both gates, but the logic definitions are not. The AND gate can also be drawn as an OR gate if inversion "bubbles" are added to both the inputs and the output to indicate the active-LOW signals. The operation of the AND gate can be given by two rules.

Rule 1: If A is LOW OR B is LOW OR both are LOW, then X is LOW.
Rule 2: If A is HIGH AND B is HIGH, then X is HIGH.

A = 0
B = 0 — X = 0

A = 0
B = 1 — X = 0   } "0 **OR** 0 produces a 0"

A = 1
B = 0 — X = 0

(a)

A = 1
B = 1 — X = 1   } "1 **AND** 1 produces a 1"

(b)

FIGURE 4–1
Two distinctive shape symbols for an AND gate. The two symbols represent the same gate.

The operation can also be shown by the truth table. The AND truth table is

Inputs		Output	
A	*B*	*X*	
LOW	LOW	LOW	
LOW	HIGH	LOW	} Rule 1
HIGH	LOW	LOW	
HIGH	HIGH	HIGH	← Rule 2

Notice that the first rule describes the first *three* lines of the truth table and the second rule describes the last line of the truth table. Sometimes, it is useful to draw the gate to emphasize one or another of the rules. For this reason, there are *two* distinctive shape symbols for the AND gate. Although two rules are needed to specify completely the operation of the gate, each symbol best illustrates only one of the rules. If you are reading the symbol for a gate, read

a bubble as a logic 0 and the absence of a bubble as a logic 1.

The first three lines of the truth table are illustrated with the negative-logic OR symbol (Figure 4–1(a)); the last line of the truth table is illustrated with the positive-logic AND symbol (Figure 4–1(b)). Similar rules and logic diagrams can be written for the other basic gates.

A useful method of dealing with negative logic is to label the signal function with a bar written over the label to indicate that the signal is LOW when the stated condition is true. Figure 4–2 shows some examples of this logic, called *assertion-level* logic. You should be aware that manufacturers are not always consistent in the way labels are applied to diagrams and function tables. Assertion-level logic is frequently shown to indicate an action. As shown in Figure 4–2, the action to read (R) is asserted (1) when the input line is HIGH; the opposite action is to write ($\overline{W}$), which is asserted (0) when the line is LOW. Other examples are shown in the figure.

The symbols for the basic logic gates are shown in Figure 4–3. The newer ANSI/IEEE rectangular symbols are shown along with the older distinctive-shape symbols. The ANSI/IEEE symbols contain a qualifying symbol to indicate the type of logic operation performed. The distinctive-shape symbols for logic gates are still very popular because they enable you to visualize the standard Boolean operations of AND, OR, and INVERT immediately. The distinctive shapes also enable you to analyze logic networks because each gate can be represented with a positive logic symbol or an equivalent negative logic symbol. Both shapes are used in this experiment.

In addition to the AND, OR, and INVERT functions, two other basic gates are very important to logic designers. These are the NAND and NOR gates, in which the output of AND and OR, respectively, have been negated. These gates are important because of their "universal" property; they can be used to synthesize the other Boolean logic functions including AND, OR, and INVERT functions.

FIGURE 4–2
Examples of assertion logic.

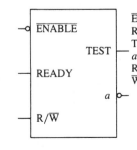

$\overline{\text{ENABLE}}$ is asserted (TRUE) when LOW.
READY is asserted (TRUE) when HIGH.
TEST is asserted (TRUE) when HIGH.
a is asserted (TRUE) when LOW (See 7447A)
R is asserted (TRUE) when HIGH.
$\overline{W}$ is asserted (TRUE) when LOW.

72

FIGURE 4–3
Basic logic gates.

Distinctive shape symbols   Rectangular outline symbols (ANSI/IEEE symbols)

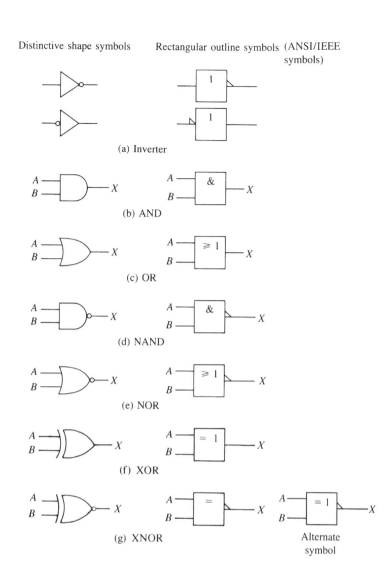

(a) Inverter

(b) AND

(c) OR

(d) NAND

(e) NOR

(f) XOR

(g) XNOR   Alternate symbol

Two gates that are sometimes classified with the basic gates are the exclusive-OR (abbreviated XOR) and the exclusive-NOR (abbreviated XNOR) gates. These gates always have two inputs. The symbols are shown in Figure 4–3(f) and (g). The output of the XOR gate is HIGH when either *A* or *B* is HIGH, but not both (inputs "disagree"). The XNOR is just the opposite; the output is HIGH only when the inputs are the same (agree). For this reason, the XNOR gate is sometimes called a COINCIDENCE gate.

The logical operation of any gate can be summarized with a truth table, which shows all the possible inputs and outputs. The truth tables for AND, OR, INVERT, XOR, and XNOR are shown in Table 4–1 (a) through (e). The tables are shown with 1 and 0 to represent positive logic HIGH and LOW, respec-

tively. Except in Figure 4–1 (where negative logic is illustrated), only positive logic is used in this lab book and 1 and 0 mean HIGH and LOW, respectively.

In this experiment, you will test the truth tables for NAND and NOR gates as well as those for several combinations of these gates. Keep in mind that if any two truth tables are identical, then the logic circuits that they represent are equivalent.

Pre-lab Questions

1. Explain the difference between positive logic and negative logic.
2. What gates are considered to be "universal" gates? Explain your answer.
3. What is meant by assertion-level logic?

73

TABLE 4–1(a)
Truth table for inverter.

Input	Output
A	X
0	1
1	0

TABLE 4–1(b)
Truth table for 2-input AND gate.

Inputs		Output
A	B	X
0	0	0
0	1	0
1	0	0
1	1	1

TABLE 4–1(c)
Truth table for 2-input OR gate.

Inputs		Output
A	B	X
0	0	0
0	1	1
1	0	1
1	1	1

TABLE 4–1(d)
Truth table for XOR gate.

Inputs		Output
A	B	X
0	0	0
0	1	1
1	0	1
1	1	0

TABLE 4–1(e)
Truth table for XNOR gate.

Inputs		Output
A	B	X
0	0	1
0	1	0
1	0	0
1	1	1

TTL

Procedure

Logic Functions

1. Find the connection diagram for the 7400 quad 2-input NAND gate and the 7402 quad 2-input NOR gate in the manufacturer's specification sheet.* Note that there are four gates on each of these ICs. Apply V_{CC} and ground to the appropriate pins. Then test one of the NAND gates by connecting all possible combinations of inputs, as listed in Table 4–2 of the report. Apply a logic 1 through a series

*See Appendix A.

1.0 kΩ resistor and a logic 0 by connecting directly to ground. Show the logic output (1 or 0) as well as the measured output voltage in Table 4–2. Use the DMM to measure the output voltage.

2. Repeat Step 1 for one of the NOR gates; tabulate your results in Table 4–3 of the report.

3. Connect the circuits of Figures 4–4 and 4–5. Connect the input to a 0 and a 1, measure each output voltage, and complete truth Tables 4–4 and 4–5 for the circuits.

4. Construct the circuit shown in Figure 4–6 and complete truth Table 4–6. This circuit may appear at first to have no application, but in fact can be used as a buffer. Because of amplification within the IC, a buffer provides more drive current.

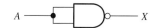

FIGURE 4–4

FIGURE 4–5

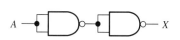

FIGURE 4–6

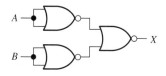

FIGURE 4–7

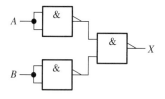

FIGURE 4–8

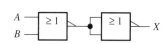

FIGURE 4–9

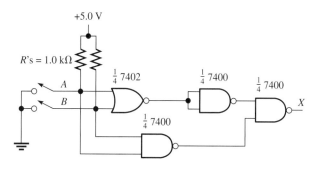

FIGURE 4–10

5. Construct the circuit shown in Figure 4–7 and complete truth Table 4–7. Notice that the truth table for this circuit is the same as the truth table for one of the single gates. (What does this imply about the circuit?)

6. Repeat Step 5 for the circuits shown in Figures 4–8 and 4–9. Complete truth Tables 4–8 and 4–9.

For Further Investigation

The circuit shown in Figure 4–10 has the same truth table as one of the truth tables shown in Figure 4–1 (a) through (e). Test all input combinations and complete truth Table 4–10. What is the equivalent gate?

Report for Experiment 4

Name: _____ Date: _____ Class: _____

Data and Observations:

TABLE 4–2
NAND gate.

Inputs		Output	Measured Output Voltage
A	B	X	
0	0		
0	1		
1	0		
1	1		

TABLE 4–3
NOR gate.

Inputs		Output	Measured Output Voltage
A	B	X	
0	0		
0	1		
1	0		
1	1		

TABLE 4–4
Truth table for Figure 4–4.

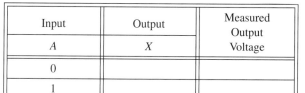

Input	Output	Measured Output Voltage
A	X	
0		
1		

TABLE 4–5
Truth table for Figure 4–5.

Input	Output	Measured Output Voltage
A	X	
0		
1		

TABLE 4–6
Truth table for Figure 4–6.

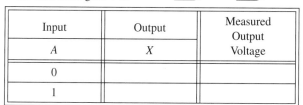

Input	Output	Measured Output Voltage
A	X	
0		
1		

TABLE 4–7
Truth table for Figure 4–7.

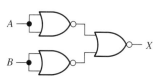

Inputs		Output	Measured Output Voltage
A	B	X	
0	0		
0	1		
1	0		
1	1		

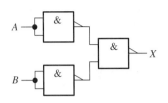

TABLE 4–8
Truth table for Figure 4–8.

Inputs		Output	Measured Output Voltage
A	B	X	
0	0		
0	1		
1	0		
1	1		

TABLE 4–9
Truth table for Figure 4–9.

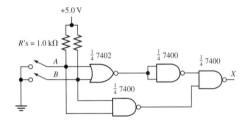

Inputs		Output	Measured Output Voltage
A	B	X	
0	0		
0	1		
1	0		
1	1		

Results and Conclusion:

Further Investigation Results:

TABLE 4–10
Truth table for Figure 4–10.

Inputs		Output	Measured Output Voltage
A	B	X	
0	0		
0	1		
1	0		
1	1		

Review Questions (TTL)

1. Look over the truth tables in your report.

   a. What circuits did you find that are equivalent to inverters? _____

   b. What circuit is equivalent to a 2-input AND gate? _____

   c. What circuit is equivalent to a 2-input OR gate? _____

2. A car burglar alarm has a normally LOW switch on each of its four doors when they are closed. If any door is opened, the alarm is set off. The alarm requires an active-HIGH output. What type of basic gate is needed to provide this logic?

Program Overview

Normal TTL logic cannot provide sufficient current to light an LED when it is HIGH. The PLD *can* light an LED with a HIGH signal (with low current). Consequently, an LED that is ON represents a LOW in the TTL portion of this experiment but represents a HIGH on all project boards except for the DeVry eSOC board, which uses a LOW to turn on LEDs.

In all of the VHDL experiments, the project board toggle switches are used to supply the input logic, and LEDs are used to read the output logic. Refer to the *Project Board Familiarization* section, Table PB–1, for mapping information of the PLD pins to the toggle switches for your particular board. Table PB–3 has mapping information of the PLD pins to the LEDs.

In the two VHDL programs in this experiment, the internal definitions mimic the names in the pin descriptions of the TTL fixed-function logic given in manufacturers' specification sheets. Each program has three simulated gates, which will be internal to the PLD. The inputs for the first gate are named *A1* and *B1*, the second gate has inputs named *A2* and *B2*, and the third gate has inputs named *A3* and *B3*. The corresponding outputs are named *X1, X2,* and *X3*. Because these names are assigned as internal inputs and outputs, the VHDL keyword **signal** is used to define them. Inputs to the PLD from the switches and outputs to the LEDs are defined in the **entity** section because they are outside the PLD. The inputs are labeled *A, B,* and *C* and the outputs are labeled *LED1, LED2,* and *LED3*.

The keywords **NAND** and **NOR** are introduced in the two programs in this experiment. The logical operations and examples of the syntax for these keywords are shown in Table 4–11. The programs are designed to show you how a PLD can implement gate logic, just as you would do with fixed-function logic. All of the student programs, including the two

used in this experiment, are on the CD packaged with this manual and can be "copied and pasted" directly into the text editor.

As an optional exercise, your instructor may want you to measure the output voltages on the board in this experiment. *You should never hook a probe directly to the PLD.* Great care must be taken to avoid shorting any pins (and damaging the board) with the DMM or other instrument. If directed by your instructor, use a DMM to measure the output voltages. A space is provided in the tables in the report for this optional measurement.

Procedure

Logic Functions

1. Connect the project board to a computer as described in *Project Board Familiarization* and review *VHDL Software Familiarization*. The tutorial can serve as a model for compiling and downloading programs for all of the VHDL experiments.

2. Figure 4–11 shows a program named *NandGate* that is a PLD implementation of three 2-input NAND gates. Enter the NandGate program into the VHDL text editor by either typing it or copying it from the CD and pasting it into the editor.

3. Compile and download the NandGate program to the project board.

4. The NAND gate shown in Figure 4–12 reads two inputs *A* and *B*, which are renamed *A1* and *B1* within the program to look like the fixed-function description of a single gate. The output *X1* is connected to LED1. Test the function of the NAND gate logic controlling LED1 by connecting all four combinations of inputs as listed in Table 4–12 of the report. Show the logic output (1 or 0) based on LED1. (*Optional:* If directed by your instructor, carefully use the DMM to measure the output voltage.)

5. The circuit in Figure 4–13 is represented in the program by internally connecting the switch input, *A*, to signals *A2* and *B2*, which represent the inputs to the second NAND gate. This gate has one output labeled *X2*, which controls LED2. Test the logic by connecting *A* to a 1 and a 0 as listed in Table 4–13. Show the output logic (1 or 0) for each input.

6. The circuit in Figure 4–14 is represented in the program as two NAND gates. The *X2* output from gate 2 (Figure 4–13) is connected to the third NAND gate, with inputs *A3* and *B3* and with the output labeled *X3*, which is connected to LED3. Notice that the inputs of both gates are connected together. Test the logic controlling LED3 by connecting both a 1 and a 0 to the *A* input. Show the logic output (1 or 0) in Table 4–14.

TABLE 4–11

Operator	Description	Syntax Example
NAND	Returns HIGH when any input is LOW.	X1 <= A1 **nand** B1;
NOR	Returns LOW when any input is HIGH.	X1 <= A1 **nor** B1;

```
--This program simulates three 2-input nand gates
entity NandGate is
  port (A, B: in bit;
        LED1, LED2, LED3: out bit);
end entity NandGate;

architecture GateBehavior of NandGate is
signal A1, B1, A2, B2, A3, B3, X1, X2, X3 : bit;
begin
  A1 <= A; B1 <= B;
  A2 <= A; B2 <= A;
  A3 <= X2; B3 <= X2;
  X1 <= A1 nand B1; -- Figure 4-12
  X2 <= A2 nand B2; -- Figure 4-13
  X3 <= A3 nand A3;
  LED1 <= X1;
  LED2 <= X2;
  LED3 <= X3;
end architecture GateBehavior;
```

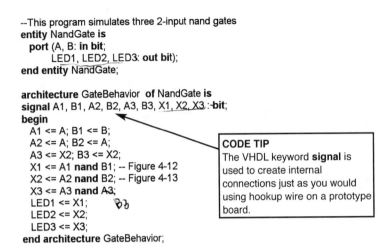

CODE TIP
The VHDL keyword **signal** is used to create internal connections just as you would using hookup wire on a prototype board.

FIGURE 4–11

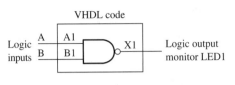

FIGURE 4–12

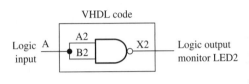

FIGURE 4–13

7. Figure 4–15 shows a new program named *NorGate* that is a PLD implementation of three 2-input NOR gates. The **entity** section describes the two inputs *A* and *B* as well as three outputs *LED1*, *LED2*, and *LED3*. The VHDL keyword **signal** is again used to define internal signal identifiers, which are named *A1*, *B1*, *X1*, and so forth. Enter the VHDL program into the text editor by typing it or copying it from the CD.

8. Compile and download your program.

9. Select and test the NOR gate controlling LED1 as shown in Figure 4–16 by connecting all possible combinations of the two inputs (*A* and *B*) as listed in Table 4–15. Show the output logic (1 or 0) observed on LED1.

10. The circuit in Figure 4–17 is represented in the program by connecting the switch input *A* to internal signals *A2* and *B2*. Signals *A2* and *B2* drive a NOR gate to form the output *X2*. Test the NOR gate logic controlling LED2 by connecting both a 1 and a 0 to the single inputs as listed in Table 4–16. Show the output logic (1 or 0).

11. The circuit in Figure 4–18 is represented in code by tying the second NOR gate output, *X2*, to

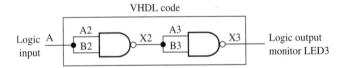

FIGURE 4–14

```
entity NorGate is
  port (A, B: in bit;
        LED1, LED2, LED3: out bit);
end entity NorGate;

architecture GateBehavior of NorGate is
signal A1, B1, A2, B2, A3, B3, X1, X2, X3 : bit;
begin
  A1 <= A; B1 <= B;
  A2 <= A; B2 <= A;
  A3 <= X2; B3 <= X2;
  X1 <= A1 nor B1; -- Figure 4-16
  X2 <= A2 nor B2; -- Figure 4-17
  X3 <= A3 nor A3;
  LED1 <= X1;
  LED2 <= X2;
  LED3 <= X3;
end architecture GateBehavior;
```

FIGURE 4–15

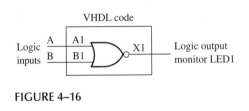

FIGURE 4–16

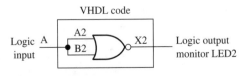

FIGURE 4–17

FIGURE 4–18

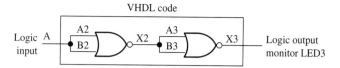

FIGURE 4–19

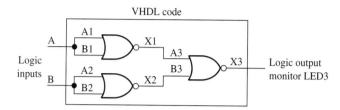

internal signals *A3* and *B3* to form the inputs to the third NOR gate. Test the overall circuit by connecting both a 1 and a 0 to the input. Show the output logic (1 or 0) for each input in Table 4–17.

For Further Investigation

Modify the current VHDL program to represent the gate logic of Figure 4–19. The *LED1* and *LED2* outputs can be ignored. Test all input combinations and complete truth Table 4–18. What is the equivalent gate?

Report for Experiment 4

Name: _____ Date: _____ Class: _____

Data and Observations:

TABLE 4–12
NAND gate.

Inputs		Output	(Optional) Measured Voltage
A	B	X	
0	0		
0	1		
1	0		
1	1		

TABLE 4–13
Truth table for Figure 4–13.

Input	Output	(Optional) Measured Voltage
A	X	
0		
1		

TABLE 4–14
Truth table for Figure 4–14.

Input	Output	(Optional) Measured Voltage
A	X	
0		
1		

TABLE 4–15
NOR gate.

Inputs		Output	(Optional) Measured Voltage
A	B	X	
0	0		
0	1		
1	0		
1	1		

TABLE 4–16
Truth table for Figure 4–17.

Input	Output	(Optional) Measured Voltage
A	X	
0		
1		

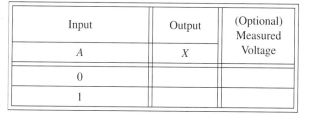

TABLE 4–17
Truth table for Figure 4–18.

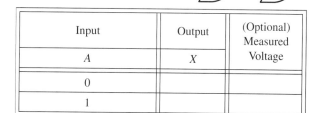

Input	Output	(Optional) Measured Voltage
A	X	
0		
1		

Further Investigation Results:

TABLE 4–18
Truth table for Figure 4–19.

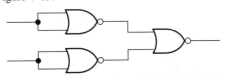

Inputs		Output	(Optional) Measured Voltage
A	*B*	*X*	
0	0		
0	1		
1	0		
1	1		

Results and Conclusion:

Review Questions (VHDL)

1. Explain what happens after the statement **OUT := A NOR B** is executed.

2. Write a single VHDL statement to perform the logic in Table 4–17.

5

More Logic Gates

Objectives

After completing this experiment, you will be able to
□ Determine experimentally the truth tables for OR and XOR.
□ Test OR and XOR logic gates with pulse waveforms.
□ Use OR and XOR gates to form a circuit that performs the 1's or 2's complement of a 4-bit binary number.

Reference Reading

Floyd, *Digital Fundamentals with VHDL*, Chapter 3, "Logic Gates"

Materials Needed (TTL)

ICs: one 7432 OR gate, one 7486 XOR gate
Four LEDs
Resistors: nine 330 Ω, one 1.0 kΩ
One 4-position DIP switch
One SPST switch (wire may substitute)

For Further Investigation:
Three additional 1.0 kΩ resistors

Materials Needed (VHDL)

Project Board

Summary of Theory

In this experiment, you will test the OR and XOR gates but go one step further and use these gates in an application.

The truth table for an OR gate is shown in Table 5–1(a) for a two-input OR gate. OR gates are available with more than two inputs. The operation of an n-input OR gate is summarized in the following rule:

The output is HIGH if any input is HIGH, otherwise it is LOW.

The XOR gate is a 2-input gate. Recall that the truth table is similar to the OR gate except for when both inputs are HIGH; in this case, the output is LOW. The truth table for a 2-input XOR gate can be summarized with the statement

The output is HIGH only if one input is HIGH; otherwise it is LOW.

The truth table for XOR is shown in Table 5–1(b).

Pre-lab Questions

1. Assume you have two inputs A and B and their complements, $\bar{A}$ and $\bar{B}$, available. Show how you could use 2-input NAND gates to implement the XOR function.
2. Assume you have 2-input OR gates but needed to implement a 4-input OR function. Show how to connect the gates to implement the 4-input requirement.

TABLE 5–1(a)
Truth table for 2-input OR gate.

Inputs		Output
A	B	X
0	0	0
0	1	1
1	0	1
1	1	1

TABLE 5–1(b)
Truth table for XOR gate.

Inputs		Output
A	B	X
0	0	0
0	1	1
1	0	1
1	1	0

Procedure

Logic Functions for the OR and XOR Gates

1. Find the connection diagram for the 7432 quad 2-input OR gate and the 7486 quad 2-input XOR gate in the manufacturer's specification sheet.* Note that there are four gates on each of these ICs. Apply V_{CC} and ground to the appropriate pins. Then test one of the OR gates in the 7432 by connecting all possible combinations of inputs, as listed in Table 5–2 of the report. Apply a logic 1 through a series 1.0 kΩ resistor and a logic 0 by connecting directly to ground. Show the logic output (1 or 0) as well as the measured output voltage in Table 5–2. Use the DMM to measure the output voltage.

2. Repeat Step 1 for one of the XOR gates in the 7486; tabulate your results in Table 5–3 of the report.

3. The XOR gate has a very useful feature enabling selective inversion of a waveform. Construct the circuit shown in Figure 5–1. The input on pin 2 is from your pulse generator, which should be set to a TTL compatible pulse. Set the frequency for 1 kHz and observe the input and the output simultaneously with S_1 open. Then close S_1 and observe the input

*See Appendix A.

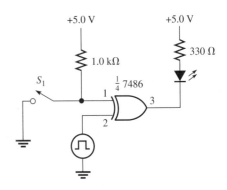

FIGURE 5–1

and the output. Sketch the observed waveforms in Plot 1 of the report.

4. In this step, you will test a circuit that uses combinations of OR and XOR gates and complete the truth table for the circuit. The purpose of the circuit is to use the selective inversion property of the XOR gate to produce either the 1's complement or the 2's complement of a 4-bit number. Both the input and output number are read from the LEDs; the LEDs are on when the bit shown is LOW in keeping with TTL current specifications. Construct the circuit shown in Figure 5–2. You will need to assign pin numbers to the various pins.

5. Open the complement switch, and test the data switches. If the circuit is working properly, each output LED should be the exact opposite of the corresponding input LED. If this isn't what you observe, stop and troubleshoot your circuit.

6. Now test the circuit with the complement switch closed. Complete the truth table in the report (Table 5–4) for all possible inputs. Keep in mind that a 0 is indicated with an LED that is ON.

7. Table 5–5 (in the report) gives several possible problems that could occur in the complement circuit. For each problem given, list one or two likely causes that would produce the problem. As a check on your idea, you may want to test your idea on the circuit.

EWB/MSM Troubleshooting

The CD packaged with this lab manual contains Electronics Workbench (.ewb) and Multisim (.msm) files. Open the file named Exp-05.ewb on the CD packaged with this lab manual. The file contains two circuits. The first one has no fault and is the 1's and 2's complement circuit you tested in this experiment (Figure 5–2). The second has a fault. Analyze the fault by changing the input switches and observing the outputs. From your observations, deduce the most likely fault and state how you would isolate it.

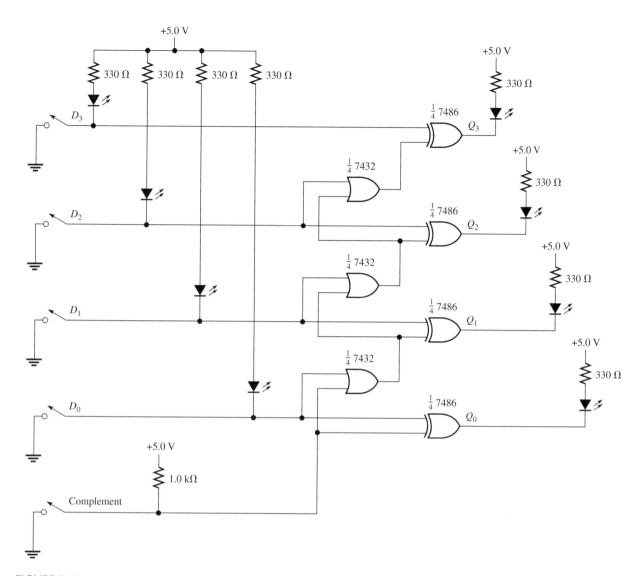

FIGURE 5–2

87

For Further Investigation

Another interesting circuit that can be constructed with XOR gates is the solution to the logic problem of controlling a light or other electrical device from several different locations. For two locations, the problem is simple and switches are made to do just that. The circuit shown in Figure 5–3 can control an LED from any of four locations. Construct and test the circuit; summarize your results in the report.

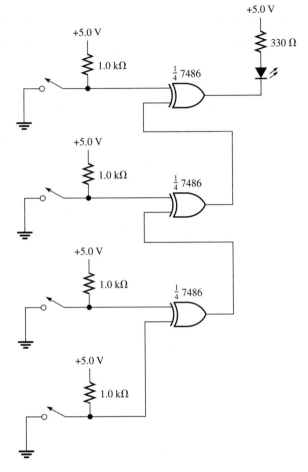

FIGURE 5–3

Report for Experiment 5

Name: _____ Date: _____ Class: _____

Data and Observations:

TABLE 5–2
OR gate.

Inputs		Output	Measured Output Voltage
A	B	X	
0	0		
0	1		
1	0		
1	1		

TABLE 5–3
XOR gate.

Inputs		Output	Measured Output Voltage
A	B	X	
0	0		
0	1		
1	0		
1	1		

TABLE 5–4

Inputs	Outputs
$D_3 D_2 D_1 D_0$	$Q_3 Q_2 Q_1 Q_0$
0 0 0 0	
0 0 0 1	
0 0 1 0	
0 0 1 1	
0 1 0 0	
0 1 0 1	
0 1 1 0	
0 1 1 1	
1 0 0 0	
1 0 0 1	
1 0 1 0	
1 0 1 1	
1 1 0 0	
1 1 0 1	
1 1 1 0	
1 1 1 1	

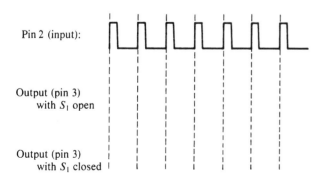

Pin 2 (input):

Output (pin 3)
  with S_1 open

Output (pin 3)
  with S_1 closed

PLOT 1

TABLE 5–5

Symptom Number	Symptom	Possible Cause
1	None of the LEDs operate; the switches have no effect.	
2	LEDs on the output side do not work; those on the input side do work.	
3	The LED representing Q_3 is sometimes on when it should be off.	
4	The complement switch has no effect on the outputs.	

Results and Conclusion:

EWB/MSM Troubleshooting:

Most likely problem: _____ _____

_____

Further Investigation Results:

Review Questions (TTL)

1. Step 3 mentions the selective inversion feature of an XOR gate. Explain how you can choose to invert or not invert a given signal.

2. The circuit in Figure 5–2 is limited to a 4-bit input. Show how you could expand the circuit to 8 bits by adding more ICs.

Program Overview

In Experiment 4, it was mentioned that an LED that is ON represents a LOW in the TTL section of this experiment but a HIGH in the VHDL section (except for the DeVry eSOC board). As in the previous programs, the toggle switches and LEDs on the project board are used for inputs and outputs. You will need to do the pin mapping for inputs and outputs as described in the section entitled *Project Board Familiarization.*

In the first two VHDL programs for this experiment, you will be introduced to the VHDL keywords **OR** and **XOR.** The logical operation and examples of the syntax for these keywords are shown in Table 5–6. The inputs to the first two programs are named *A* and *B* and the output is named *LED1.* These are defined in the **entity** section of the programs.

The third program will use both OR and XOR in a small system. Also, you will use an external pulse generator to supply a TTL compatible pulse to the board and an oscilloscope to view the input and output. Although the board has a high-speed oscillator available, it is more versatile to be able to use a pulse generator that has a frequency control. Prior to connecting the pulse generator, the pin assignment in the program needs to be changed. The procedure for connecting the pulse generator to your board is in *Project Board Familiarization,* section 4b, p. 20. A color photo of the correct hookup for the pulse generator and the oscilloscope is shown on the back cover for each board.

Procedure

Logic Functions for the OR and XOR Gates

1. Connect the project board to a computer as described in *Project Board Familiarization* and review *VHDL Software Familiarization.*

2. Figure 5–4 shows a program named *More-Gates* that is a PLD implementation of a 2-input OR gate. Enter the VHDL program into the text editor by either typing it or "copying and pasting" it from the CD.

3. Compile and download the MoreGates program to the project board.

4. The program simulates the OR gate circuit shown in Figure 5–5. The inputs *A* and *B* are from switches and are defined internally in the program as *A1* and *B1.* The output *X1* is sent to LED1. Test the function of the OR gate by connecting all four combinations of the two inputs as listed in Table 5–7 in the report. Show the logic output (1 or 0) in the table. (*Optional:* If directed by your instructor, carefully use the DMM to measure the output voltage for each case. Do not connect a DMM directly to the PLD.)

5. In this step, you will modify one line of the program. In the text editor, change the line defining *X1* from OR to XOR as shown in Figure 5–6. This change will cause the program to simulate the XOR gate shown in Figure 5–7. Recompile and download the modified program.

6. Just as before, the XOR gate program reads two inputs *A* and *B* but now uses an XOR gate from the output *X1* that lights LED1. Test the function of the XOR gate controlling LED1 by connecting all four combinations of the two inputs as listed in Table 5–8 (in the report). Show the logic output (1 or 0) in the table.

7. In this step, you will change the program so that it will be ready for a pulse generator input. Find the pin used for the pulse generator in Section 4b of *Project Board Familiarization.* In the pin assignment section of the Altera or Xilinx program, change the pin assignment of the *B* input to the pin used for the pulse generator. Recompile the program and download the revised program to your project board.

8. Connect a pulse generator to your project board according to the steps given in Section 4b of *Project Board Familiarization.* Verify that you have a TTL level pulse BEFORE connecting the pulse generator to the project board to avoid damaging

TABLE 5–6

Operator	Description	Syntax Example
OR	Returns HIGH when any input is HIGH.	X1 <= A1 **or** B1;
XOR	Returns HIGH when all inputs are HIGH and LOW when all inputs are LOW.	X1 <= A1 **xor** B1;

```
--This program simulates a 2-input OR gate
entity MoreGates is
    port (A, B: in bit;
        LED1: out bit);
end entity MoreGates;

architecture GateBehavior of MoreGates is
signal A1, B1, X1: bit;
begin
    A1 <= A; B1 <= B;
    X1 <= A1 or B1;
    LED1 <= X1;
end architecture GateBehavior;
```

FIGURE 5–4

```
--This program simulates a 2-input xor gate
entity MoreGates is
    port (A, B: in bit;
        LED1: out bit);
end entity MoreGates;

architecture GateBehavior of MoreGates is
signal A1, B1, X1 : bit;
begin
    A1 <= A; B1 <= B;
    X1 <= A1 xor B1;
    LED1 <= X1;
end architecture GateBehavior;
```

FIGURE 5–6

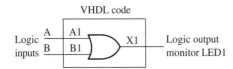

FIGURE 5–5

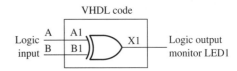

FIGURE 5–7

your board. When you have verified the level, connect the pulse generator.

9. The *B* input is now from your pulse generator as shown in Figure 5–8. Set the frequency of the pulse generator to 1 kHz and observe the input and the output simultaneously with the *A* input HIGH. Then change input *A* to a logic LOW and observe the

input and output. Sketch the results in Plot 2 of the report.

Putting It All Together

10. In this step, you will test digital logic that uses combinations of OR and XOR gates and complete the truth table for the circuit. The purpose of the logic system is to use the selective inversion property of an XOR gate to produce either the 1's complement or the 2's complement of a 4-bit number. Both the input and output numbers are read from the LEDs. Enter the VHDL program in Figure 5–9 by typing it into the text editor or by "copying and pasting" it from the CD. The program simulates the circuit shown in Figure 5–10.

11. Compile and download the program.

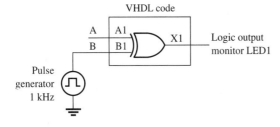

FIGURE 5–8

```
entity LabOrXor is
    port ( A, B, C, D, Complement : in bit;
        LED0, LED1, LED2, LED3, LED4, LED5, LED6, LED7:  out bit);
end entity LabOrXor;

architecture GateBehavior of LabOrXor is
begin
    LED0 <= A;
    LED1 <= B;
    LED2 <= C;
    LED3 <= D;
    LED4 <=(((Complement or A) or  B) or C) xor D;
    LED5 <=((Complement or A) or  B) xor C;
    LED6 <= (Complement or A) xor B;
    LED7 <= Complement xor A;
end architecture GateBehavior;
```

CODE TIP
VHDL uses parentheses to group logic to force precedence of operations and clarify the program.

FIGURE 5–9

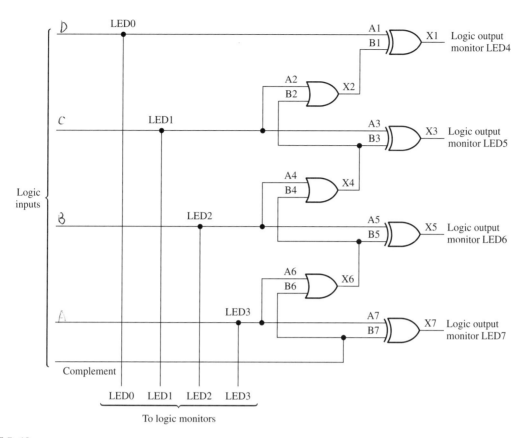

FIGURE 5–10
The numbers shown with the gates are for reference only.

12. Set the complement switch to a HIGH and test the data switches. Each output LED should be exact opposite of the corresponding input LED.

13. Set the complement switch to a LOW and test the data switches. Complete the truth table in the report (Table 5–9) for all 16 possible inputs.

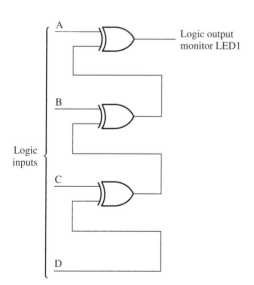

FIGURE 5–11

For Further Investigation

Another interesting circuit that can be constructed with XOR logic is the solution to the logic problem of controlling a light or other electrical device from several different locations. For two locations, the problem is simple and switches are made to do that. The circuit shown in Figure 5–11 can control an LED from any of four locations. Test the VHDL program (Figure 5–12) that represents this logic system; summarize your results in the report.

```
entity Lab5FI is
    port ( A, B, C, D, Complement : in bit;
        LED1: out bit);
end entity Lab5FI;

architecture Behavior of Lab5FI is
begin
    LED1 <= (( D xor C ) xor B ) xor A;
end architecture Behavior;
```

FIGURE 5–12

93

VHDL

Report for Experiment 5

Name: _____ Date: _____ Class: _____

Data and Observations:

TABLE 5–7
Truth table for 2-input OR gate.

Inputs		Output	(Optional) Measured Voltage
A	B	X	
0	0		
0	1		
1	0		
1	1		

TABLE 5–8
Truth table for 2-input XOR gate.

Inputs		Output	(Optional) Measured Voltage
A	B	X	
0	0		
0	1		
1	0		
1	1		

TABLE 5–9

Inputs				Outputs
D	C	B	A	LED7 LED6 LED5 LED4
0	0	0	0	
0	0	0	1	
0	0	1	0	
0	0	1	1	
0	1	0	0	
0	1	0	1	
0	1	1	0	
0	1	1	1	
1	0	0	0	
1	0	0	1	
1	0	1	0	
1	0	1	1	
1	1	0	0	
1	1	0	1	
1	1	1	0	
1	1	1	1	

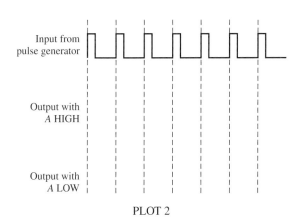

Input from pulse generator

Output with *A* HIGH

Output with *A* LOW

PLOT 2

Results and Conclusion:

Further Investigation Results:

Review Questions (VHDL)

1. Explain what would happen if the XOR gates in Figure 5–11 were replaced with OR gates in the program from Step 10.

2. A 3-bit binary counter produces a sequence of binary numbers from 000 to 111. Can you think of a way to produce a logic 1 when the output of the counter is 001, 010, 011, or 100 and a LOW for all other outputs? Use OR and XOR gates in a VHDL statement to accomplish this.

6

Interpreting Manufacturer's Data Sheets

Objectives

After completing this experiment, you will be able to
☐ Measure the static electrical specifications for TTL and CMOS logic.
☐ Interpret manufacturer's data sheets including voltage and current requirements and limits.
☐ Measure the transfer curve for a TTL inverter.

Reference Reading

Floyd, *Digital Fundamentals with VHDL,* Chapter 3, "Logic Gates," and Chapter 14, "Integrated Circuit Technologies"

Materials Needed

7404 hex inverter
4081 quad AND gate
One 10 kΩ variable resistor
Resistors (one of each): 300 Ω, 1.0 kΩ, 15 kΩ, 1.0 MΩ, load resistor (to be calculated)

Summary of Theory

In this experiment, you will start by testing a TTL (transistor-transistor logic) 7404 hex inverter, a single package containing six inverters. As you know, an inverter performs the NOT or complement function. Ideally, the output is in either of two defined states. As long as the manufacturer's specifications

are not exceeded, these conditions will hold and the logic will not be damaged.

TTL logic is designed to have conventional current (plus to minus) flowing into the output terminal of the gate when the output is LOW. This current, called *sink* current, is shown on a data sheet as a *positive* current, indicating that it is flowing into the gate. Conventional current leaves the gate when the output is HIGH. This current is indicated on the data sheet as a *negative* current and is said to be *source* current. TTL logic can sink much larger current than it can source.

In the last part of this experiment, you will test CMOS (complementary metal-oxide semiconductor) logic. An important advantage to CMOS logic is its low power consumption. When it is not switching from one logic level to another, the power dissipation in the IC approaches zero; however, at high frequencies the power dissipation increases. Other advantages include high fanout, high noise immunity, temperature stability, and ability to operate from power supplies from 3 V to 15 V.

CMOS logic uses field-effect transistors, whereas TTL uses bipolar transistors. This results in significantly different characteristics. Consequently, CMOS and TTL logic cannot be connected directly to each other without due consideration of their specifications, since voltage levels and current sourcing and sinking capabilities differ. Interfacing between various types of logic is determined by these specifications. In addition, all MOS families of

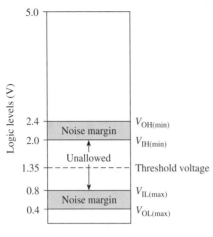

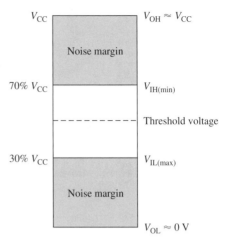

(a) TTL levels and noise margin

(b) CMOS levels and noise margin.

FIGURE 6–1

logic are more sensitive to static electricity, and special precautions to avoid static damage should be observed when handling MOS devices. In addition to static handling precautions, you should use the following operating precautions:

1. Unused inputs must NOT be left open even on gates that are not being used. They should be tied to V_{CC}, ground, or an input signal.
2. Power supply voltages must always be on when signal voltages are present at the inputs. Signal voltage must never exceed the power supply.
3. CMOS devices must never be inserted into or removed from circuits with the power on.

One important specification for any logic family is *noise margin*. Noise margin is the voltage difference that can exist between the output of one gate and the input of the next gate and still maintain guaranteed logic levels. For TTL, this difference is 0.4 V, as illustrated in Figure 6–1(a). For CMOS, the voltage thresholds are approximately 30% and 70% of V_{CC}. The noise margin is 30% of the supply voltage, as illustrated in Figure 6–1(b). A technique that is used to avoid noise problems in logic circuits is to place a small bypass capacitor (about 0.1 μF) between the supply and ground near every IC in a circuit.

A graphic tool to help visualize the characteristics of a circuit is called the *transfer curve*. The transfer curve is a graph of the input voltage plotted along the *x*-axis against the corresponding output voltage plotted along the *y*-axis. A linear circuit should have a straight-line transfer curve. On the other hand, a digital circuit has a transfer curve with a sharp transition between a HIGH and a LOW value. In the Further Investigation section, you will investigate the transfer curve for a 7404 inverter.

Pre-lab Questions

1. A hypothetical logic family has the following characteristics: $V_{IL} = +0.5$ V; $V_{IH} = +3.0$ V; $V_{OL} = +0.2$ V; $V_{OH} = +3.5$ V. Compute the LOW and HIGH noise margin for this family.

   V_{NL} (LOW) = _____; V_{NL} (HIGH) = _____

2. What is a transfer curve? Which variable is plotted on the *x*-axis and which variable is plotted on the *y*-axis?

Procedure

1. The data table in the Report section is from the manufacturer's specified characteristics for the 7404 inverter. You will be measuring many of these characteristics in this experiment and entering your measured value next to the specified value. Begin by connecting the circuit shown in Figure 6–2(a). Inputs that are connected HIGH are normally connected through a resistor to protect the input from voltage surges and the possibility of shorting the power supply directly to ground in case the input is grounded.

2. Measure the voltage at the input of the inverter, with respect to ground, as shown in Figure 6–2(b). Since the input is pulled HIGH, this voltage will be labeled V_{IH}. Enter your measured voltage in Table 6–1, line a. (Note that the specified V_{IH} is a *minimum* level; your measured value is probably much higher.)

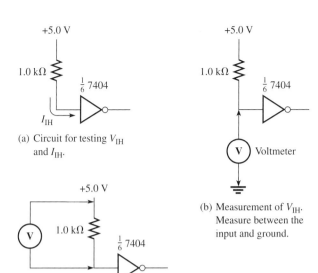

+5.0 V

1.0 kΩ

$\frac{1}{6}$ 7404

I_{IH}

(a) Circuit for testing V_{IH} and I_{IH}.

+5.0 V

1.0 kΩ

$\frac{1}{6}$ 7404

V Voltmeter

(b) Measurement of V_{IH}. Measure between the input and ground.

+5.0 V

V

1.0 kΩ

$\frac{1}{6}$ 7404

(c) Measure across the input resistor to calculate I_{IH}.

FIGURE 6–2

3. Measure the voltage *across* the 1.0 kΩ resistor, as shown in Figure 6–2(c). TTL logic requires a very small input current to pull it HIGH. Using your measured voltage and Ohm's law, calculate the current in the resistor. This current is the input HIGH current, abbreviated I_{IH}. Enter your measured current in Table 6–1, line g. Compare your measured value with the specified maximum I_{IH}. Since conventional current is into the IC, the sign of this current is positive.

4. Measure the output voltage with respect to ground. Since the input is HIGH, the output is LOW. This voltage is called V_{OL}. Do not record this voltage; you will record V_{OL} in Step 5. Notice that without a load, the V_{OL} is much lower than the maximum specified level.

5. In order to determine the effect of a load on V_{OL}, look up the maximum LOW output current I_{OL} for the 7404. Then connect a resistor, R_{LOAD}, between the output and +5.0 V that allows $I_{OL(max)}$ to flow. Assume 4.8 V is dropped *across* the load resistor. Using Ohm's law, determine the appropriate load resistor, measure it, and place it in the circuit of

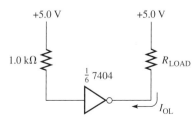

+5.0 V

+5.0 V

1.0 kΩ

R_{LOAD}

$\frac{1}{6}$ 7404

I_{OL}

FIGURE 6–3

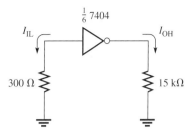

$\frac{1}{6}$ 7404

I_{IL}

I_{OH}

300 Ω

15 kΩ

FIGURE 6–4

Figure 6–3. Then measure V_{OL} and record it in Table 6–1, line f.

6. Measure the voltage drop across R_{LOAD}, and apply Ohm's law to determine the actual load current. Record the measured load current as I_{OL} in Table 6–1, line d.

7. Change the previous circuit to the one shown in Figure 6–4. Measure V_{IL} and V_{OH}, and record the measured voltages in Table 6–1, lines b and e.

8. Calculate I_{IL} by applying Ohm's law to the 300 Ω input resistor in Figure 6–4. (Note the sign.) Record the measured I_{IL} in Table 6–1, line h.

9. Measure the output load current by applying Ohm's law to the 15 kΩ load resistor. Record this current, I_{OH}, in Table 6–1, line c. Note the units and the sign. The minus sign indicates that the current is leaving the IC. This current, called *source* current, is significantly lower than the maximum LOW current, I_{OL}, which is positive current, or *sink* current.

10. In this and remaining steps, you will test a CMOS IC for several important characteristics. CMOS is static sensitive and it should be handled with special care. Avoid touching the pins. Always remove power before installing or removing a CMOS IC.* Disconnect power from your protoboard and replace the 7404 with a 4081 quad AND gate. Although in practice you could test any CMOS gate, this gate will be used because it is needed in the next experiment and you have already tested an inverter. Check the manufacturer's specification sheet.** Enter the specified values for $V_{OL(max)}$, $V_{OH(min)}$, $V_{IL(max)}$, $V_{IH(min)}$, $I_{OL(min)}$, $I_{OH(min)}$ and $I_{IN(typ)}$ for a supply voltage of +5.0 V and a temperature of 25°C in Table 6–2. Notice on the pinout that the power is supplied to a pin labeled V_{DD} and ground is supplied to a pin labeled V_{SS}. Although this convention is commonly used, both pins are actually connected to transistor drains; V_{DD} is used to indicate the positive supply. (For +5.0 V supplies, the supply is often referred to as V_{CC}.)

*More precautions are given in Section 14–2 of the text.
**See Appendix A.

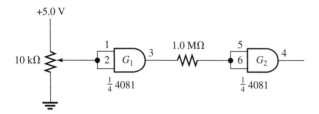

FIGURE 6–5

11. Connect the circuit shown in Figure 6–5 and ground the inputs to all other gates except the two gates you are using. Reconnect the power supply and keep it at $+5.0$ V for these tests. Adjust the input voltage using the potentiometer to the manufacturer's specified value of $V_{IH(min)}$ for $V_{DD} = +5.0$ V. Record your measured value of the $V_{IH(min)}$ on line d of Table 6–2.

12. Read the output voltage of the first AND gate at pin 3. Notice the difference between the CMOS gate and the TTL gate you tested earlier. Since the output is HIGH, record it as $V_{OH(min)}$ in Table 6–2, line b.

13. Measure the voltage *across* the 1.0 MΩ test resistor. A very high impedance meter is necessary to make an accurate measurement in this step. Determine the current flowing into the input of the second gate by applying Ohm's law to the test resistor. Record this as the input current in Table 6–2, line g.

14. Adjust the potentiometer until the input voltage on the first AND gate is at the specified value of $V_{IL(max)}$. Record the measured input voltage in Table 6–2, line c. Measure the output voltage on pin 3 and record this as $V_{OL(max)}$ in Table 6–2, line a.

15. Turn off the power supply and change the circuit to that of Figure 6–6(a). The potentiometer is moved to the output and the 1.0 MΩ resistor is used as a pull-up resistor on the input. This circuit will be used to test the HIGH output current of the gate. After connecting the circuit, restore the power and adjust the potentiometer until the output voltage is 4.6 V (see manufacturer's stated conditions for spec-

ification of output current). Remove the power, measure the potentiometer's resistance, and apply Ohm's law to determine the output current I_{OH}. Record your measured current in Table 6–2, line f.

16. Change the circuit to that of Figure 6–6(b). Restore the power and adjust the potentiometer until the output voltage is 0.4 V. Remove the power, measure the potentiometer's resistance, and apply Ohm's law to determine the output current I_{OL}. Remember, Ohm's law is applied by substituting the voltage measured *across* the resistor, not the output voltage. Record your measured current in Table 6–2, line e.

For Further Investigation

1. To investigate further the voltage characteristics of TTL, connect the circuit shown in Figure 6–7. The variable resistor is used to vary the input voltage.

2. Vary the input voltage through the range of values shown in Table 6–3. Set each input voltage; then measure the corresponding output voltage and record it in Table 6–3.

3. Plot the data from Table 6–3 onto Plot 1. Since V_{out} depends on V_{in}, plot V_{out} on the y-axis and V_{in} on the x-axis. This graph is called the *transfer curve* for the inverter.

4. Label the region on the transfer curve for V_{OH}, V_{OL}, and the threshold. The threshold is the region where the transition from HIGH to LOW takes place.

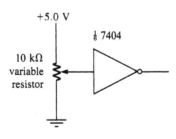

FIGURE 6–7

FIGURE 6–6

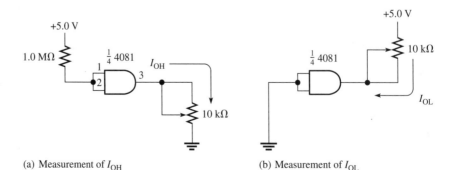

(a) Measurement of I_{OH} (b) Measurement of I_{OL}

Report for Experiment 6

Name: _____ Date: _____ Class: _____

Data and Observations:

TABLE 6–1
TTL 7404.

Recommended Operating Conditions		DM5404			DM7404				
Symbol	Parameter	Min	Nom	Max	Min	Nom	Max	Units	Measured Value
V_{CC}	Supply voltage	4.5	5	5.5	4.75	5	5.25	V	
V_{IH}	High-level input voltage	2			2			V	a.
V_{IL}	Low-level input voltage			0.8			0.8	V	b.
I_{OH}	High-level output current			−0.4			−0.4	mA	c.
I_{OL}	Low-level output current			16			16	mA	d.
T_A	Free air operating temperature	−55		125	0		70	°C	

Electrical Characteristics Over Recommended Operating Free Air Temperature (unless otherwise noted)							
Symbol	Parameter	Conditions	Min	Typ	Max	Units	
V_I	Input clamp voltage	V_{CC} = Min, I_I = −12 mA			−1.5	V	
V_{OH}	High-level output voltage	V_{CC} = Min, I_{OH} = Max V_{IL} = Max	2.4	3.4		V	e.
V_{OL}	Low-level output voltage	V_{CC} = Min, I_{OL} = Max V_{IH} = Min		0.2	0.4	V	f.
I_I	Input current @ max input voltage	V_{CC} = Max, V_I = 5.5 V			1	mA	
I_{IH}	High-level input current	V_{CC} = Max, V_I = 2.4 V			40	μA	g.
I_{IL}	Low-level input current	V_{CC} = Max, V_I = 0.4 V			−1.6	mA	h.

TABLE 6–2
CMOS CD4081.

	Quantity	Manufacturer's Specified Value	Measured Value
(a)	$V_{OL(max)}$, low-level output voltage		
(b)	$V_{OH(min)}$, high-level output voltage		
(c)	$V_{IL(max)}$, low-level input voltage		
(d)	$V_{IH(min)}$, high-level input voltage		
(e)	$I_{OL(min)}$, low-level output current		
(f)	$I_{OH(min)}$, high-level output current		
(g)	$I_{IN(typ)}$, input current		

Results and Conclusion:

Further Investigation Results:

TABLE 6–3

V_{in} (V)	0.4	0.8	1.2	1.3	1.4	1.5	1.6	2.0	2.4	2.8	3.2	3.6	4.0
V_{out} (V)													

Review Questions (TTL/CMOS)

1. In Step 4, you observed V_{OL} with no load resistor. In Step 5, you measured V_{OL} with a load resistor. What is the effect of a load resistor on V_{OL}?

2. Assume a TTL logic gate has a logic HIGH output voltage of +2.4 V. Using the maximum specified I_{OH} from Table 6–1, determine the *smallest* output resistor that can be connected between the output and ground.

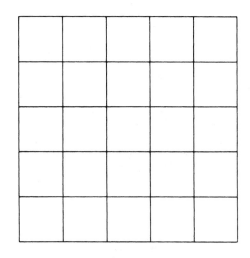

PLOT 1

3. Assume you connected the inputs of a TTL AND gate together and plotted the transfer curve. Sketch the shape of the curve and label the threshold.

7

Boolean Laws and DeMorgan's Theorem

Objectives

After completing this experiment, you will be able to
□ Experimentally verify several of the rules for Boolean algebra.
□ Implement logic to prove Rules 10 and 11.
□ Experimentally determine the truth tables for circuits with three input variables, and use DeMorgan's theorem to prove algebraically whether they are equivalent.

Reference Reading

Floyd, *Digital Fundamentals with VHDL,* Chapter 4, "Boolean Algebra and Logic Simplification"

Materials Needed (CMOS)

4071 quad 2-input OR gate
4069 hex inverter
4081 quad 2-input AND gate
One LED
Four-position DIP switch
Four 1.0 kΩ resistors
Three 0.1 μF capacitors

Materials Needed (VHDL)

Project Board

Summary of Theory

Boolean algebra consists of a set of laws that govern logical relationships. Unlike ordinary algebra, where an unknown can take any value, the elements of Boolean algebra are binary variables and can have only one of two values: 1 or 0.

Symbols used in Boolean algebra include the overbar, which is the NOT or complement; the connective $+$, which implies logical addition and is read "OR"; and the connective $\cdot$, which implies logical multiplication and is read "AND." The dot is frequently eliminated when logical multiplication is shown. Thus $A \cdot B$ is written AB. The basic rules of Boolean algebra are listed in Table 7–1 for convenience.

The Boolean rules shown in Table 7–1 can be applied to actual circuits, as this experiment demonstrates. For example, Rule 1 states $A + 0 = A$ (remember to read $+$ as "OR"). This rule can be demonstrated with an OR gate and a pulse generator, as shown in Figure 7–1. The signal from the pulse generator is labeled A and the ground represents the logic 0. The output, which is a replica of the pulse generator, represents the ORing of the two inputs—hence, the rule is proved. Figure 7–1 illustrates this rule.

In addition to the basic rules of Boolean algebra, there are two additional rules called DeMorgan's theorems that allow simplification of logic expressions that have an overbar covering more than one quantity.

DeMorgan wrote two theorems for reducing these expressions. His first theorem is

The complement of two or more variables ANDed is equivalent to the OR of the complements of the individual variables.

Algebraically, this can be written as

$$\overline{X \cdot Y} = \overline{X} + \overline{Y}$$

His second theorem is

The complement of two or more variables ORed is equivalent to the AND of the complements of the individual variables.

Algebraically, this can be written as

$$\overline{X + Y} = \overline{X} \cdot \overline{Y}$$

As a memory aid for DeMorgan's theorems, some people like to use the rule "Break the bar and change the sign." The dot between ANDed quantities is implied if it is not shown, but it is given here to emphasize this idea.

The circuits constructed in this experiment use CMOS logic. You should use static protection as to prevent damage to your ICs.

Pre-lab Questions

1. Which Boolean rule is represented by two inverters in series?
2. The equation $X = A (A + B) + C$ is equivalent to $X = A + C$. Prove this with Boolean algebra.
3. What are DeMorgan's theorems?

Procedure

1. Construct the circuit shown in Figure 7–1. Set the power supply to $+5.0$ V and use a $0.1 \ \mu\text{F}$ capacitor between V_{CC} and ground for each IC throughout this experiment.* If your pulse generator has a variable output, set it to a frequency of 10 kHz with a 0 to $+4$ V level on the output. Observe the signals from the pulse generator and the output at the same time on your oscilloscope. If you are using an analog scope, you need to be sure to trigger the scope on one channel only; otherwise a timing error

---

* In keeping with standard practice, capacitors are specified, particularly with CMOS devices, to return switching current "spikes" to the source through the shortest possible path.

104

TABLE 7–1
Basic rules of Boolean algebra.

1. $A + 0 = A$
2. $A + 1 = 1$
3. $A \cdot 0 = 0$
4. $A \cdot 1 = A$
5. $A + A = A$
6. $A + \overline{A} = 1$
7. $A \cdot A = A$
8. $A \cdot \overline{A} = 0$
9. $\overline{\overline{A}} = A$
10. $\overline{A} + AB = \overline{A} + B$
11. $A + \overline{A}B = A + B$
12. $(A + B)(A + C) = A + BC$

NOTE: A, B, or C can represent a single variable or a combination of variables.

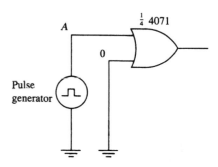

FIGURE 7–1

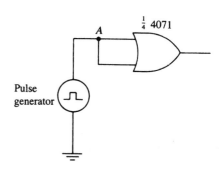

FIGURE 7–2

can occur with some signals. The timing diagram and Boolean rule for this circuit has been completed in Table 7–2 in the report as an example.

2. Change the circuit from Step 1 to that of Figure 7–2. Complete the second line in Table 7–2.

3. Connect the circuit shown in Figure 7–3. Complete the third line in Table 7–2.

4. Change the circuit in Step 3 to that of Figure 7–4. Complete the last line in Table 7–2.

5. Design a circuit that will illustrate Rule 10. The pulse generator is used to represent the A input and a switch is used for the B input. Switch B is open

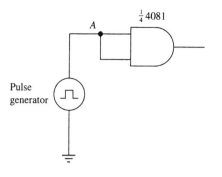

FIGURE 7–3

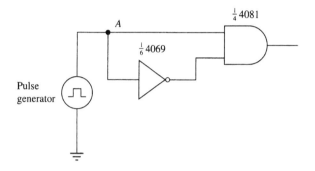

FIGURE 7–4

for $B = 1$ and closed for $B = 0$. Complete the schematic, build your circuit, and draw two timing diagrams in the space provided in Table 7–3. The first timing diagram is for the condition $B = 0$ and the second is for the condition $B = 1$.

6. Design a circuit that illustrates Rule 11. Draw your schematic in the space provided in Table 7–4. Construct the circuit and draw two timing diagrams for the circuit in Table 7–4.

For Further Investigation

1. Build the circuit shown in Figure 7–5. Test each combination of input variables by closing the appropriate switches as listed in truth Table 7–5 in the report. Using the LED as a logic monitor, read the output logic, and complete Table 7–5.

2. Construct the circuit of Figure 7–6. Again, test each combination of inputs and complete truth Table 7–6 in the report. Observe the two truth tables. Can you prove (or disprove) that the circuits perform equivalent logic?

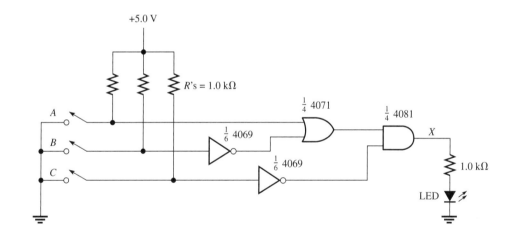

FIGURE 7–5

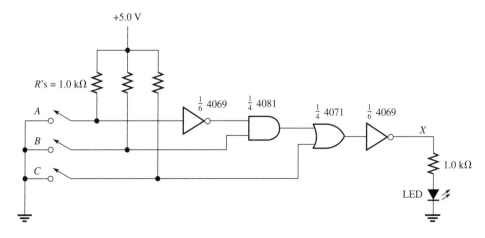

FIGURE 7–6

Report for Experiment 7

Name: _____ Date: _____ Class: _____

Data and Observations:

TABLE 7–2

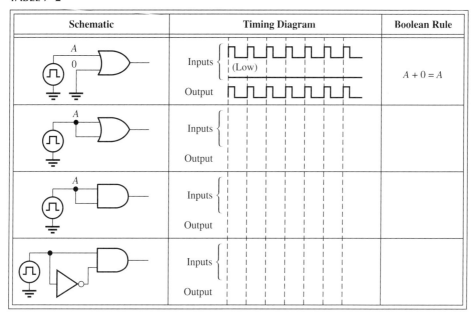

Schematic	Timing Diagram		Boolean Rule
	Inputs	(Low)	$A + 0 = A$
	Output		
	Inputs		
	Output		
	Inputs		
	Output		
	Inputs		
	Output		

TABLE 7–3

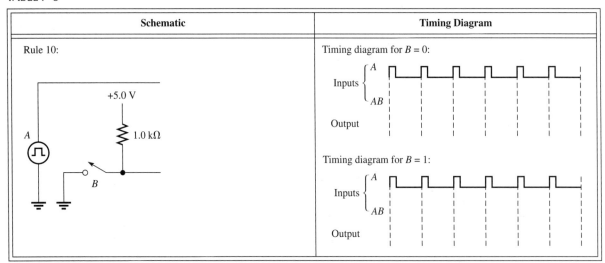

TABLE 7–4

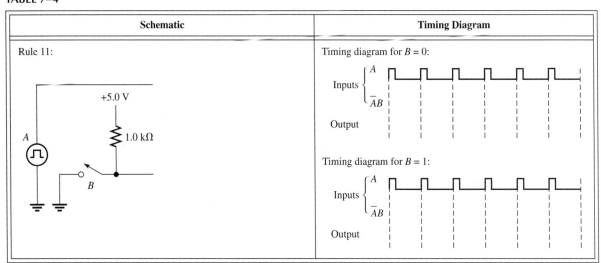

Results and Conclusion:

Further Investigation Results:

TABLE 7–5
Truth table for Figure 7–5.

Inputs			Output
A	B	C	X
0	0	0	
0	0	1	
0	1	0	
0	1	1	
1	0	0	
1	0	1	
1	1	0	
1	1	1	

TABLE 7–6
Truth table for Figure 7–6.

Inputs			Output
A	B	C	X
0	0	0	
0	0	1	
0	1	0	
0	1	1	
1	0	0	
1	0	1	
1	1	0	
1	1	1	

Write the Boolean expression for each circuit.

Review Questions (CMOS)

1. Draw two equivalent circuits that could prove Rule 12. Show the left side of the equation as one circuit and the right side as another circuit.

2. Determine whether the circuits in Figures 7–5 and 7–6 perform equivalent logic. Then, using DeMorgan's theorem, prove your answer.

VHDL

```
--This program simulates a 2-input or gate
entity LogicGates is
    port (A, B: in  bit;
             X: out bit);
end entity LogicGates;

architecture GateBehavior of LogicGates is
begin
    X <= A or B;
end architecture GateBehavior
```

FIGURE 7–7

Program Overview

In this experiment, you will be introduced to additional VHDL keywords **AND** and **NOT.** The keyword **OR** is used again. The logical operations and examples of the syntax for these keywords are shown in Table 7–7. The PLD will be programmed to simulate basic gates that perform these operations to show the relation between the gate logic and Boolean algebra. Most VHDL compilers will reduce unnecessary gate logic automatically, minimizing the PLD logic required.

As in Experiment 5, you will use a TTL compatible pulse for one of the logic inputs and you will view the logic on an oscilloscope. Before connecting the pulse generator to your board, you should review the method in section 4b, p. 20 in *Project Board Familiarization.* A color photo of the correct hookup for the pulse generator and the oscilloscope is shown on the back cover for each board.

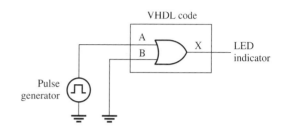

FIGURE 7–8

signal from the pulse generator and the output signal X at the same time on your oscilloscope. The timing diagram and Boolean rule for this condition have been completed in Table 7–8 in the report as an example.

6. Notice what happens when *B* is switched to a HIGH. The circuit no longer represents the circuit in Figure 7–8 but represents the second circuit in Table 7–8. Complete this line of the table by showing the output and indicate the Boolean rule.

7. In this step, you will modify the program by connecting both gate inputs to the pulse generator as in Figure 7–9. Change the **entity** section by removing the *B* identifier. Then modify the **architecture** statement "X <= A **or** B;" to become "X <= A **or** A;". Remove the pin assignment for the *B* identifier.

8. Recompile and download your modified program to the project board.

9. Observe the output on the oscilloscope and complete the third line in Table 7–8.

10. Modify the VHDL program to represent the circuit of Figure 7–10 by changing the **or** gate in the **architecture** section to an **and** gate. The **architecture** statement should now read "X <= A **and** A;".

Procedure

Boolean Laws and DeMorgan's Theorem

1. Connect the project board to a computer as described in *Project Board Familiarization* and review *VHDL Software Familiarization.*

2. Figure 7–7 shows a program named *LogicGates* that is a PLD implementation of a 2-input OR gate. Enter the VHDL program into the text editor.

3. Find the pin used for the pulse generator in Section 4b of *Project Board Familiarization.* In the pin assignment section of the Altera or Xilinx program, assign input *A* to the pin used for a pulse generator. Assign pin *B* to a switch.

4. Compile and download the program to the project board.

5. Connect a TTL compatible pulse generator set to a frequency of 10 kHz to your project board. Connect *B* to a logic LOW. Your program now represents the circuit shown in Figure 7–8. Observe the

TABLE 7–7

Operator	Description	Syntax Example
OR	Returns HIGH when any input is HIGH.	X<= A **OR** B
AND	Returns HIGH only when all inputs are HIGH.	X<= A **NOR** B;
NOT	Returns HIGH if input is LOW, and LOW if input is HIGH.	X<= **NOT** A;

111

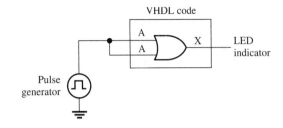

FIGURE 7–9

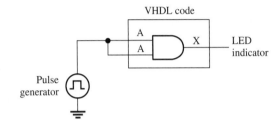

FIGURE 7–10

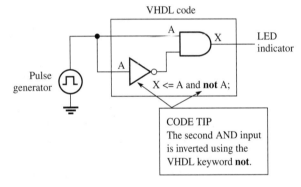

CODE TIP
The second AND input
is inverted using the
VHDL keyword **not**.

FIGURE 7–11

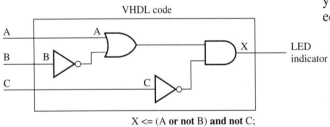

$X <= (A \textbf{ or not } B) \textbf{ and not } C;$

FIGURE 7–12

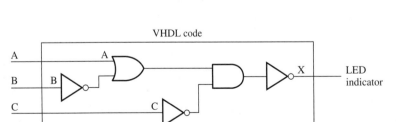

FIGURE 7–13

11. Recompile and download your modified program. Then observe the output on the oscilloscope and complete the fourth line in Table 7–8.

12. Add the keyword **not** to the assignment of X as shown in Figure 7–11. Recompile and download the revised program. Complete the last line in Table 7–8.

13. Complete the circuit diagram in Table 7–9 to illustrate Rule 10. Modify the program to simulate the circuit. You will need to reassign B in the **entity** section. Recompile and download the program. The pulse generator is used for the A input. Use a switch for the B input. Draw the two timing diagrams in the space provided in Table 7–9. The first timing diagram is for the condition $B = 0$ and the second is for condition $B = 1$.

14. Complete the circuit diagram in Table 7–10 to illustrate Rule 11. Modify the program to simulate the circuit. Recompile and download the program. Again, the pulse generator is used for the A input and a switch is used for the B input. Draw the two timing diagrams in Table 7–10.

For Further Investigation

1. Modify the VHDL program to simulate the logic in Figure 7–12. You will need to create a new input identifier C in the **entity** section and enter the new Boolean expression for X given on the circuit diagram. Test each combination of input variables by closing the appropriate switches as listed in Table 7–11 in the report. Complete the table.

2. Modify the VHDL code to simulate the circuit of Figure 7–13. Indicate in your report the correct expression for X for this circuit. Again, test each combination of inputs and complete Table 7–12. Can you prove (or disprove) that the circuits perform equivalent logic?

Report for Experiment 7

Name: _____ Date: _____ Class: _____

Data and Observations:

TABLE 7–8

Schematic	Timing Diagram	Boolean Rule
A 0	Inputs { (LOW) / Output	$A + 0 = A$
A 1 +5 V	Inputs { (HIGH) / Output (high)	$A + 1 = 1$
A	Inputs { / Output	$A + A = A$
A	Inputs { / Output	$A \cdot A = A$
	Inputs { / Output (Low)	$A \cdot \overline{A} = 0$

TABLE 7–9

Schematic	Timing Diagram
Rule 10: 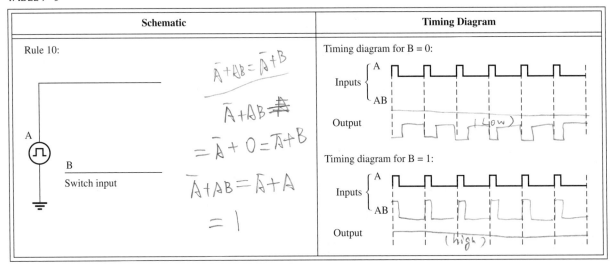	

(Handwritten work in Schematic column:)

$$\overline{A} + AB = \overline{A} + B$$

$$\overline{A} + AB \neq$$

$$= \overline{A} + 0 = \overline{A} + B$$

$$\overline{A} + AB = \overline{A} + A$$

$$= 1$$

(Timing Diagram column:)

Timing diagram for B = 0:

Inputs { A, AB } Output (Low)

Timing diagram for B = 1:

Inputs { A, AB } Output (high)

TABLE 7–10

Schematic	Timing Diagram
Rule 11: 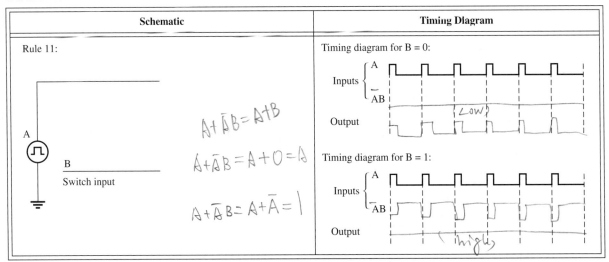	

(Handwritten work in Schematic column:)

$$A + \overline{A}B = A + B$$

$$A + \overline{A}B = A + 0 = A$$

$$A + \overline{A}B = A + \overline{A} = 1$$

(Timing Diagram column:)

Timing diagram for B = 0:

Inputs { A, $\overline{A}$B } Output (Low)

Timing diagram for B = 1:

Inputs { A, $\overline{A}$B } Output (high)

Results and Conclusion:

114

Further Investigation Results:

TABLE 7–11
Truth table for Figure 7–12.

Inputs			Output
A	B	C	X
0	0	0	
0	0	1	
0	1	0	
0	1	1	
1	0	0	
1	0	1	
1	1	0	
1	1	1	

TABLE 7–12
Truth table for Figure 7–13.

Inputs			Output
A	B	C	X
0	0	0	
0	0	1	
0	1	0	
0	1	1	
1	0	0	
1	0	1	
1	1	0	
1	1	1	

Write the Boolean expression used in the program for X in both circuits.

Review Questions (VHDL)

1. Explain how the VHDL compiler optimization feature can benefit your design implementation.

2. **a.** Write a VHDL assignment statement for the logic exactly as shown in Figure 7–14 that assigns this logic to a variable named X.

   b. Simplify the logic and write the simplified expression for X in VHDL.

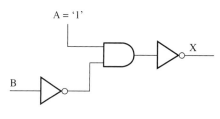

FIGURE 7–14

Logic Circuit Simplification

Objectives

After completing this experiment, you will be able to
- ☐ Develop the truth table for a BCD-invalid code detector.
- ☐ Use a Karnaugh map to simplify the expression.
- ☐ Build and test logic that implements the simplified expression.

Reference Reading

Floyd, *Digital Fundamentals with VHDL,* Chapter 4, "Boolean Algebra and Logic Simplification"

Materials Needed (TTL)

7400 NAND gate
LED
Resistors: one 330 Ω, four 1.0 kΩ
One 4-position DIP switch

Materials Needed (VHDL)

Project Board

Summary of Theory

With combinational logic circuits, the outputs are determined solely by the inputs. For simple combinational circuits, truth tables are used to summarize all possible inputs and outputs; the truth table completely describes the desired operation of the circuit. The circuit may be realized by simplifying the ex-

pression for the output function as read from the truth table.

A powerful mapping technique for simplifying combinational logic circuits was developed by M. Karnaugh and was described in a paper he published in 1953. The method involved writing the truth table into a geometric map in which adjacent cells (squares) differ from each other in only one variable. (Adjacent cells share a common border horizontally or vertically.) When you are drawing a Karnaugh map, the variables are written in a Gray code sequence along the sides and tops of the map. Each cell on the map corresponds to one row of the truth table. The output variables appear as 0's and 1's on the map in positions corresponding to those given in the truth table.

As an example, consider the design of a 2-bit comparator. The inputs will be called A_2A_1 and B_2B_1. The desired output is HIGH if A_2A_1 is equal to or greater than B_2B_1. To begin, the desired output is written in the form of a truth table, as given in Table 8–1. All possible inputs are clearly identified by the truth table and the desired output for every possible input is given.

Next the Karnaugh map is drawn, as shown in Figure 8–1. In this example, the map is drawn using numbers to represent the inputs. The corresponding values for the output function are entered from the truth table. The map can be read in sum-of-products (SOP) form by grouping adjacent cells containing 1's (or X's) on the map. The size of the groups must be an integer power of 2 (1, 2, 4, 8, etc.) and should contain only 1's. The largest possible group should

TABLE 8–1
Truth table for comparator.

Inputs		Output
$A_2 A_1$	$B_2 B_1$	X
0 0	0 0	1
0 0	0 1	0
0 0	1 0	0
0 0	1 1	0
0 1	0 0	1
0 1	0 1	1
0 1	1 0	0
0 1	1 1	0
1 0	0 0	1
1 0	0 1	1
1 0	1 0	1
1 0	1 1	0
1 1	0 0	1
1 1	0 1	1
1 1	1 0	1
1 1	1 1	1

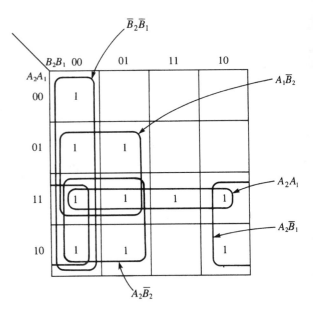

FIGURE 8–1
Karnaugh map for the truth table shown in Table 8–1.

be taken; all 1's must be in at least one group and may be taken in more than one group if helpful.

After grouping the 1's on the map, the output function can be determined. Each group is read as one of the product terms in the reduced output function. Within each group larger than one, adjacent boundaries will be crossed, causing the variable that changes to be eliminated from the output expression. A group of two adjacent 1's will have a single adjacent boundary and will eliminate one variable. A group of four 1's will eliminate two variables and a group of eight 1's will eliminate three variables. Figure 8–1 shows the groupings for the 2-bit comparator. Since each group in this case is a group of four 1's, each product term contains two variables (two were eliminated from each term). The resulting expression is the sum of all of the product terms. The circuit can be drawn directly, as shown in Figure 8–2.

In this experiment, you will use the Karnaugh mapping method, similar to the one described previously, to design a BCD-Invalid code detector. The detector is an enhancement to the tablet counting and control system described in the text. You will design a circuit to assure that only valid BCD codes are present in Register A and to signal a warning if an in-

valid BCD code is detected. Your circuit will be designed for 4 bits, but could easily be expanded to 8 bits for Register A.

Pre-lab Questions

1. What type of code is used along the side and top of a Karnaugh map?
2. Summarize the rules for grouping the 1's and X's on a Karnaugh map.

Procedure

BCD Invalid Code Detector

Figure 8–3 illustrates the tablet control system with the invalid code detector. As you know, BCD is a 4-bit binary code that represents the decimal numbers 0 through 9. The binary numbers 1010 through 1111 are invalid in BCD.

1. Complete the truth table shown as Table 8–2 in the report. Assume the output for the ten valid BCD codes is a 0 and for the six invalid BCD codes is a 1. As usual for representing numbers, the most significant bit is represented by the letter D and the least significant bit by the letter A.

2. Complete the Karnaugh map shown as Figure 8–4 in the report. Group the 1's according to the rules given in the text and the Summary of Theory. Find the expression of the invalid codes by reading the minimum SOP from the map. Write the Boolean expression in the space provided in the report.

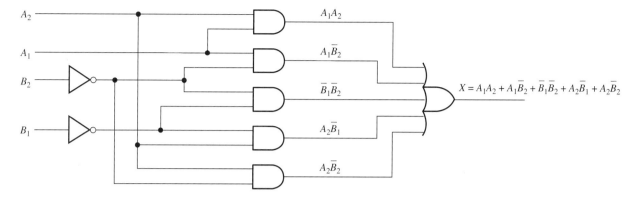

FIGURE 8–2

Circuit implementation of the comparator given by truth table in Table 8–1.

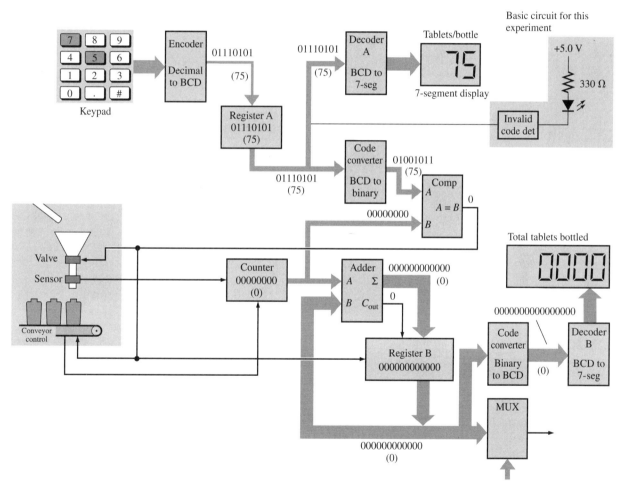

FIGURE 8–3

Tablet control system.

119

FIGURE 8–5

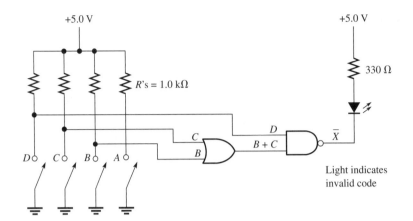

3. If you have correctly written the expression in Step 2, there are two product terms and you will see that the letter D appears in both terms. This expression could be implemented directly as a satisfactory logic circuit. By factoring D from each term, you will arrive at another expression for invalid codes. Write the new expression in the space provided in the report.

4. Recall that, for TTL logic, a LOW can light an LED without violating the I_{OL} (16 mA) specification but a HIGH causes the I_{OH} (400 µA) specification to be exceeded. To avoid this, the output is inverted and $\overline{X}$ is used to light the LED with a LOW logic level. The circuit shown in Figure 8–5 implements the expression from Step 3 but with the output inverted in order *sink* rather than *source* current.

5. Although the circuit shown in Figure 8–5 satisfies the design requirements with only two gates, it requires two *different* ICs. In some cases, this might be the best design. However, using the universal properties of the NAND gate, the OR gate could be replaced with three NAND gates. This change allows the circuit to be implemented with only *one* IC—a quad 7400. Change the circuit in Figure 8–5 by replacing the OR gate with three NAND gates. Draw the new circuit in the space provided in the report.

6. Construct the circuit you drew in Step 5. Test all combinations of the inputs and complete truth Table 8–3 in the report. If you have constructed and tested the circuit correctly, the truth table will be the same as Table 8–2.

7. For each problem listed in Table 8–4, state what effect it will have on your circuit. (Some "problems" may have no effect). If you aren't sure, you may want to simulate the problem and test the result.

EWB/MSM Troubleshooting

The CD packaged with this lab manual contains Electronics Workbench (.ewb) and Multisim (.msm) files. Open the file named Exp-08. The file has three circuits that are the same as Figure 8–5. Each of the three circuits has a fault. Analyze the logic indicators and determine the most likely fault in each circuit.

For Further Investigation

Design a circuit that will indicate if a BCD number is evenly divisible by three (3, 6, or 9). The input is a valid BCD number—assume that invalid numbers have already been tested and rejected by your earlier circuit! Since invalid numbers are now impossible, the Karnaugh map will contain "don't care" entries. An "X" on the map means that if the input is *not possible,* then you *don't care* about the outcome.

1. Complete the truth Table 8–5 in the report for the problem stated above. Enter 0's for BCD numbers that are not divisible by three and 1's for BCD numbers that are divisible by three. Enter an "X" to indicate an invalid BCD code.

2. Complete the Karnaugh map shown as Figure 8–6. Group the 1's on the map in groups of 2, 4, 8, etc. Do not take any 0's but do take X's if you can obtain a larger group. Read the minimum SOP from the map and show your expression in the space provided in the report.

3. Draw a circuit using only NAND gates that will implement the expression. The LED should be turned ON with a LOW output. Build the circuit and test each of the possible inputs to see that it performs as expected.

Report for Experiment 8

Name: _____ Date: _____ Class: _____

Data and Observations:

TABLE 8–2
Truth table for BCD-invalid code detector.

Inputs				Output
D	C	B	A	X
0	0	0	0	0
0	0	0	1	0
0	0	1	0	0
0	0	1	1	0
0	1	0	0	0
0	1	0	1	0
0	1	1	0	0
0	1	1	1	0
1	0	0	0	0
1	0	0	1	0
1	0	1	0	1
1	0	1	1	1
1	1	0	0	1
1	1	0	1	1
1	1	1	0	1
1	1	1	1	1

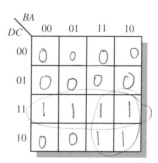

FIGURE 8–4
Karnaugh map of truth table for invalid BCD code detector.

Minimum sum-of-products read from map:

$X =$ $DC + DB$

Factoring D from both product terms gives:

$X =$ $D(C+B)$

Step 5. Circuit for BCD-invalid code detector:

TABLE 8–3

Truth table for BCD-invalid code detector constructed in step 6.

Inputs				Output
D	C	B	A	X
0	0	0	0	1
0	0	0	1	1
0	0	1	0	1
0	0	1	1	1
0	1	0	0	1
0	1	0	1	1
0	1	1	0	1
0	1	1	1	1
1	0	0	0	1
1	0	0	1	1
1	0	1	0	0
1	0	1	1	0
1	1	0	0	0
1	1	0	1	0
1	1	1	0	0
1	1	1	1	0

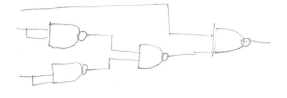

TABLE 8–4

Problem Number	Problem	Effect
1	The pull-up resistor for the D switch is open.	$D = X$
2	The ground to the NAND gate is open.	not work properly
3	A 3.3 kΩ resistor was accidently used in place of the 330 Ω resistor.	Led off
4	The LED was inserted backward.	Led off
5	Switch A is shorted to ground.	$A = 0$

Results and Conclusion:

$$\overline{D(B+C)} = \overline{DB + DC} = \overline{DB} \cdot \overline{DC}$$

$$\overline{B+C} = \overline{B} \cdot \overline{C}$$

EWB/MSM Troubleshooting:

Circuit 1 Most likely problem: _____

_____

Circuit 2 Most likely problem: _____

_____

Circuit 3 Most likely problem: _____

_____

Further Investigation Results:

TABLE 8–5
Truth table for BCD numbers divisible by three.

Inputs				Output
D	C	B	A	X
0	0	0	0	
0	0	0	1	
0	0	1	0	
0	0	1	1	
0	1	0	0	
0	1	0	1	
0	1	1	0	
0	1	1	1	
1	0	0	0	
1	0	0	1	
1	0	1	0	
1	0	1	1	
1	1	0	0	
1	1	0	1	
1	1	1	0	
1	1	1	1	

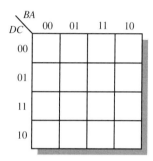

FIGURE 8–6
Karnaugh map of truth table for BCD numbers divisible by three.

Minimum sum-of-products read from map:

$X=$ _____

Circuit:

Review Questions (TTL)

1. Assume that the circuit in Figure 8–5 was constructed but doesn't work correctly. The output is correct for all inputs except $DCBA = 1000$ and 1001. Suggest at least two possible problems that could account for this and explain how you would isolate the exact problem.

2. Assume a circuit already had a 7442 BCD decoder in it and you wanted to add a BCD-invalid code detector to the circuit. Design a circuit that uses only one 3-input NAND gate and the 7442 to turn on an LED for invalid codes. (*Hint:* Use two outputs from the 7442 and one input to the 7442.)

3. The circuit shown in Figure 8–7 has an output labeled $\overline{X}$. Write the expression for $\overline{X}$; then, using DeMorgan's theorem, find the expression for X.

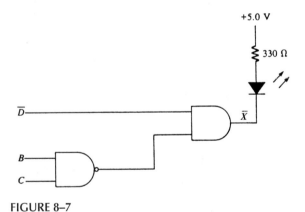

FIGURE 8–7

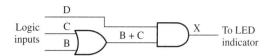

FIGURE 8–9

Program Overview

The basic rules of Boolean algebra can be used to create simple and compact VHDL programs. Although most VHDL compilers will try to optimize the logic in your output file, it is better to start with concise logic for efficiency and maintainability. In this VHDL exercise, you will simplify a Boolean logic expression to its most compact form using Karnaugh mapping. You will need to complete the VHDL program by writing the logic equation from the Karnaugh map results.

Procedure

Figure 8–3 illustrates the tablet control system with the binary invalid code detector. As you know, BCD is a 4-bit binary code that represents the decimal numbers 0 through 9. The binary numbers 1010 through 1111 are invalid in BCD.

1. Complete the truth table shown as Table 8–6 in the report. Assume the output for the ten valid BCD codes is a 0 and the six invalid BCD codes is a 1. As usual for representing numbers, the most significant bit is represented by the letter D and the least significant bit is represented by the letter A.

2. Complete the Karnaugh map shown as Figure 8–8 in the report. Group the 1's according to the rules given in the text and the Summary of Theory. Find the expression of the invalid codes by reading the minimum SOP from the map. Write the Boolean expression in the space provided in the report.

3. If you have correctly written the expression in step 2, there are two product terms and you will see that the letter D appears in both terms. An alternate expression for invalid codes can be arrived at by factoring D. Either expression can be implemented in the VHDL program for this experiment.

VHDL Design Implementation

4. Connect the project board to a computer as described in *Project Board Familiarization* and review *VHDL Software Familiarization*.

5. The circuit shown in Figure 8–9 satisfies the design requirements for the invalid code detector using AND and OR logic. Complete the VHDL pro-

gram in Figure 8–10 in the report by completing the expression for X with the equation you found in step 3. Then enter the completed program into the text editor. Notice that the input A is not required for the invalid code detector.

6. Assign inputs B, C, and D to switches and output X to an LED. Compile and download the invalid code detector program to the project board.

7. Recall that input A is ignored in the invalid code detector in Figure 8–9. This means that a logic 1 or a 0 on input A has no effect on the output. Test all combinations of the inputs and complete truth Table 8–7. Your completed truth table should look the same as Table 8–6.

For Further Investigation

Design the VHDL program and develop the circuit that will indicate if a BCD number is evenly divisible by three (3, 6, or 9). The input is a valid BCD number – assuming that invalid numbers have already been tested and rejected by your earlier circuit! Since invalid numbers are now impossible, the Karnaugh map will contain "don't care" entries. An "X" on the map means that if the input is *not possible,* then you *don't care* about the outcome.

1. Complete the truth Table 8–8 in the report for the problem stated above. Enter 0's for BCD numbers that are not divisible by three and 1's for BCD numbers that are divisible by three. Enter an "X" to indicate an invalid BCD code.

2. Complete the Karnaugh map shown as Figure 8–11. Group the 1's on the map in groups of 2, 4, 8, etc. Do not take any 0's but do take X's if you can obtain a larger group. Read the minimum SOP from the map and show your expression in the space provided in the report.

3. Complete the VHDL program in Figure 8–12 of the report by completing the expression for X. Use NAND logic in the expression.

4. Compile and download your VHDL application. Then test each of the possible input combinations to see that it performs as expected.

Report for Experiment 8

Name: _____ Date: _____ Class: _____

Data and Observations:

TABLE 8–6
Truth table for BCD-invalid code detector.

Inputs				Output
D	C	B	A	X
0	0	0	0	0
0	0	0	1	0
0	0	1	0	0
0	0	1	1	0
0	1	0	0	0
0	1	0	1	0
0	1	1	0	0
0	1	1	1	0
1	0	0	0	0
1	0	0	1	0
1	0	1	0	1
1	0	1	1	1
1	1	0	0	1
1	1	0	1	1
1	1	1	0	1
1	1	1	1	1

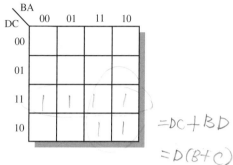

$$= DC + BD$$
$$= D(B + C)$$

FIGURE 8–8
Karnaugh map of the truth table for invalid BCD code detector.

Minimum sum-of-products read from map:

$X =$ _____

Factoring D from both product terms gives:

$X =$ _____

```
entity lab8 is
   port (B, C, D: in bit;  X: out bit);
end entity lab8;

architecture Invalid of lab8 is
begin
   X <= D and (B or C)
end architecture Invalid;
```

FIGURE 8–10

TABLE 8–7

Truth table for BCD-invalid code detector constructed in step 7.

Inputs				Output
D	C	B	A	X
0	0	0	0	0
0	0	0	1	0
0	0	1	0	0
0	0	1	1	0
0	1	0	0	0
0	1	0	1	0
0	1	1	0	0
0	1	1	1	0
1	0	0	0	0
1	0	0	1	0
1	0	1	0	1
1	0	1	1	1
1	1	0	0	1
1	1	0	1	1
1	1	1	0	1
1	1	1	1	1

Results and Conclusion:

Further Investigation Results:

TABLE 8–8
Truth table for BCD numbers divisible by three.

Inputs				Output
D	C	B	A	X
0	0	0	0	0
0	0	0	1	0
0	0	1	0	0
0	0	1	1	1
0	1	0	0	0
0	1	0	1	0
0	1	1	0	1
0	1	1	1	0
1	0	0	0	0
1	0	0	1	1
1	0	1	0	✕
1	0	1	1	✕
1	1	0	0	✕
1	1	0	1	✕
1	1	1	0	✕
1	1	1	1	✕

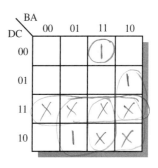

FIGURE 8–11
Karnaugh map of the truth table for BCD numbers divisible by three.

Minimum sum-of-products read from map:

$X =$ _____

Circuit:

```
entity lab8FI is
  port (A, B, C, D: in bit; X: out bit);
end lab8FI;

architecture Div3 of lab8FI is
begin
  X <=                          ;
end architecture Div3;
```

FIGURE 8–12

Review Questions (VHDL)

1. In the **entity** section of the program in Figure 8–10, the A input is not listed. Explain why not.

2. Implement the equivalent circuit in Figure 8–9 in VHDL using only NOR gates.

9 ✓

The Perfect Pencil Machine

Objectives

After completing this experiment, you will be able to

☐ Design and implement the combinational portion of a logic circuit that delivers a "pencil" and "change" based on the value of "coins" that are entered.

☐ Write a report describing your circuit and results.

Reference Reading

Floyd, *Digital Fundamentals with VHDL,* Chapter 5, "Combinational Logic"

Materials Needed (TTL)

Four LEDs
One 4-position DIP switch
Resistors: four 1.0 kΩ, four 330 Ω
Other materials as determined by student

Materials Needed (VHDL)

Project Board

Summary of Theory

Most digital logic circuits require more than simple combinational logic. They require the ability to respond to a series of events. For example, a coin-operated machine must "remember" the amount of money that has been inserted previously and compare it with the price of the product. When the amount of money is equal or greater than the price of the product, the machine delivers the product and any necessary change. This is an example of a sequential machine; the key difference between it and a combinational machine is memory. Any circuit that contains memory is considered to be a sequential circuit.

For analysis purposes, sequential circuits can be broken into memory units and combinational units. A coin-operated machine actually contains both sequential (memory) and combinational portions. For simplification, we will focus only on the combinational logic in this experiment. You will complete the design of the combinational logic portion of a coin-operated machine that has multiple outputs. The outputs consist of a product and various coins for change.

To design the combinational logic portion of the machine, you will need a separate Karnaugh map for each output. Keep in mind that logic needed for one of the outputs sometimes appears in the equation for the other output, and this logic may simplify the total circuit.

As an example, the Model-1 perfect pencil machine design is shown (see Figure 9–1). This machine (which was built shortly after the invention of the pencil) uses combinational logic to determine if the mechanical hand holding the pencil should open. Back then, pencils sold for ten cents and the original pencil machine could accept either two nickels or one dime but nothing else. If someone first dropped in a nickel and then a dime, the machine was smart enough to give a nickel change.

The Model-1 perfect pencil machine was designed by first filling out a truth table showing all possibilities for the input coins. There were two switches for nickels, labeled N_1 and N_2, and one switch for a dime, labeled D. The truth table is shown as Table 9–1. The truth table lists two outputs; a pencil, labeled P, and a nickel change, labeled NC. A 1 on the truth table indicates that the coin has been placed in the machine or a product (pencil or change) is to be delivered; a 0 indicates the absence of a coin or that no product is to be delivered.

In the Model-1 machine, the two nickel switches are stacked on top of each other (see Figure 9–1), forming a mechanical version of sequential logic. It is *not possible* for the second nickel to be placed in the machine until the first nickel has been placed in the machine. The coins must be placed in the machine sequentially; as soon as ten cents is added, the pencil is delivered. It is not possible for three coins to be placed in the machine as any combination of two coins will deliver a pencil. For these reasons, several lines on the truth table are shown as "don't care" (X). "Don't cares" appear on the table because if the input is *not possible,* then we *don't care* what the output does.

The information from the truth table was entered onto two Karnaugh maps—one for each output (see Figure 9–2). The maps were read by taking "don't care" wherever it would help. This, of course, greatly

TABLE 9–1
Truth table for the Model-1 perfect pencil machine.

Inputs			Outputs	
N_1	N_2	D	P	NC
0	0	0	0	0
0	0	1	1	0
0	1	0	X	X
0	1	1	X	X
1	0	0	0	0
1	0	1	1	1
1	1	0	1	0
1	1	1	X	X

simplifies the resulting logic. The Boolean expressions that resulted surprised no one—not even the company president! From the Boolean sum-of-products (SOP), it was a simple matter to implement the Model-1 perfect pencil machine, as shown in Figure 9–3.

Pre-lab Questions

1. When is an X entered in a truth table or a Karnaugh map?
2. What is the form of the expression as read directly from a Karnaugh map?

FIGURE 9–1
Model-1 perfect pencil machine.

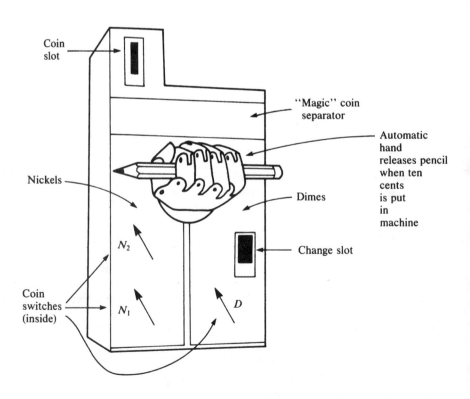

Coin slot

"Magic" coin separator

Automatic hand releases pencil when ten cents is put in machine

Nickels

Dimes

N_2

Change slot

Coin switches (inside)

N_1

D

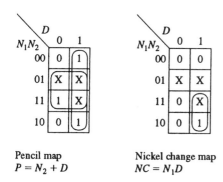

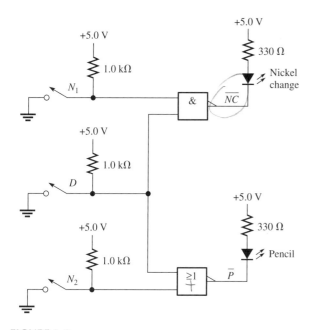

Pencil map
$P = N_2 + D$

Nickel change map
$NC = N_1 D$

FIGURE 9–2
Karnaugh maps for Model-1 perfect pencil machine.

FIGURE 9–3
Model-1 perfect pencil machine.

TTL

Procedure

The Model-2 Perfect Pencil Machine

1. The logic for the new Model-2 perfect pencil machine must be designed and ready for testing by next week. Your job is to design the combinational logic portion of the new machine and test it (using LEDs for the outputs) to assure that it works. You must then write a report for the director of engi-

neering summarizing your design and test results. The problem statement is given as follows.

Problem statement: The new Model-2 perfect pencil machine sells pencils for fifteen cents (due to inflation). The machine will be designed to accept one nickel, two dimes, a quarter, or certain combinations of these. (The president of the company was heard to say that anyone who put three nickels in the machine deserved to lose them!) The coins for the combinational logic are represented by four input switches—a nickel (N), two dimes (D_1 and D_2), and a quarter (Q). The first dime in the machine will always turn on the D_1 switch and the second dime in the machine will always turn on the D_2 switch. As in the Model-1 design, there are certain combinations that are impossible. This is due to the fact that the automatic hand (holding the pencil) begins to open as soon as 15 cents is in the machine. This implies that no more than 2 coins can be put in the machine. Also, it is not possible to activate the second dime switch before the first dime switch. To clarify the combinations, the director of engineering has started filling out the truth table (see Table 9–2 in the Report section) but was called to a meeting.

There are four outputs from the Model-2 perfect pencil machine, as listed on the truth table. They are pencil (P), nickel change (NC), the first dime change (DC_1), and the second dime change (DC_2). You will need to complete the truth table and Karnaugh maps and read the output logic to deliver the correct product and change.

Oh!—and the director of engineering says she would like to have you use no more than two ICs! Good luck!

2. Draw the complete circuit for the Model-2 perfect pencil machine in the space provided in the report.

For Further Investigation

After the Model-2 perfect pencil machine was designed, the purchasing department found out that 2-input NAND gates were on sale and they purchased several million of them. (The head purchasing agent used to work for the government!) The problem is that you will need to modify your circuit to use the 2-input NAND gates throughout. Your boss muttered, "It may mean more ICs, but we've got to use up those NAND gates!" Show in the report how you will help the company in your design.

TTL

Report for Experiment 9

Name: ______________________ Date: ____________ Class: ______________________

Data and Observations:

TABLE 9–2
Truth table for Model-2 perfect pencil machine.

5¢ 10 10 25 pencil nickle change first dime change second dime change

Inputs				Outputs			
N	D_1	D_2	Q	P	NC	DC_1	DC_2
0	0	0	0	0	0	0	0
0	0	0	1	1	0	1	0
0	0	1	0	X	X	X	X
0	0	1	1	X	X	X	X
0	1	0	0	0	0	0	0
0	1	0	1	1	0	1	1
0	1	1	0	1	1	0	0
0	1	1	1	X	X	X	X
1	0	0	0	0	0	0	0
1	0	0	1	1	1	1	0
1	0	1	0	X	X	X	X
1	0	1	1	X	X	X	X
1	1	0	0	1	0	0	0
1	1	0	1	X	X	X	X
1	1	1	0	X	X	X	X
1	1	1	1	X	X	X	X

Step 2. Circuit:

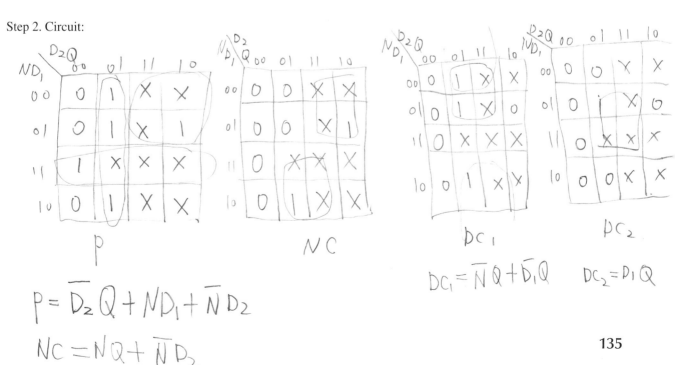

P

ND_1 \ D_2Q	00	01	11	10
00	0	1	X	X
01	0	1	X	1
11	1	X	X	X
10	0	1	X	X

NC

ND_1 \ D_2Q	00	01	11	10
00	0	0	X	X
01	0	0	X	1
11	0	X	X	X
10	0	1	X	X

DC_1

ND_1 \ D_2Q	00	01	11	10
00	0	1	X	X
01	0	1	X	0
11	0	X	X	X
10	0	1	X	X

DC_2

ND_1 \ D_2Q	00	01	11	10
00	0	0	X	X
01	0	1	X	0
11	0	X	X	X
10	0	0	X	X

$DC_1 = \overline{N}Q + \overline{D_1}Q$

$DC_2 = D_1 Q$

$P = \overline{D_2}Q + ND_1 + \overline{N}D_2$

$NC = NQ + \overline{N}D_2$

Results and Conclusions:

Further Investigation Results:

Review Questions (TTL)

1. In Table 9–2, the second and third lines are shown with X's in the output. Explain why.

2. How many variables are eliminated on a Karnaugh map if a particular group includes 4 squares?

Program Overview

Recall the rules for simplifying logic using Karnaugh maps. In this VHDL portion of the experiment, you will use Karnaugh map simplification to determine the sum-of-product (SOP) equations. These equations will be used to complete the VHDL program for the new Model-2 Perfect Pencil Machine.

The lead software engineer has completed the VHDL program except for the logic equations. The partially completed truth table is given in Table 9–3 and the partially completed program is shown in Figure 9–4. The outputs P, NC, DC_1, and DC_2 are used to turn on LEDs on the project board. Notice that a 1 is shown on the truth table for delivering a pencil or change.

Procedure

1. Connect the project board to a computer as described in *Project Board Familiarization* and review *VHDL Software Familiarization.*

2. The logic for the new Model-2 perfect pencil machine must be designed and ready for testing by next week. Your job is to design and implement the combinational logic portion of the new machine using VHDL and test it (using LEDs for the outputs) to assure that it works. You must then write a report for the director of engineering summarizing your design and test results. The problem statement is given as follows:

Problem Statement: The new Model-2 perfect pencil machine sells pencils for fifteen cents (due to inflation). The machine will be designed to accept one nickel, two dimes, a quarter, or certain combinations of these. (The president of the company was heard to say that anyone who puts three nickels in the machine deserved to lose them!) The coins for the combinational logic are represented by four input switches–a nickel (N), two dimes (D_1 and D_2), and a quarter (Q). The first dime in the machine will always turn on the D_1 switch and the second dime in the machine will always turn on the D_2 switch. As in the Model-1, there are certain combinations that are impossible. This is due to the fact that the automatic hand (holding the pencil) begins to open as soon as fifteen cents is in the machine. This implies that no more than 2 coins can be put in the machine. Also, it is not possible to activate the second dime switch before the first dime switch. To clarify the combinations, the director of engineering has started filling out the truth table (see Table 9–3 in the Report section) but was called to a meeting.

There are four outputs for the Model-2 perfect pencil machine, as listed on the truth table. They are pencil (P), nickel change (NC), the first dime change (DC_1), and the second dime change (DC_2). You will need to deliver the correct product and change.

For Further Investigation

After you completed the design of the model-2 machine using VHDL, your boss had a change of heart. "We should allow three nickels to be considered to be a valid input and deliver a pencil. While there are other valid inputs, we will ignore them in the Model-2 machine." Show the changes you would make to the VHDL program to allow this input. Compile and test your program.

Report for Experiment 9

Name: _____ Date: _____ Class: _____

Data and Observations:

TABLE 9–3
Truth table for Model-2 perfect pencil machine.

Inputs				Outputs			
N	D_1	D_2	Q	P	NC	DC_1	DC_2
0	0	0	0	0	0	0	0
0	0	0	1	1	0	1	0
0	0	1	0	X	X	X	X
0	0	1	1	X	X	X	X
0	1	0	0				
0	1	0	1				
0	1	1	0				
0	1	1	1				
1	0	0	0				
1	0	0	1				
1	0	1	0				
1	0	1	1				
1	1	0	0				
1	1	0	1				
1	1	1	0				
1	1	1	1				

```
-- This partially completed program implements the
-- logic for the new Model-2 Perfect Pencil Machine.
entity Pencil is
    port(N,D1,D2,Q:in bit; -- Nickel Dime1 Dime2 Quarter
         P,NC,DC1,DC2:out bit); --Pencil Nickel change, Dime1 change Dime2 change
end entity Pencil;
architecture PencilBehavior of Pencil is
begin
    P <=                    ; -- Pencil delivered
    NC <=                   ; -- Nickel change
    DC1 <=                  ; -- Dime 1 change
    DC2 <=                  ; -- Dime 2 change
end architecture PencilBehavior;
```

FIGURE 9–4

$P <= ($ not D_2 and $Q)$ or $(N$ and $D_1)$ or $($ not N and $D_2)$

$NC <= (N$ and $Q)$ or $($ not N and $D_2)$

$DC_1 <= ($ not N and $Q)$ or $($ not D_1 and $Q)$

$DC_2 <= D_1$ and Q

Further Investigation Results:

Review Questions (VHDL)

1. Is there an advantage to reducing the expressions for the pencil machine prior to writing the expressions into the VHDL program? Explain your answer.

2. Suppose the price of pencils went to 20 cents. What is the advantage of VHDL for implementing this change over fixed-function logic?

10 ✓

The Molasses Tank

Objectives

After completing this experiment, you will be able to
- ☐ Design and implement the logic for a control process that involves feedback.
- ☐ Write a report describing your circuit and results.

Reference Reading

Floyd, *Digital Fundamentals with VHDL,* Chapter 5, "Combinational Logic"

Materials Needed (TTL)

Four LEDs
One four-position DIP switch
Resistors: four 1.0 kΩ, four 330 Ω
Other materials as determined by the student

Materials Needed (VHDL)

Project Board

Summary of Theory

Control systems typically use sophisticated programmable controllers to provide flexibility in implementing changes. For very simple systems, the control logic could be designed using small-scale integrated circuits. The problem posed in this experiment is a simple system that will provide you with an opportunity to test your skill at designing, testing, and reporting on a combinational logic problem with a limited number of inputs and outputs.

The Crumbly Cookie Company has a problem with the storage tank for its new line of molasses cookies. The problem is that the molasses in the winter months runs too slow for the batch process. As a new employee, you have been assigned to design logic for the model-2 tank controller that will assure that the molasses is warm enough before the outlet valve, V_{OUT}, is opened. After it is opened, it must remain open until the lower sensor is uncovered, indicating the tank is empty.

The best way to understand the problem is to review the model-1 tank controller design, which did not have a temperature sensor. In the model-1 design, the molasses tank had two level sensors, one high, L_H, and one low, L_L. The tank was emptied (outlet valve opened) only when molasses reached the upper sensor. After opening, the valve was closed only when the lower sensor was uncovered. The tank is illustrated in Figure 10–1.

As mentioned, the model-1 system opens the outlet valve *only* when both sensors are covered but, once opened, it remains open until both sensors are uncovered. This concept requires knowing the current state of the output valve; hence in the design, it is considered as both an *output* and an *input* to the logic. This idea is summarized with the truth table shown as Table 10–1. Because the system is designed for TTL logic, the outlet valve is *opened* with a LOW signal.

FIGURE 10–1
Molasses vat.

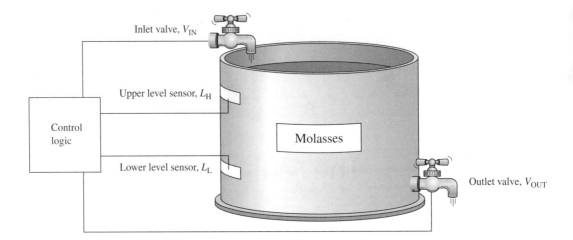

A Karnaugh map that represents the truth table is shown in Figure 10–2. From the map, the minimum logic is determined. The circuit for the outlet valve of the model-1 tank controller is shown in Figure 10–3. Notice how V_{OUT} is returned to one of the inputs.

After constructing the circuit for the outlet valve of the model-1 tank controller, it was tested using switches for the inputs and an LED to represent the outlet valve. The test begins with both switches closed, meaning the level inputs are both LOW. As the tank fills, L_L is covered, so it will open and changes to a HIGH level. The LED, representing the valve, remains OFF. Later, L_H is covered, so it is opened and changes to a HIGH level. This causes the LED to turn ON. At this point, closing the high level switch will have no effect on the LED as it remains ON until L_L is again covered, represented by a LOW.

Pre-lab Questions

1. In Table 10–1, why is V_{OUT} shown as both an input and an output?
2. The Model-1 controller is shown in Figure 10–3 with five gates. Show how an equivalent NOR implementation can simplify the circuit to four gates.

TABLE 10–1
Truth table for the model-1 outlet valve.

L_H	L_L	V_{OUT}	V_{OUT}	Action
0	0	0	1	Close valve.
0	0	1	1	Leave valve closed.
0	1	0	0	Valve is open; leave open.
0	1	1	1	Valve is closed; leave closed.
1	0	0	0	Sensor error; open valve.
1	0	1	0	Sensor error; open valve.
1	1	0	0	Sensors covered; leave valve open.
1	1	1	0	Sensors covered; open valve.

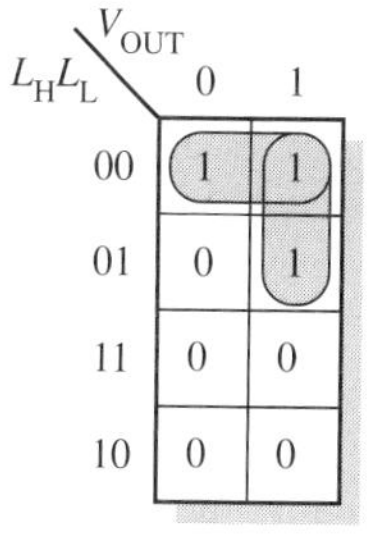

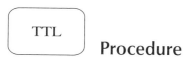

$$V_{OUT} = \overline{L_H}\,\overline{L_L} + \overline{L_H}V_{OUT}$$

FIGURE 10–2
Karnaugh map simplification for the outlet valve of the model-1 tank controller.

TTL

Procedure

Design the logic for the outlet valve, V_{OUT}, and the alarm, *A,* for the model-2 molasses tank controller. Test the design and submit a report showing the schematic and test results for this portion of the controller. The design requirements are given with the problem statement.

Problem Statement: The model-2 molasses tank controller has three inputs and four outputs. The inputs are two level sensors, L_L and L_H, and a temperature sensor, T_C. If the temperature is too cold for the molasses to flow properly, the "cold" temperature sensor will indicate this with a logic 1. The outputs are two valves, V_{IN}, and V_{OUT}, an alarm, *A,* and a heater, *H,* to warm the molasses sufficiently for it to flow properly. You need to design the logic for the outlet valve, V_{OUT}, the inlet valve, V_{IN}, and the alarm, *A*. The truth table for V_{OUT} has been prepared (with comments) as Table 10–2 to illustrate the logic. The partially completed truth table, which you need to finish, is shown as Table 10–3 in the report. Blank Karnaugh maps are provided in the report.

As in the model-1 controller, when the upper level sensor indicates it is covered, the outlet valve should open but only if the temperature sensor indicates the molasses is not too cold. The valve should remain open until the lower sensor is uncovered or if the molasses cools off so that it will not flow properly.

The alarm logic is designed to alert operators if a failure is detected in a sensor. This can occur if the upper level sensor indicates that it is covered but the lower sensor does not indicate that it is covered. Under this condition, an alarm should be indicated by an LED. The active level for the alarm should be LOW. Construct and test the logic for V_{OUT} and *A*. Describe your results.

For Further Investigation

Construct and test the logic for the inlet valve, V_{IN}. The valve should be open only when the outlet valve is closed and the upper level sensor is not covered. Describe the results of your test in the report.

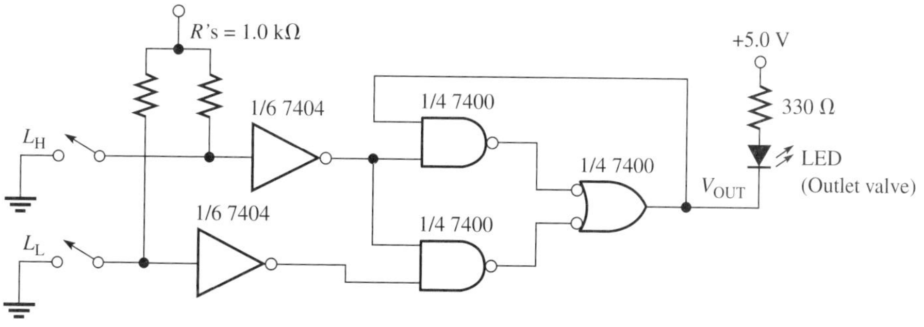

FIGURE 10–3
Schematic for the outlet valve logic of the model-1 tank controller.

TABLE 10–2

Truth table for the output valve of the model-2 tank controller.

L_H	L_L	T_C	V_{OUT}	V_{OUT}	Action
0	0	0	0	1	Close valve.
0	0	0	1	1	Leave valve closed.
0	0	1	0	1	Close valve.
0	0	1	1	1	Leave valve closed.
0	1	0	0	0	Valve is already open; leave open.
0	1	0	1	1	Valve is closed; leave closed.
0	1	1	0	1	Close valve; temp too cold.
0	1	1	1	1	Leave valve closed; temp too cold.
1	0	0	0	0	Sensor error; open valve.
1	0	0	1	0	Sensor error; open valve.
1	0	1	0	0	Sensor error; open valve.
1	0	1	1	0	Sensor error; open valve.
1	1	0	0	0	Tank full; leave valve open.
1	1	0	1	0	Tank full; open valve.
1	1	1	0	1	Tank full but too cold, close valve.
1	1	1	1	1	Tank full but too cold, keep valve closed.

Report for Experiment 10

Name: _____ Date: _____ Class: _____

Data and Observations:

TABLE 10–3
Truth table for Model-2 controller.

L_H	L_L	T_C	V_{OUT}	V_{OUT}	V_{IN}	A
0	0	0	0	1		
0	0	0	1	1		
0	0	1	0	1		
0	0	1	1	1		
0	1	0	0	0		
0	1	0	1	1		
0	1	1	0	1		
0	1	1	1	1		
1	0	0	0	0		
1	0	0	1	0		
1	0	1	0	0		
1	0	1	1	0		
1	1	0	0	0		
1	1	0	1	0		
1	1	1	0	1		
1	1	1	1	1		

Karnaugh maps:

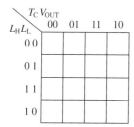

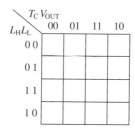

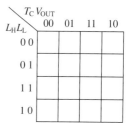

Results and Conclusion:

Further Investigation Results:

Review Questions (TTL)

1. Assume the level of the molasses in the model-2 controller causes the HIGH level sensor to "stick" in the open (logic 1) position. Will the alarm be activated as a result? Explain your answer.

2. Assume the level of the molasses in the model-2 controller causes the LOW level sensor to "stick" in the closed (logic 0) position. Will the alarm be activated as a result? Explain your answer.

Program Overview

A common method of circuit development involves the use of *feedback loops* where the output from a set of combinational logic is connected to its own input as shown in Figure 10–3. To accomplish this in VHDL, there is a special VHDL mode called **inout.** VHDL supports three basic modes within the entity portion of a VHDL application. These modes are **in, out,** and **inout.** Mode **in** is used for identifiers that name input signals. Mode **out** is used for identifiers that name output signals. Mode **inout** is used to represent bidirectional identifiers. In this experiment, you will use the **inout** mode to build the model-2 tank controller based on the model-1 tank controller design.

The model-1 tank controller was described in the Summary of Theory along with the Karnaugh map and the circuit for the V_{OUT} logic. Notice that in the TTL version of the experiment, 0's were entered on the truth table and the Karnaugh map in Figure 10–2 to represent active-LOW outputs. In the circuit implementation in Figure 10–3, V_{OUT} was connected directly to an active-LOW LED. In this case, a 0 was assumed to open a valve or activate the alarm and turn on the LED. In the VHDL program for the model-1 controller, the output logic was changed to active-HIGH. This is simple to do in the program and does not require new truth tables or maps. The program is shown in Figure 10–4.

The original expression with an active-LOW output for V_{OUT} (as read from the map) is

$$V_{OUT} = \overline{L_H}\,\overline{L_L} + \overline{L_H}V_{OUT}$$

Notice that *two* changes are required to implement this with active-HIGH logic in the VHDL program. The first change is to apply the **not** operator to the entire expression. The second change is more subtle. Recall that V_{OUT} is both an input and an output, so the V_{OUT} that is an input (right side of the equation) must also be inverted so that the correct logic is fed back. You will need to apply this same idea in the model-2 design.

In the VHDL program, it is a very simple addition to include the logic for the inlet valve, V_{IN} (given in the TTL version as a further investigation). By including a single equation, the inlet valve logic is added to the system. You will need to map this logic, and reduce it before entering it in the program.

Procedure

1. Connect the project board to a computer as described in *Project Board Familiarization* and review the *VHDL Software Familiarization.* Examine the program named *Molasses1* shown in Figure 10–4, which is written for the outlet valve of the model-1 tank controller. The circuit shown in Figure 10–3 is simulated in this program except the logic was converted from an active-LOW output in the circuit to an active-HIGH output in the program as explained in the Program Overview.

2. Design the logic for the outlet valve, V_{OUT}, the inlet valve, V_{IN}, and the alarm, A, for the model-2 molasses tank controller by reading through the problem statement and completing the truth table (Table 10–4) and Karnaugh maps in the report. The active level on the maps for all three outputs is to be a LOW (that is, assume a LOW signal opens a valve or turns on the alarm). The truth table for the V_{OUT} is completed as an example.

3. Complete the program *Molasses2* shown in Figure 10–5 of the report by adding the equations for V_{OUT}, V_{IN}, and A in the architecture section. Although the active level is LOW on the truth table and maps, write the equations in the program for active HIGH outputs as was done in the model-1 program.

4. Enter your completed program into the VHDL text editor. Assign inputs L_H, L_L, and T_C to on-board switches. Assign the outputs V_{OUT}, V_{IN}, and A to output LEDs.

FIGURE 10–4

Model-1 tank controller program.

```
library IEEE;
use IEEE.std_logic_1164.all;

entity Molasses1 is
    port (Lh, Ll: in std_logic;
            Vout: inout std_logic);
end entity Molasses1;

architecture Behavior of Molasses1 is
begin
    Vout <= not ((not Lh and not Vout) or (not Lh and not Ll));
end architecture Behavior;
```

CODE TIP
To reverse the output from an active LOW to an active HIGH, the keyword **not** is used in front of the entire expression and in front of Vout in the feedback path.

5. Compile and download the completed program *Molasses2* to the project board.

6. Test your program by exercising the L_H, L_L, and T_C inputs as shown in Table 10–4. If your program is working correctly, you should observe latching action for the V_{OUT} logic. With T_C LOW, close the L_L switch. After the L_L switch is closed, close and open the L_H switch. The V_{OUT} LED should indicate that the outlet valve remains open during this process. It will only close if the temperature is too low or if the L_L sensor is uncovered. Verify that for each combination of inputs the circuit responds correctly.

For Further Investigation

Modify the Molasses2 program by adding the heater logic. The heater should be on if the molasses is too cold and the lower-level sensor is covered. Show your modification in the report.

VHDL

Report for Experiment 10

Name: _____ Date: _____ Class: _____

Data and Observations:

TABLE 10–4
Truth table for model-2 controller.

L_H	L_L	T_C	V_{OUT}	V_{OUT}	V_{IN}	A
0	0	0	0	1	0	0
0	0	0	1	1	1	0
0	0	1	0	1	0	0
0	0	1	1	1	1	0
0	1	0	0	0	0	0
0	1	0	1	1	1	0
0	1	1	0	1	0	0
0	1	1	1	1	1	0
1	0	0	0	0	0	1
1	0	0	1	0	0	1
1	0	1	0	0	0	1
1	0	1	1	0	0	1
1	1	0	0	0	0	0
1	1	0	1	0	0	0
1	1	1	0	1	0	0
1	1	1	1	1	0	0

Karnaugh maps:

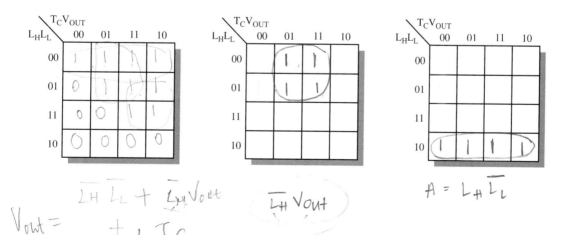

$$V_{out} = L_H \overline{L_L} + \overline{L_H} V_{out} + L_L T_C$$

$$\overline{L_H} V_{out}$$

$$A = L_H \overline{L_L}$$

149

```vhdl
library IEEE;
use IEEE.std_logic_1164.all;

entity Molasses2 is
  port (Lh, Ll, Tc: in std_logic;
        Vout, Vin, A: inout std_logic);
end entity Molasses2;

architecture Behavior of Molasses2 is
begin
  Vout <=          ;
  Vin  <=          ;
  A <=             ;
end architecture Behavior;
```

FIGURE 10–5

$$Vout <= ((\text{not } Lh \text{ and not } Ll) \text{ or } (\text{not } Lh \text{ and not } Vout) \text{ or } (Ll \text{ and } Tc));$$
$$Vin <= (\text{not } Lh \text{ and not } Vout);$$
$$A <= (Lh \text{ and not } Ll);$$

Further Investigation Results:

Review Questions (VHDL)

1. Could the VHDL mode **in** be used in place of **inout?**

2. Explain the importance of a bidirectional mode to VHDL.

3. Why are some lines of the truth table not directly testable in the Molasses2 program?

150

11

Adder and Magnitude Comparator

Objectives

After completing this experiment, you will be able to
- Complete the design, implement, and test a 4-bit binary to Excess-3 code converter.
- Complete the design of a signed number adder with overflow detection.

Reference Reading

Floyd, *Digital Fundamentals with VHDL*, Chapter 6, "Functions of Combinational Logic"

Materials Needed (TTL)

7483A 4-bit binary adder
7485 4-bit magnitude comparator
7404 hex inverter
7410 triple 3-input NAND gate
Five LEDs
One 4-position DIP switch
Resistors: five 330 Ω, eight 1.0 kΩ

Materials Needed (VHDL)

Project Board

Summary of Theory

This experiment introduces you to two important MSI circuits—the 4-bit adder and the 4-bit magnitude comparator. The TTL version of a 4-bit adder, with full look-ahead carry, is the 7483A. The truth table for this device is given in the manufacturer's specification sheet. The TTL version of the 4-bit magnitude comparator is the 7485 which includes $A > B$, $A < B$, and $A = B$ outputs. It also has $A > B$, $A < B$, and $A = B$ inputs for the purpose of cascading comparators. Be careful to note inputs and outputs when you are connecting a comparator.

One difference in the way adders and comparators are labeled needs to be clarified. A 4-bit adder contains a carry-in, which is considered the least significant bit so it is given a *zero* subscript (C_0). The next least significant bits are contained in the two 4-bit numbers to be added, so they are identified with a *one* subscript (A_1, B_1). On a comparator, there is no carry-in, so the least significant bits are labeled with a *zero* subscript (A_0, B_0).

In this experiment, an adder and comparator are used to convert a 4-bit binary code to Excess-3 code. The approach is somewhat unorthodox but shows how adders and magnitude comparators work. Although the technique could be applied to larger binary numbers, better methods are available. To familiarize you with the experiment, a similar circuit is described in the following example.

Example: A 4-Bit Binary to BCD Converter

Recall that a 4-bit binary number between 0000 and 1001 (decimal 9) is the same as the BCD number. If we add zero to these binary numbers, the result is unchanged and still represents BCD. Binary numbers from 1010 (ten) to 1111 (fifteen) can be converted to BCD by simply adding 0110 (six) to them.

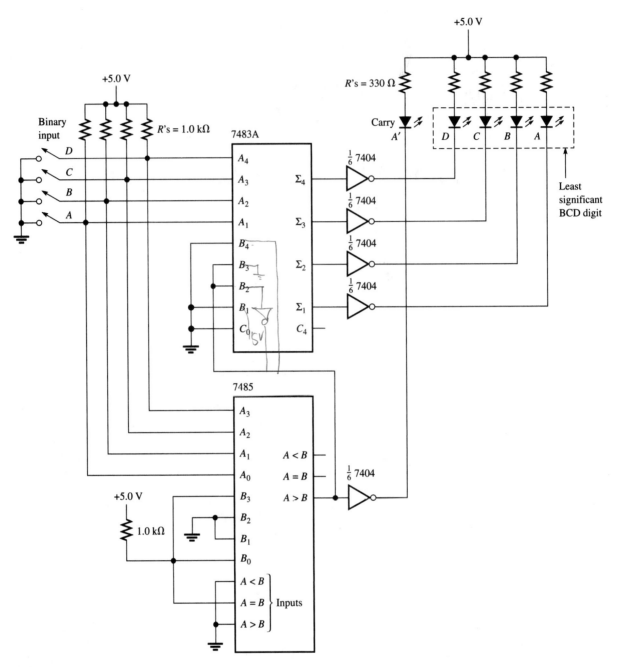

FIGURE 11–1
Binary to BCD converter.

The circuit that accomplishes this is illustrated in Figure 11–1. Notice that the B input of the comparator is connected to 1001. If the binary number on the A input of the comparator is greater than 1001, the $A > B$ output is asserted. This action causes the adder to add 0110 to the binary input. Notice how the $A > B$ output of the comparator is connected to the B side of the adder. Only bits B_2 and B_3 will be high when $A > B$ is asserted; otherwise, all bits are low. This causes the adder to either add 0000 or 0110 to the binary input. The situation is summarized in Table 11–1. Notice in the table that bits B_2 and B_3 have the same "sense" as the $A > B$ output—they are 0 when $A > B$ is 0 and 1 when $A > B$ is 1. Bits B_4 and B_1 are always 0, hence these inputs are connected to ground.

TABLE 11–1

Binary to BCD.

Comparator $A > B$ Output	Adder Input				Comment
	B_4	B_3	B_2	B_1	
0	0	0	0	0	input is less than ten, add 0000
1	0	1	1	0	input is greater than nine, add 0110

Pre-lab Questions

1. Explain why the LSB on a comparator has a different subscript than the LSB of an adder.
2. What is the purpose of the comparator in Figure 11–1?

TTL

Procedure

1. Figure 11–2 (in the report) shows a partially completed schematic of a binary to Excess-3 code conversion circuit. It uses the basic idea described by the example in the Summary of Theory except it needs to add either 0011 or 1001 to the binary input number. The adder must add 0011 (decimal 3) to the binary input number if it is between 0000 and 1001 but add 1001 (nine) to the number if it is greater than nine in order to convert the 4-bit binary number to Excess-3. The problem is summarized in Table 11–2. Decide how to connect the open inputs on the 7483A, and complete the schematic.

2. From your schematic, build the circuit. Test all possible inputs as listed on truth Table 11–3 (in the report). The outputs can be read directly from the LEDs. Assume an LED that is ON represents a logic 1 and an LED that is OFF represents a logic 0.

For Further Investigation

Overflow Detection

Fixed-point signed numbers are stored in most computers in the manner illustrated in Table 11–4. Positive numbers are stored in true form and negative numbers are stored in 2's complement form. If two numbers with the same sign are added, the answer can be too large to be represented with the number of bits available. This condition, called *overflow,* occurs when an addition operation causes a carry into the sign bit position. As a result, the sign bit will be in error, a condition easy to detect. When two numbers with the opposite sign are added, overflow cannot occur, so the sign bit will always be correct. Figure 11–3 illustrates overflow for 4-bit numbers.

In this part of the experiment we will step through the design of a 4-bit adder for signed numbers that detects the presence of an overflow error and lights an LED when overflow occurs. We can start with the 7483A adder and a 7404 hex inverter as shown in Figure 11–4 (in the report).

1. Consider the problem of detecting an overflow error. We need consider only the sign bit for each number to be added and the sign bit for the answer. Complete truth Table 11–5 (in the report) for all possible combinations of the sign bit, showing a 1 whenever an overflow error occurs.

TABLE 11–2

Binary to Excess-3.

Comparator $A > B$ Output	Adder Input				Comment
	B_4	B_3	B_2	B_1	
0	0	0	1	1	input is less than ten, add 0011
1	1	0	0	1	input is greater than nine, add 1001

TABLE 11–4
Representation of 4-bit signed numbers.

Base Ten Number	Computer Representation	
+7	0111	
+6	0110	
+5	0101	
+4	0100	Numbers in
+3	0011	true form
+2	0010	
+1	0001	
0	0000	
−1	1111	
−2	1110	
−3	1101	
−4	1100	Numbers in 2's
−5	1011	complement
−6	1010	form
−7	1001	
−8	1000	

↑
Sign bit

Numbers with opposite signs: Overflow into sign position cannot occur.

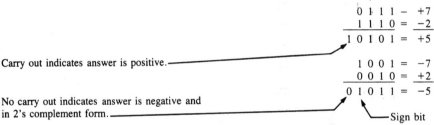

Carry out indicates answer is positive.

No carry out indicates answer is negative and
in 2's complement form.

Numbers with the same sign: Overflow into sign position can occur.

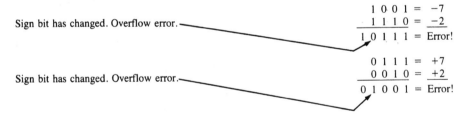

Sign bit has changed. Overflow error.

Sign bit has changed. Overflow error.

FIGURE 11–3
Overflow that can occur with 4-bit signed numbers. The concept shown here is applied to large binary numbers.

2. Complete the Karnaugh map of the output (shown in the report as Figure 11–5) to see whether minimization is possible.

3. Write the Boolean expression for detection of an overflow error in your report.

4. Note that the signals going into the box in Figure 11–4 are A_4, B_4, and $\overline{\Sigma_4}$. If you apply DeMorgan's theorem to one term of your Boolean expression, you can draw a circuit that uses only these inputs. Draw the circuit in the box. If directed by your instructor, build and test your circuit.

Report for Experiment 11

Name: _____ Date: _____ Class: _____

Data and Observations:

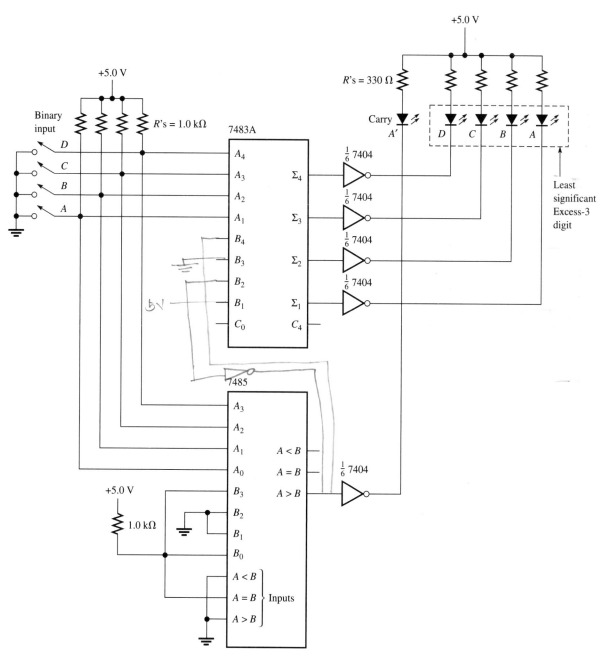

FIGURE 11–2
Binary to Excess-3 converter.

TABLE 11–3

Truth table for Figure 11–2.

Inputs (Binary)				Outputs Excess-3				
D	C	B	A	A'	D	C	B	A
0	0	0	0					
0	0	0	1					
0	0	1	0					
0	0	1	1					
0	1	0	0					
0	1	0	1					
0	1	1	0					
0	1	1	1					
1	0	0	0					
1	0	0	1					
1	0	1	0					
1	0	1	1					
1	1	0	0					
1	1	0	1					
1	1	1	0					
1	1	1	1					

Results and Conclusion:

Further Investigation Results:

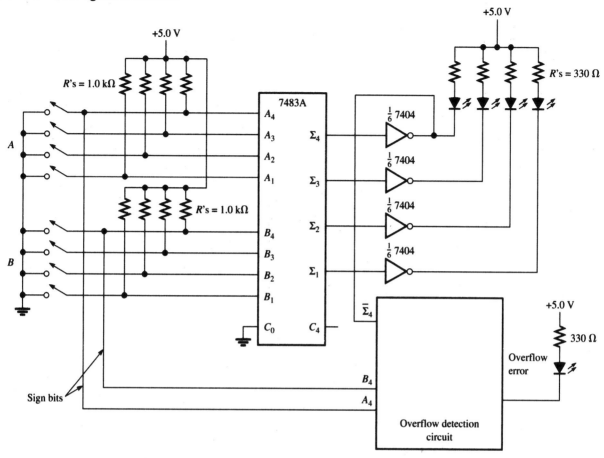

FIGURE 11–4
Signed number adder.

TABLE 11–5
Truth table for overflow error.

Sign Bits			Error
A_4	B_4	Σ_4	X
0	0	0	
0	0	1	
0	1	0	
0	1	1	
1	0	0	
1	0	1	
1	1	0	
1	1	1	

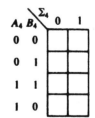

FIGURE 11–5
Karnaugh map for overflow error.

Boolean expression for overflow error:

$X = $ _____

Review Questions (TTL)

1. In the space below, show how two 7483A adders could be cascaded to add two 8-bit numbers.

2. The circuit in Figure 11–4 is designed to add two 4-bit signed numbers. Recall that negative numbers are stored in 2's complement form. To change the circuit into a subtracting circuit ($A - B$) you need to 2's complement the B (subtrahend) inputs. Inverting the B inputs forms the 1's complement. What else must be done in order to cause the circuit to form the 2's complement of the B input?

3. Figure 6–12 of the text shows a simple six-position voting machine module. What change could you make to the module to allow a seventh position? (*Hint:* no ICs are needed!)

Program Overview

VHDL can implement functions like adders and comparators very easily. These two functions are explored in the first programs in this experiment. Both of these functions are more efficient if the input variables (identifiers) are treated as a one-dimensional array (list) of numbers. In the first two programs, the inputs A and B will each be 4 bits. The **integer** data type assigns related bits into a collection of bits that can be treated as one number. The **integer** data type is used in the **entity** section of these programs to represent the input and output identifiers. Assignments to array elements must include a numeric index starting with 0. (Notice that this convention differs from traditional adders). Thus, the A identifier has elements A_0, A_1, A_2, and A_3 and the B array has elements B_0, B_1, B_2, and B_3.

In the comparator program, the same **integer** data type is used to assign the inputs to 4-bit arrays. In addition, the VHDL key words **when** and **else** will be used to determine if the value A is less than, equal to, or greater than the value B.

After exploring the adder and comparator functions, a VHDL program is given that converts binary code to excess-3 code as described in the Summary of Theory. Although the TTL experiment used the adder and comparator circuits to accomplish this, it is more complicated than necessary for the VHDL program, hence it is not used. The VHDL program still tests the input and adds a value based on the result, but it can be accomplished in a single line of code!

In the For Further Investigation section, a VHDL program is given that performs the overflow detection logic described in the TTL experiment. You can test this program and develop the truth table.

Procedure

1. Connect the project board to a computer as described in *Project Board Familiarization* and review *VHDL Software Familiarization*.

2. Enter the program named *FourBitAdd* shown in Figure 11–6 of the report into the text editor. The adder program adds two 4-bit identifiers A and B. The summation of A and B is assigned to a 5-bit identifier named *Sum*. The fifth bit in *Sum* is the carry-out bit. In Tables 11–6 and 11–9, the standard mathematical Σ is used for the sum.

3. Assign A and B to four switches each and *Sum* to five LEDs. A and B are each 4-bit arrays because they are assigned as data type **integer** (see Program Overview). After assigning the identifiers, compile and download the program to the project board.

4. Test the FourBitAdd program by entering the values for A and B shown in Table 11–6 of the report and entering the sum in the space provided. Notice that the sum of A and B can produce five bits because of carries. The test values given in Table 11–6 represent only a sample of possible inputs. A full test of a 4-bit adder is not reasonable.

5. Enter the program named *Comparator* shown in Figure 11–7 of the report into the text editor. The two 4-bit inputs A and B are compared and the output assigned to one of three single bit outputs representing either less than "$<$", equal to "$=$", or greater than "$>$".

6. Assign inputs A and B to switches and outputs *Less, Equal,* and *Greater* to LEDs. Compile and download the program to the project board.

7. Test the Comparator program by completing the output section of Table 11–7 in the report. Again, a full test is not reasonable, so sample values are entered in Table 11–7.

Excess-3 Code

8. Excess-3 code is a 4-bit binary code used in early computers. It uses the basic idea described in the Summary of Theory. To convert BCD numbers to Excess-3, the value 3 is added to the input when it is less then 10; otherwise, nine is added as shown in Table 11–2. Examine the Excess-3 converter by entering the program *BinaryToExcess3* (in Figure 11–8 in the report) into the text editor and downloading it to the project board adding comments to describe how it works.

9. Assign input A to four switches and output X to five LEDs. Compile and download the program to the project board.

10. Test the program and complete the truth Table 11–8 in the report.

For Further Investigation

Overflow Detection

Fixed-point signed numbers are stored in most computers in the manner illustrated in Table 11–4. Positive numbers are stored in true form and negative numbers are stored in 2's complement form. If two numbers with the same sign are added, the answer can be too large to be represented with the number of bits available. This condition, called *overflow,* occurs when an addition operation causes a carry into the sign bit position. As a result, the sign bit will be in error, a condition easy to detect. When two numbers with the opposite sign are added, overflow cannot occur, so the sign will always be correct. Figure 11–3 illustrates overflow for 4-bit numbers.

In this investigation, a simple detector for an overflow error is developed. The output will control an LED when this occurs.

1. Consider the problem of detecting an overflow error. Consider only the sign bit for each number to be added and the sign bit for the answer. Complete truth Table 11–9 for all possible combinations of the sign bit, showing a 1 whenever an overflow error occurs.

2. Complete the Karnaugh map of the output (shown in the report as Figure 11–9) to see whether minimization is possible.

3. Write the Boolean expression for detection of an overflow error in your report.

4. Implement the Boolean expression by supplying the equation for X in program *OverFlow* shown in Figure 11–10.

5. Assign *A4, B4,* and *Sum4* to switches and output X to an LED. Then compile and download the program to the project board.

6. Demonstrate that the output of the OverFlow program agrees with Table 11–9 of the report.

Report for Experiment 11

Name: _____ Date: _____ Class: _____

Data and Observations:

```
entity FourBitAdd is
    port (A, B : in integer range 0 to 15;  -- Array of 4 bits
          Sum : out integer range 0 to 31); -- Array of 5 bits
end entity FourBitAdd;

architecture AdderBehavior of FourBitAdd is
begin
    Sum <= A + B;
end architecture AdderBehavior;
```

> **CODE TIP**
> The INTEGER data can be used to identify a group of related bits in a convenient format. Grouping related bits allows for simplified programs that are easier to understand. The keyword RANGE is used to constrain the INTEGER data type to a specific range of values, also defining the number of required hardware bits.

FIGURE 11–6
Program for the 4-bit adder.

```
library IEEE;
use IEEE.std_logic_1164.all;

entity Comparator is
    port (A, B : in integer range 0 to 15; -- Bit arrays of 4 bits
          Less, Equal, Greater: out std_logic);
end entity Comparator;

architecture Comp_behavior of Comparator is
begin
    Less    <= '1' when (A < B) else '0';
    Equal   <= '1' when (A = B) else '0';
    Greater <= '1' when (A > B) else '0';
end architecture Comp_behavior;
```

FIGURE 11–7
Program for the 4-bit comparator.

```
library IEEE;
use IEEE.std_logic_1164.all;
entity BinaryToExcess3 is
    port (A : in integer range 0 to 15;  --  4 bit input
          X : out integer range 0 to 31); -- 5 bit output

end entity BinaryToExcess3;

architecture Converter of BinaryToExcess3 is
begin
-- Program Comments
--
--
--
--
    X <= A + 3 when A < 10 else A + 9;
end architecture Converter;
```

FIGURE 11–8
Program for Excess-3 converter.

TABLE 11–6
Summation of registers A and B.

Inputs (Binary)								Output				
A_3	A_2	A_1	A_0	B_3	B_2	B_1	B_0	C_4	Σ_3	Σ_2	Σ_1	Σ_0
0	0	0	0	0	0	0	0					
0	0	0	0	0	1	1	1					
0	0	0	1	0	1	1	1					
0	1	1	1	0	1	1	0					
0	1	1	0	0	1	0	0					
0	1	1	0	1	1	0	0					
0	1	1	0	1	1	1	0					
1	1	1	0	1	0	0	0					
1	0	0	0	1	0	0	0					
1	0	0	0	1	0	0	1					
1	0	1	0	1	0	0	1					
1	0	1	0	1	0	1	0					
1	0	1	1	1	0	1	0					
1	1	0	0	1	0	1	1					
1	1	1	0	1	1	1	1					
1	1	1	1	1	1	1	1					

TABLE 11–7
4-bit comparator.

Inputs (Binary)								Output (bit)		
A_3	A_2	A_1	A_0	B_3	B_2	B_1	B_0	Less	Equal	Greater
0	0	0	0	0	0	0	0			
0	0	0	0	0	1	1	1			
0	0	0	1	0	1	1	1			
0	1	1	1	0	1	1	0			
0	1	1	0	0	1	0	0			
0	1	1	0	1	1	0	0			
0	1	1	0	1	1	1	0			
1	1	1	0	1	0	0	0			
1	0	0	0	1	0	0	0			
1	0	0	0	1	0	0	1			
1	0	1	0	1	0	0	1			
1	0	1	0	1	0	1	0			
1	0	1	1	1	0	1	0			
1	1	0	0	1	0	1	1			
1	1	1	0	1	1	1	1			
1	1	1	1	1	1	1	1			

TABLE 11–8
Truth table for Excess-3.

Inputs (Binary)				Outputs (Excess-3)				
A_3	A_2	A_1	A_0	X_4	X_3	X_2	X_1	X_0
0	0	0	0	0	0	0	1	1
0	0	0	1	0	0	1	0	0
0	0	1	0					
0	0	1	1					
0	1	0	0					
0	1	0	1					
0	1	1	0					
0	1	1	1					
1	0	0	0					
1	0	0	1					
1	0	1	0					
1	0	1	1					
1	1	0	0					
1	1	0	1					
1	1	1	0					
1	1	1	1					

Further Investigation Results:

TABLE 11–9
Truth table for overflow error.

Sign Bits			Error
A_4	B_4	Σ_4	X
0	0	0	
0	0	1	
0	1	0	
0	1	1	
1	0	0	
1	0	1	
1	1	0	
1	1	1	

FIGURE 11–9
Karnaugh map for overflow error.

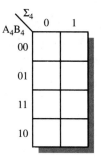

```
entity OverFlow is
   port (A4, B4, Sum4: in bit; X: out bit);
end entity OverFlow;

architecture OverFlowBehavior of OverFlow is
begin
   X <=                              ;
end architecture OverFlowBehavior;
```

FIGURE 11–10
Program for overflow error.

Boolean expression of overflow error:

$X = $ _____

Review Questions (VHDL)

1. In step 4, it is mentioned that a full test of a 4-bit adder is not reasonable. Why?

2. What is the advantage of writing the Excess-3 logic without using the user-defined Comparator and Adder as a **component**?

12

Combinational Logic Using Multiplexers

Objectives

After completing this experiment, you will be able to

☐ Use a multiplexer to implement a comparator and a parity generator and test the circuit.

☐ Use an *N*-input multiplexer to implement a truth table containing 2*N* inputs.

☐ Troubleshoot a simulated failure in a test circuit.

Reference Reading

Floyd, *Digital Fundamentals with VHDL,* Chapter 6, "Functions of Combinational Logic"

Materials Needed (TTL)

74151A data selector/multiplexer
7404 hex inverter
One LED
Resistors: one 330 Ω, four 1.0 kΩ

Materials Needed (VHDL)

Project Board

Summary of Theory

The *multiplexer* or *data selector* connects any one of several inputs to a single output. The opposite function, in which a single input is directed to one of several outputs, is called a *demultiplexer* or a *decoder.* These definitions are illustrated in Figure 12–1.

Control is determined by additional logic signals called the *select* (or *address*) inputs.

Multiplexers (MUXs) and demultiplexers (DMUXs) have many applications in digital logic. One useful application for MUXs is implementation of combinational logic functions directly from the truth table. For example, an overflow error detection circuit is described by the truth table shown in Figure 12–2(a). Each output row containing a "1" represents a minterm. (*Minterm* is a Boolean term in which all input variables appear either in "NOTed" or "true" form. For example, if there are 4 inputs labeled *A, B, C,* and *D,* then $A\overline{B}C\overline{D}$ and $\overline{A}BCD$ are both minterms but *ABC* is not.) If the logic for that minterm is connected to the data inputs of a MUX, and if the data selected are controlled by the input variables, the truth table has been implemented

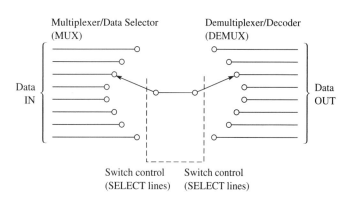

FIGURE 12–1

FIGURE 12-2

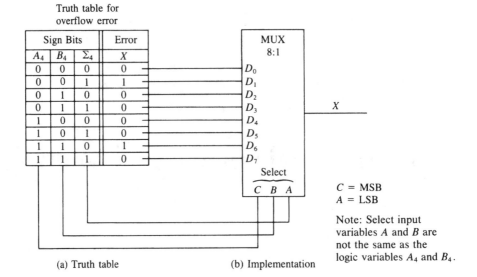

Truth table for
overflow error

(a) Truth table

(b) Implementation

C = MSB
A = LSB

Note: Select input
variables A and B are
not the same as the
logic variables A_4 and B_4.

directly. Figure 12–2(b) illustrates this idea conceptually for the overflow detector.

Actually, an 8-input MUX is not required to implement the overflow detection logic. Any N-input MUX can generate the output function for $2N$ inputs. To illustrate, we reorganize the truth table in pairs, as shown in Figure 12–3(a). The inputs labeled A_4 and B_4 are used to select a data line. Connected to that line can be a logic 0, 1, Σ_4, or $\overline{\Sigma}_4$. For example, from the truth table, if $A_4 = 0$ and $B_4 = 1$, the D_1 input is selected. Since both outputs are the same (in this case a logic 0), then D_1 is connected to a logic 0. If the outputs were different, such as in the first and fourth rows, then the third input variable, Σ_4, would be compared with the output. If the desired Output X is the same as the Data Input Σ_4, then it is selected as the input to the MUX. If the desired Output X is opposite to the Data Input Σ_4, then $\overline{\Sigma}_4$ is selected as the input to the MUX. The results are shown conceptually in Figure 12–3(b), which is equivalent to but simpler than the circuit in Figure 12–2(b). This circuit is also on the EWB/MSM CD packaged with the text.

In this experiment you will use an 8:1 MUX to implement a 4-input truth table (with 16 combinations). First you will develop the circuit to implement a special comparator. In the For Further Investigation section the circuit is modified to make a parity generator for a 4-bit code. *Parity* is an extra bit attached to a code to check that the code has been received correctly. *Odd parity* means that the number of 1's in the code, including the parity bit, is an odd number. Odd or even parity can be generated with exclusive-OR gates, and parity generators are available in IC form. However, the implementing of an arbitrary truth table using MUXs is the important concept.

Pre-lab Questions

1. Summarize the operation of a multiplexer.
2. Summarize the operation of a demultiplexer.

TTL

Procedure

Special 2-Bit Comparator

1. Assume you needed to compare two 2-bit numbers called A and B to find whether A is equal to or greater than B. You could use a comparator and OR the $A > B$ and $A = B$ outputs. Another technique is to use an 8:1 MUX with the method shown in the Summary of Theory section. The partially completed truth table for the comparator is shown as Table 12–1 in the report. The inputs are A_2, A_1 and B_2, B_1, representing the two numbers to be compared. Notice that the A_2, A_1, and B_2 bits are connected to the SELECT inputs of the MUX. The B_1 bit is available to be connected as needed. It is therefore listed in a separate column of the truth table. Determine the logic in which the output represents $A > B$ and complete the X column of Table 12–1. The first two entries are completed as an example.

2. Look at the output X, in groups of two. The first pair of entries in X is the complement of the corresponding entries in B_1; therefore, the data should be connected to $\overline{B}_1$, as shown in the first line. Complete Table 12–1 by filling in the last column with either 0, 1, B_1, or $\overline{B}_1$.

3. Using the data from Table 12–1, complete the circuit drawing shown as Figure 12–4 in the report. From the manufacturer's specification sheet, determine how to connect the STROBE input

FIGURE 12–3　　　　　Truth table for overflow error

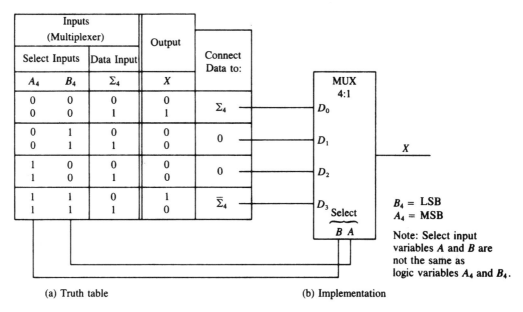

Inputs (Multiplexer)			Output	Connect Data to:
Select Inputs		Data Input		
A_4	B_4	Σ_4	X	
0	0	0	0	Σ_4
0	0	1	1	
0	1	0	0	0
0	1	1	0	
1	0	0	0	0
1	0	1	0	
1	1	0	1	$\overline{\Sigma_4}$
1	1	1	0	

(a) Truth table　　　　　　　　　　　　　　　(b) Implementation

B_4 = LSB
A_4 = MSB

Note: Select input variables A and B are not the same as logic variables A_4 and B_4.

(labeled $\overline{G}$). Construct the circuit and test its operation by checking every possible input. Demonstrate your working circuit to your instructor.

EWB/MSM Troubleshooting

The CD packaged with this lab manual contains Electronics Workbench (.ewb) and Multisim (.msm) files.

The overflow error circuit discussed in the Summary of Theory and shown in Figure 12–3 is given as Exp-12. Two versions are given; the first has no fault and can be used as a reference. The second circuit has a fault. Analyze the circuit. In the space provided in the report, indicate the most likely problem.

For Further Investigation

Parity Generator Using a Multiplexer

1. The technique to implement an arbitrary function can also generate either odd or even parity. The MUX can generate *both* odd and even parity at the same time because there are two complementary outputs. One interesting aspect of the parity generator circuit is that any of the four inputs can turn the LED on or off in a manner similar to the way in which 3-way switches can turn a light on or off from more than one location. The truth table is shown in the report as Table 12–2. Four of the bits (A_3 through A_0) represent the information, and the fifth bit (X), which is the output, represents the parity bit. The requirement is for a circuit that generates both odd and even parity; however, the truth table will be set up for even parity. Even parity means that the sum of the 5 bits, *including the output parity bit,* must be equal to an even number. Complete Table 12–2 to reflect this requirement. The first line has been completed as an example.

2. Using the truth table completed in Step 1, complete the schematic for the even parity generator that is started in Figure 12–5 of the report. Change your original circuit into the parity circuit and test its operation.

Report for Experiment 12

Name: _____ Date: _____ Class: _____

Data and Observations:

TABLE 12–1
Truth table for 2-bit comparator, $A \geq B$.

Inputs				Output	Connect Data to:
A_2	A_1	B_2	B_1	X	
0	0	0	0	1	$\overline{B_1}$
0	0	0	1	0	
0	0	1	0		
0	0	1	1		
0	1	0	0		
0	1	0	1		
0	1	1	0		
0	1	1	1		
1	0	0	0		
1	0	0	1		
1	0	1	0		
1	0	1	1		
1	1	0	0		
1	1	0	1		
1	1	1	0		
1	1	1	1		

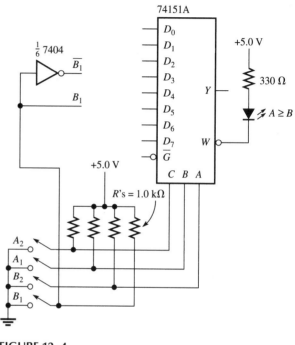

FIGURE 12–4

Results and Conclusion:

EWB/MSM Troubleshooting:

Most likely problem: _____

Further Investigation Results:

TABLE 12–2
Truth table for even parity generator.

Inputs				Output	Connect
A_3	A_2	A_1	A_0	X	Data to:
0	0	0	0	0	A_0
0	0	0	1	1	
0	0	1	0		
0	0	1	1		
0	1	0	0		
0	1	0	1		
0	1	1	0		
0	1	1	1		
1	0	0	0		
1	0	0	1		
1	0	1	0		
1	0	1	1		
1	1	0	0		
1	1	0	1		
1	1	1	0		
1	1	1	1		

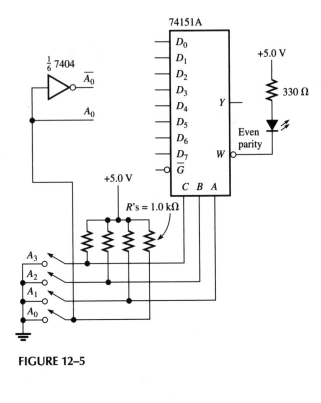

FIGURE 12–5

Review Questions (TTL)

1. How can both odd and even parity be obtained from the circuit in Figure 12–5?

2. Assume the circuit shown in Figure 12–4 had the correct output for the first half of the truth table but had some incorrect outputs for the second half of the truth table. You decide to change ICs (not necessarily the best choice!) but the problem persists. What is the most likely cause of the problem? How could you test the circuit for your suspected problem?

Program Overview

One method of modeling VHDL applications is called structural modeling. In structural modeling, blocks of logic are defined such as the function of a common fixed function IC. In this experiment, you will see an application of structural modeling to simulate the performance of a fixed function 8:1 MUX.

In combinational logic, an N-input MUX can be used to generate the output function for $2N$ inputs. In this experiment, you will model an 8:1 MUX in VHDL and then use this MUX to compare two 2-bit numbers A and B as described in the Summary of Theory. The output will control an LED on your project board if the A input is equal to or greater than the B input.

Procedure

1. Assume you needed to compare two 2-bit numbers called A and B to find whether A is equal to or greater than B using an 8:1 MUX. The partially completed truth table for the comparator is shown in Table 12–3 in the report section. The inputs are labeled A_2, A_1, and B_2, B_1 and represent the two numbers to be compared. Notice that the A_2, A_1, and B_2 bits are connected to the SELECT inputs of the MUX. The B_1 bit (and its complement $\overline{B_1}$) are available to be assigned as data inputs to the MUX. It is therefore listed in a separate column of the truth table. Determine the logic in which the output represents $A \geq B$ and complete the X column of Table 12–3. The first two entries are completed as an example.

2. Look at the output X, in the groups of two. The first pair of entries in X is the complement of the corresponding entries in B_1; therefore, the data should be connected to B_1, as shown in the first line. Complete Table 12–3 by filling in the last column with either 1 (HIGH), 0 (LOW), B_1, or $\overline{B_1}$.

3. Using the data from Table 12–3, complete the circuit drawing shown as Figure 12–6 in the report. The circuit drawing will be the basis for the VHDL implementation of the 2-bit comparator.

Creating the 8:1 MUX

4. Connect the project board to a computer as described in *Project Board Familiarization* and review appropriate *VHDL Software Familiarization*.

5. Enter the program *MUX8_1* in Figure 12–7 into the text editor.

6. The SELECT logic for the MUX program is supplied by inputs S_0, S_1, and S_2, which will be represented by input switches on your project board. Input data to be selected are bits D_0 through D_7 and are also represented by switches on your project board. Assign input switches to the select and data inputs. Assign an LED to output X. Note if you are using the PLDT-1 board, you can use PLD global pins located on B_1 for S_0, S_1, and S_2 as inputs.

7. Compile and download the program to the project board.

8. Test the 8:1 MUX by observing output X for each input selection D_0 through D_7. Record your observations in Table 12–4 in the report.

Creating the 2-Bit Comparator

9. Use the VHDL MUX in Figure 12–6 as a guide to write the equations for d(2) through d(7) for program *TwoBitCompare* in Figure 12–8. d(0) and d(1) are completed as an example.

10. Enter your program into the text editor.

11. Assign inputs A_2, A_1, B_2, and B_1 to switches. Assign the output X to an LED. Then compile and download your program to the project board.

12. Exercise the 2-bit comparator application by asserting the inputs for A_2, A_1, B_2, and B_1 as listed in Table 12–3. Verify that the program complies with the output column in Table 12–3. Record your observations and complete the table.

For Further Investigation

Parity Generator Using a Multiplexer

1. The technique to implement an arbitrary function can also generate either odd or even parity. A MUX can generate *both* odd and even parity at the same time because there are two complementary outputs. One interesting aspect of the parity generator is that any of the four inputs can turn the LED on or off in a manner similar to the way in which 3-way switches can turn a light on or off from more than one location. The truth table is shown in the report as Table 12–5. Four of the bits (A_3 through A_0) represent the information, and the fifth bit (X), which is the output, represents the parity bit. The requirement is for a logic system that generates both odd and even parity. Even parity means that the sum of the 5 bits, *including the output parity bit,* must be equal to an even number. Complete Table 12–5 to reflect this requirement. The first line has been completed as an example.

2. Using the truth table completed in Step 1, complete the design for the even parity checker in Figure 12–9.

3. Using the truth table from Step 1, complete the equations for d(2) through s(2) for program *ParityChecker* in Figure 12–10 of the report. Modify your original program to implement the parity checker using the same input switches and output LED.

4. Compile and download program *ParityChecker* to the project board.

5. Exercise the parity checker application by asserting the inputs for A_3, A_2, A_1, and A_0 as listed in Table 12–5. Verify that the circuit complies with the output column in Table 12–5. Record your observations in the Output Observed column to complete the table.

Report for Experiment 12

Name: _____ Date: _____ Class: _____

Data and Observations:

TABLE 12–3
Truth table for 2-bit comparator, $A \geq B$.

Inputs				Output		Connected Data to:
A_2	A_1	B_2	B_1	X	Observed on Project Board	
0	0	0	0	1		$\overline{B_1}$
0	0	0	1	0		
0	0	1	0			
0	0	1	1			
0	1	0	0			
0	1	0	1			
0	1	1	0			
0	1	1	1			
1	0	0	0			
1	0	0	1			
1	0	1	0			
1	0	1	1			
1	1	0	0			
1	1	0	1			
1	1	1	0			
1	1	1	1			

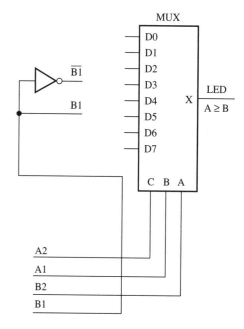

FIGURE 12–6

```
entity MUX8_1 is
  port( D: in bit_vector(0 to 7);
        S: in bit_vector(0 to 2);
        X: out bit);
end entity MUX8_1;

architecture Behavior of MUX8_1 is
begin
  X <= D(0) when (S = "000") else
       D(1) when (S = "001") else
       D(2) when (S = "010") else
       D(3) when (S = "011") else
       D(4) when (S = "100") else
       D(5) when (S = "101") else
       D(6) when (S = "110") else
       D(7) when (S = "111");
end architecture Behavior;
```

CODE TIP
Input S represents MUX inputs C, B, and A as shown in Figure 12–6.

FIGURE 12–7
Program for the 8:1 MUX.

TABLE 12–4
Truth Table for 8:1 MUX.

Data		Select			Output
		S_0	S_1	S_2	
D_0	1	0	0	0	
	0				
D_1	1	0	0	1	
	0				
D_2	1				
	0				
D_3	1				
	0				
D_4	1				
	0				
D_5	1				
	0				
D_6	1				
	0				
D_7	1				
	0				

```
entity TwoBitCompare is
  port (A2, A1, B2, B1: in bit;
        X : out bit);
end entity TwoBitCompare;

architecture Behavior of TwoBitCompare is
signal High, Low ,B1Not: bit;

component MUX8_1 is
  port( D: in bit_vector(0 to 7);
        S: in bit_vector(0 to 2);
        X: out bit);
end component MUX8_1;

begin
  High <= '1';    -- High is used where a logic 1 is needed.
  Low <= '0';     -- Low is used where a logic 1 is needed.
  B1Not <= not B1; -- B1Not is used where you wish the invert input B1
  COMP1: MUX8_1 port map (  d(0) => B1Not  ,
                            d(1) => Low,
                            d(2) =>           ,
                            d(3) =>           ,
                            d(4) =>           ,
                            d(5) =>           ,
                            d(6) =>           ,
                            d(7) =>           ,
                            s(0) => A2,
                            s(1) => A1,
                            s(2) => B2,
                            X => X);

end architecture Behavior;
```

FIGURE 12–8

Further Investigation Results:

TABLE 12–5

Truth table for even parity generator.

Inputs				Output		Connected Data to:
A_3	A_2	A_1	A_0	X	Observed on Project Board	
0	0	0	0	1		$\overline{A_0}$
0	0	0	1	0		
0	0	1	0			
0	0	1	1			
0	1	0	0			
0	1	0	1			
0	1	1	0			
0	1	1	1			
1	0	0	0			
1	0	0	1			
1	0	1	0			
1	0	1	1			
1	1	0	0			
1	1	0	1			
1	1	1	0			
1	1	1	1			

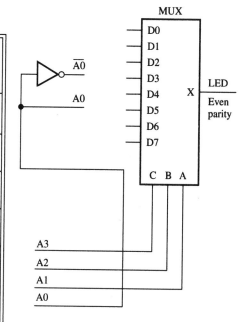

FIGURE 12–9

FIGURE 12–10

```
entity ParityChecker is
  port (A3, A2, A1, A0 : in bit;
        X : out bit);
end entiy ParityChecker;

architecture Behavior of ParityChecker is
signal High, Low ,B1Not: bit;

component MUX8_1 is
  port( D: in bit_vector(0 to 7);
        S: in bit_vector(0 to 2);
        X: out bit);
end component MUX8_1;

begin
  High <= '1';    -- High is used where a logic 1 is needed.
  Low <= '0';     -- Low is used where a logic 1 is needed.
  A0Not <= not A0; -- B1Not is used where you wish the invert input B1
  COMP1: MUX8_1 port map ( d(0) => A0   ,
                           d(1) => A0Not,
                           d(2) =>
                           d(3) =>        ,
                           d(4) =>        ,
                           d(5) =>        ,
                           d(6) =>        ,
                           d(7) =>        ,
                           s(0) =>        ,
                           s(1) =>        ,
                           s(2) =>        ,
                           X => X);
end architecture Behavior;
```

Results and Conclusion:

Review Questions (VHDL)

1. You have seen how a MUX could be used to implement a 2-bit comparator. Investigate the flexibility of VHDL by completing the single equation for the output X in Figure 12–11 that will perform the same task. The output should be a "1" whenever $A > B$.

```
entity TwoBitCompare is
   port (A, B: in integer range 0 to 3;
         X : out bit);
end entity TwoBitCompare;

architecture Comparator of TwoBitCompare is
begin
   X => '1' when (_____) else '0';
end architecture Comparator;
```

FIGURE 12–11

2. Another way to implement a 4-bit odd parity checker is to **xor** each of the inputs.

$$A_2 \oplus A_1 \oplus B_2 \oplus B_1$$

Use the **xor** statement and complete the equation for Parity with the logic for a 4- bit odd parity checking program (Figure 12–12).

```
entity Parity is
   port (NumIn: in bit_vector (0 to 3);
         Parity: out bit);
end Parity;

architecture ParityCheck of Parity is
begin
   Parity <=                    ;
end architecture ParityCheck;
```

FIGURE 12–12

3. How would you change the ParityChecker program to show both even and odd parity?

13

Combinational Logic Using Demultiplexers

Objectives

After completing this experiment, you will be able to
- Complete the design of a multiple output combinational logic circuit using a demultiplexer.
- Use an oscilloscope to develop a timing diagram for a counter-decoder circuit.

Reference Reading

Floyd, *Digital Fundamentals with VHDL,* Chapter 6, "Functions of Combinational Logic"

Materials Needed (TTL)

7408 or 74LS08 quad AND gate
7474 dual D flip-flop
74LS139A decoder/demultiplexer
One 4-position DIP switch
LEDs: two red, two yellow, two green
Resistors: six 330 Ω, two 1.0 kΩ

For Further Investigation:
    7400 quad NAND gate

Materials Needed (VHDL)

Project Board

Summary of Theory

The demultiplexer (DMUX) can serve as a decoder or a data router. In this experiment, we will focus on the decoding function. A decoder takes binary information from one or more input lines and generates a unique output for each input combination. You are already familiar with the 7447A IC, which performs the decoding function. It converts a 4-bit binary input number to a unique code that is used to drive a 7-segment display. A DMUX can serve as a decoder by providing a unique output for every combination of input variables. The input variables are applied to the decoder's SELECT lines.

For most DMUXs, the selected output is LOW, whereas all others are HIGH. To implement a truth table that has a *single* output variable with a decoder is not very efficient and is rarely done; however, a method for doing this is shown conceptually in Figure 13–1. In this case, each line on the output represents one row on the truth table. If the decoder has active HIGH outputs, the output lines on the truth table with a 1 are ORed together, as illustrated in Figure 13–1. The output of the OR gate represents the output function. If the outputs of the decoder are active LOW, the output lines with a 1 on the truth table are connected with a NAND gate. This is shown in Figure 13–2.

A DMUX is superior for implementing combinational logic when there are several outputs for the same set of input variables. As you saw, each output line of the demultiplexer represents a line on the truth table. For active HIGH decoder outputs, OR gates are used, but a separate OR gate is required for each output function. Each OR gate output represents a different output function. In the case of active LOW decoder outputs, the OR gates are replaced by NAND gates.

FIGURE 13–1

Implementing a combinational logic
function with an active HIGH DMUX.

Truth table for overflow error

Inputs			Output
A_4	B_4	Σ_4	X
0	0	0	0
0	0	1	1
0	1	0	0
0	1	1	0
1	0	0	0
1	0	1	0
1	1	0	1
1	1	1	0

(a) Truth table

(b) Implementation

The problem presented in this experiment is the output logic for a traffic light controller.* A brief synopsis of the problem is as follows:

A digital controller is required to control traffic at a busy intersection and an occasionally used side street. The main street is to have a green light for a minimum of 25 seconds or as long as there is no vehicle on the side street. The side street is to have a green light until there is no vehicle on the side street or for a maximum of 25 seconds. There is to be a 4-second caution light (yellow) between changes from green to red on both the main street and the side street. These requirements are illustrated in the state diagram in Figure 13–3. A block diagram of the system, showing the essential details, is given in Figure 13–4.

We will focus on state decoding and output logic. The block in Figure 13–4 can be separated into a state decoder, an output logic block, and trigger logic as shown in Figure 13–5. The state decoder has two inputs (2-bit Gray code) and must have an out-

*This is described in Floyd's text.

FIGURE 13–2

Truth table for overflow error

Inputs			Output
A_4	B_4	Σ_4	X
0	0	0	0
0	0	1	1
0	1	0	0
0	1	1	0
1	0	0	0
1	0	1	0
1	1	0	1
1	1	1	0

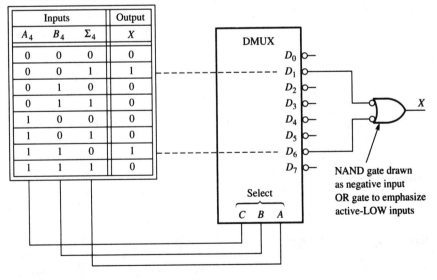

NAND gate drawn
as negative input
OR gate to emphasize
active-LOW inputs

(a) Truth table

(b) Implementation

Main   Side

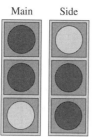

First state: 25 seconds
minimum or as long as
there is no vehicle on
side street

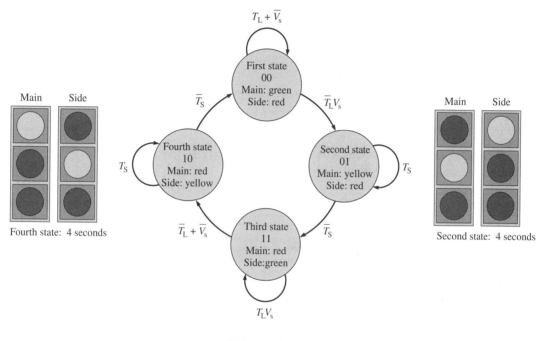

Main   Side

Fourth state: 4 seconds

Main   Side

Second state: 4 seconds

$T_L + \overline{V}_s$

First state
00
Main: green
Side: red

$\overline{T}_S$

$\overline{T}_L V_s$

Fourth state
10
Main: red
Side: yellow

T_S

Second state
01
Main: yellow
Side: red

T_S

$\overline{T}_L + \overline{V}_s$

Third state
11
Main: red
Side: green

$\overline{T}_S$

$T_L V_s$

Main   Side

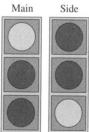

Third state: 25 seconds
maximum or until
there is no vehicle on
side street

FIGURE 13–3
Requirements for a four-state traffic light sequence.

FIGURE 13-4
System block diagram showing
essential elements.

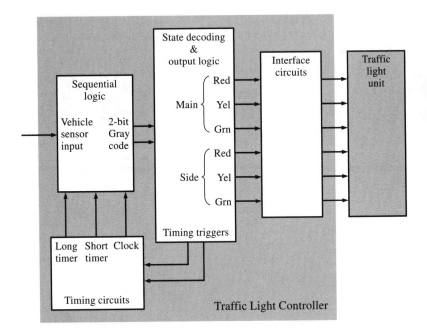

put for each of the four states. The 74LS139A is a
dual 2-line to 4-line decoder and will do the job
nicely, so it is selected.

The output logic takes the four active-LOW
states from the decoder and must produce six outputs
for activating the traffic lights. A truth table for the
decoding and output logic is given in Table 13–1. The
truth table is organized in Gray code, which is used
by the sequential logic to step through the states. The
state outputs ($\overline{SO_1}$ to $\overline{SO_4}$) are active-LOW (0) and
the output logic must be active-LOW (0) to drive
LEDs that simulate the traffic lights.

Pre-lab Questions

1. Assume a DMUX has 16 active-HIGH outputs.
   How many lines are required for the select lines?
2. A DMUX has 4 active-LOW outputs. The inputs
   include two select lines and an active-LOW enable. Assume pulses are applied to the enable,
   and both select lines are LOW. Describe each of
   the four outputs.

FIGURE 13-5
Block diagram of the state decoding
and output logic.

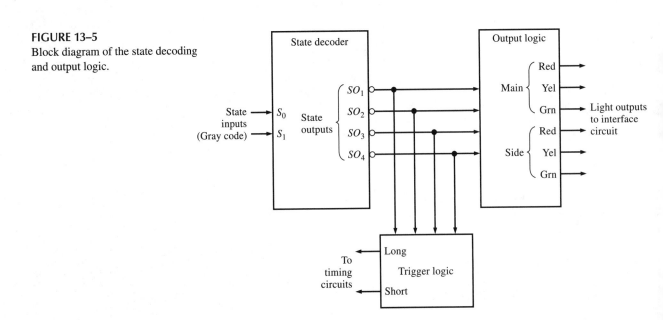

TABLE 13–1

Truth table for the decoding and output logic. State outputs are active-LOW and light outputs are active-LOW. $\overline{MR}$ = main red; $\overline{MY}$ = main yellow; etc.

State Code		State Outputs				Light Outputs					
S_1	S_0	$\overline{SO_1}$	$\overline{SO_2}$	$\overline{SO_3}$	$\overline{SO_4}$	$\overline{MR}$	$\overline{MY}$	$\overline{MG}$	$\overline{SR}$	$\overline{SY}$	$\overline{SG}$
0	0	0	1	1	1	1	1	0	0	1	1
0	1	1	0	1	1	1	0	1	0	1	1
1	1	1	1	0	1	0	1	1	1	1	0
1	0	1	1	1	0	0	1	1	1	0	1

TTL

Procedure

Traffic Light Decoder

The circuit represents the state decoder for four states and the output logic of a traffic light controller system as described in the Summary of Theory section. There are six outputs representing a red, yellow, and green traffic light on a main and side street. The outputs are shown in the desired sequence for the lights on the truth Table 13–1. A logic "0" is used to turn on an LED. For example, state 00 (the first row of the truth table) will have a green light ON for the main street and a red light ON for the side street.

1. A partially completed schematic is shown in Figure 13–6 in the report. The 74LS139A is the state decoder and the AND gates, drawn as negative NOR gates, form the output logic. Refer to the truth table and complete the schematic. You need to decide what to do with the $1\overline{G}$ input and you should draw switches with pull-up resistors to each of the decoder's select inputs. The $1Y_0$ output of the decoder (state 00) has been connected to the green LED on the main street and the red LED on the side street as an example.

2. Construct the circuit and test every combination according to the truth table. You should be able to observe the correct traffic light sequence if you open and close the switches in the same sequence as listed in truth Table 13–1.

3. Although you have not studied counters yet, the Gray-code counter shown in Figure 13–7 is simple to build and will illustrate the important role counters have in state machine design. Construct the counter, and connect the outputs to the SELECT inputs of the 74139A (switches should be removed). Set the pulse generator for 1 Hz and observe the sequence. This counter provides the correct sequence,

but it is not controlled by the inputs (vehicle sensor and timers). These improvements will be covered later.

4. In this step, you will determine the relative timing of the various signals in the system. Speed up the pulse generator to 10 kHz. Connect channel 1 of your oscilloscope to the $1B_1$ select input. Trigger the scope using channel 1; do not move channel 1 as this will serve as the reference for the various timing measurements. Connect channel 2 to the $1A_1$ input and observe the time relationship of the SELECT signals. Then observe each of the decoder outputs ($1Y_0$, $1Y_1$, $1Y_2$, and $1Y_3$) moving the channel 2 probe only. Plot the timing diagram in Figure 13–8 in the report.

For Further Investigation

An interesting application of both multiplexer (MUX) and DMUX is in time division multiplexing. Time division multiplexing is often done with displays. In this case, the DMUX is used to turn on only one 7-segment display at a time.

Time-division multiplexing is also applied to some data transmission systems. In this application, data is sent to the enable input of the DMUX and routed to the appropriate location by the DMUX. Naturally, the data and SELECT inputs have to be carefully synchronized.

A few changes to the circuit for this experiment will produce a similar idea. The simulated data is applied to the enable ($\overline{G}$) input. The particular output is addressed by the SELECT inputs, and synchronization is achieved by using the counter from Step 3 of the experiment to provide both the data and the address. The modified circuit, including the counter, is shown in Figure 13–9 in the report. The inputs to the NAND gate are not shown. Start by connecting them to the Q outputs of the counter.

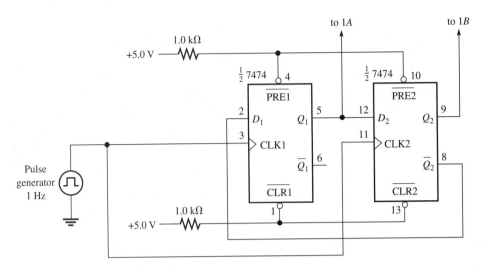

FIGURE 13–7
Gray-code counter for sequencing the traffic light decoder.

Connect the circuit and observe the results. Notice the visual appearance of the LEDs. Compare the visual appearance with the waveform viewed on the oscilloscope. Try moving the inputs of the NAND gate to the $\overline{Q}$ outputs of the counter. What happens? Connect the NAND input to other combinations of the counter output. Summarize your findings in the report.

Report for Experiment 13

Name: _____ Date: _____ Class: _____

Data and Observations:

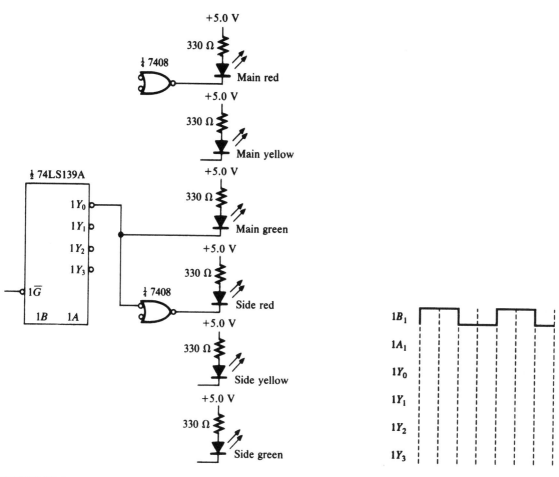

FIGURE 13–6
Traffic light output logic.

FIGURE 13–8
Timing diagram for Step 4.

Results and Conclusion:

Further Investigation Results:

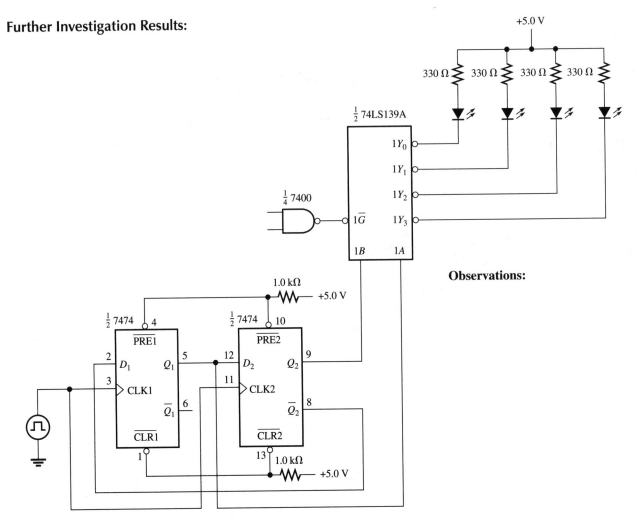

FIGURE 13–9

Review Questions (TTL)

1. Assume you needed an 8-bit decoder, but all that is available is a dual 74LS139A. Show how you could use it, along with an inverter, to form an 8-bit decoder. (*Hint:* Consider using the enable inputs.)

2. Why were the AND gates in Figure 13–6 drawn as negative-NOR gates?

3. For the circuit in Figure 13–6, what symptom would you observe if:
   a. The $1B$ select input were open?_____
   b. The $1B$ select input were shorted to ground?_____
   c. The enable ($\overline{G}$) input were open?_____

Program Overview

In this experiment, you will work with the output logic for a traffic light. The sequence for a traffic light can be thought of as a series of states that control the output. To simplify the system, you will change states by setting a binary number into two switches and observing the output. Later, in Experiment 22, this logic will be used again with additional logic to control the state.

A VHDL enumeration (programming structure) will be included in the program using the reserved word **type** as discussed in the text. One use of an enumeration is to provide a method of giving names to numbers. In the program for this experiment you will see the values *FirstState, SecondState, ThirdState,* and *FourthState,* which are selected to clarify the code and make it consistent with the textbook definitions. For example, in a state diagram, the term *FirstState* has more meaning than the value 00 (used by the state counter). The range of possible values that can be used is limited to the names used within the enumeration. There is no enumeration named *ZeroState* and therefore it could not be used. Although the program in this experiment is not a full implementation of a state machine, the concept of states is useful and will be applied to future programs.

In the program *TrafficLight,* the data type **std_logic_vector** is used to define inputs *S* and outputs *Main* and *Side* as one-dimensional arrays (lists). Recall that when making pin assignments to arrays, you must assign a separate pin for each numerically indexed bit element defined in the array.

Procedure

1. Connect the project board to a computer as described in *Project Board Familiarization* and review *VHDL Software Familiarization.*

2. Enter the partially completed TrafficLight program shown in Figure 13–10 to the text editor. This program will be used again in Experiment 22 where a complete traffic light control system is developed.

3. The truth table shown in Table 13–2 shows the decoding and output logic required for the two-bit state code, the state outputs, and the six outputs required to drive the main and side street lamps. Notice that the outputs on this table are the complements of the outputs shown in Table 13–1 because it is written for active-HIGH outputs. From this table, complete the **when** statements in the **process** *ReadState* in the program; the first two are done as an example.

4. The input states *S* in **process** *ReadState* are used to select the appropriate program state enumerated *FirstState, SecondState, ThirdState,* and *FourthState.* These enumerated inputs are the input to a second case statement in **process** *StateDiag* whose job it is to turn on the appropriate lights for the main and side streets. Notice how the output of one process is used to drive a second process. From the truth table shown in Table 13–2, complete the program *TrafficLight* by supplying the appropriate outputs for the main and side street lights for each state.

5. Assign two on-board switches for the 2-bit Gray-code input *S.* Assign three LEDs in a group for the main street traffic lights. Then assign another group of three LEDs for the side street lights. Lastly, assign two LEDs as indicators for *LongTime* and *ShortTime.* Identifiers *LongTime* and *ShortTime* are added to the current program to complete the block diagram in Figure 13–4.

TABLE 13–2

Truth table for the decoding logic. State outputs are active-HIGH and lights are active-HIGH. MR = main red, MY = main yellow, etc.

State Code		State Outputs				Light Outputs					
S_1	S_0	SO_1	SO_2	SO_3	SO_4	*MR*	*MY*	*MG*	*SR*	*SY*	*SG*
0	0	1	0	0	0	0	0	1	1	0	0
0	1	0	1	0	0	0	1	0	1	0	0
1	1	0	0	1	0	1	0	0	0	0	1
1	0	0	0	0	1	1	0	0	0	1	0

6. Test your program by sequencing the on-board switches corresponding to the state code S_1 and S_0 in Table 13–2. From your observations, complete Table 13–3 in the report, including the state of *LongTime* and *ShortTime*.

For Further Investigation

Often traffic lights are set to blink during off-peak hours. VHDL allows you to add a feature to an existing program without requiring a complete rewrite. The flashing feature will use a separate input identifier *Flash* and a clock input *Clock*.

1. Modify the **Entity** section of your program by adding the following statement in the appropriate place.

Clock, Flash: **in std_logic;**

2. Refer to the code in Figure 13–11. Add the **if** statement section as shown to cause the program to transition to *SecondState* when *Flash* is set HIGH.

3. To complete your program, refer to Figure 13–12. This section of code causes the *SecondState* to blink on and off when *Flash* is set to a HIGH. The lights blink at the rate determined by an external signal from a pulse generator.

4. Compile and download your modified program to the project board.

5. Connect a pulse generator for a TTL level pulse at 1 Hz to the clock input of your traffic light program.

6. Test the new flashing feature by setting the input *FLASH* to a LOW. Verify that your program still operates according to Table 13–2 by again sequencing the input S_0 and S_1 to each of the states.

7. Set the input *FLASH* to a HIGH. Verify that your program moves immediately to *SecondState* and the main yellow and side red lights are flashing for any combination of inputs on *S*. Show your observations in Table 13–4 of the report.

Report for Experiment 13

Name: _____ Date: _____ Class: _____

Data and Observations:

```vhdl
library IEEE;
use IEEE.std_logic_1164.all;

entity TrafficLight is
  port (S: in std_logic_vector (0 to 1);          - - array if 2 bits
        Main, Side: out std_logic_vector (0 to 2);   - - array of 3 bits
        LongTime, ShortTime: out std_logic );      - - array of 3 bits
end entity TrafficLight;

architecture Behavior of TrafficLight is
type StatesType is( FirstState, SecondState, ThirdState, FourthState); - - enumeration of 4 elements
signal State, NextState : StatesType := FirstState;

begin
  ReadState: process is
  begin
    case S is
      when "00" => State <= FirstState;
      when "10" => State <= SecondState;
      when                          :
      when                          :
      when others => state <= FirstState;
    end case;
  end process ReadState;

  StateDiag: process (State) is
  begin
    case state is
      when FirstState =>
        Main <= "001";
        Side <= "'100";
        LongTime <= '1'; -- Set Long Timer on
        ShortTime <= '0'; -- Set Short Timer off
      when SecondState =>
        Main <= "        ";
        Side <= "        ";
        LongTime <= '0'; -- Set Long Timer off
        ShortTime <= '1'; -- Set Short Timer on
      when ThirdState =>
        Main <= "        ";
        Side <= "        ";
        LongTime <= '1'; -- Set Long Timer on
        ShortTime <= '0'; -- Set Short Timer off
      when FourthState =>
        Main <= "        ";
        Side <= "        ";
        LongTime <= '0'; -- Set Long Timer off
        ShortTime <= '1'; -- Set Short Timer on
    end case;
  end process StateDiag;
end architecture Behavior;
```

FIGURE 13–10

TABLE 13–3

State Code		State Outputs						Timing Triggers	
S_1	S_0	MR	MY	MG	SR	SY	SG	LongTime	ShortTime
0	0								
0	1								
1	1								
1	0								

For Further Investigation:

```
ReadState: process is
  begin
    if Flash = '1' then
      State <= SecondState;
    else
      case S is
        when "00" => State <= FirstState;
        when "10" => State <= SecondState;
        when "11" => State <= ThirdState;
        when "01" => State <= FourthState;
        when others => state <= FirstState;
      end case;
    end if;
  end process ReadState;
```

FIGURE 13–11

```
when SecondState =>
-- Special case for flashing
  if Flash = '1' then
    LongTime <= '0'; -- Set Long Timer off
    ShortTime <= '0'; -- Set Short Timer off
    if Clock = '1' then
      Main <= "010"; -- Invert these bits
      Side <= "100"; -- for boards with active
    else
      Main <= "000"; -- low outputs.
      Side <= "000"; -- Invert for active low
    end if;
  else
    Main <= "010"; -- Invert for active low
    Side <= "100"; -- Invert for active low
    LongTime <= '0'; -- Set Long Timer off
    ShortTime <= '1'; -- Set Short Timer on
  end if;
```

FIGURE 13–12

TABLE 13–4

State Code		Flash	State Outputs 1 = flashing 0 = not flashing					
S_1	S_0		MR	MY	MG	SR	SY	SG
0	0	1						
0	1	1						
1	1	1						
1	0	1						

Review Questions (VHDL)

1. How is an enumeration defined in VHDL?

2. Suppose you need a "LEFT TURN" feature in the program *TrafficLight* in Figure 13–10 as a new *FifthState*. Identify the portions of the original code that would need to be modified.

14

The Traffic Light Timer

Objectives

After completing this experiment, you will be able to
☐ Develop multipurpose programs using VHDL.
☐ Define process variables to hold intermediate values.
☐ Build and test an event-driven timer.
☐ Explain the Boolean **if** statement.

Reference Reading

Floyd, *Digital Fundamentals with VHDL,* Chapter 7, "Additional VHDL Topics and Applications"

Materials Needed

VHDL Project Board

Summary of Theory

You have taken advantage of the VHDL concurrent statements in combinational logic circuits. Combinational logic circuits are those that the output strictly is a function of the inputs and include all of the programs up to this point. Some logic requires memory, which is how a digital system keeps track of past events. This logic is called sequential logic.

VHDL uses the term *sequential statements* for programming structures that require some form of memory. An example of sequential logic is the **if** statement, common to higher level programming languages. The VHDL **if** statement is used to evaluate the condition of a Boolean expression and ex-

ecute the appropriate set of instructions based on the result. Remember that a Boolean expression evaluates to one of two conditions: either a 0 or a 1. The syntax for an **if** statement is:

> **if** <Boolean Expression> **then**
>   <VHDL statements>
> **else**
>   <Alternate VHDL statements>
> **end if;**

The VHDL keyword **if** is followed by a conditional statement that results in a Boolean response (0 or 1), which determines the next statements to be executed. The keyword **then** follows the conditional statements. Following the keyword **then** are statements that are only executed if the Boolean response was a 1 in the conditional statement. An optional **else** statement defines a set of alternate instructions to execute if the Boolean expression evaluates to 0. Closing out the **if** statement block is the keyword **end if**.

The use of a process block variable is a convenient way to define a temporary storage area for holding values. The timer program will use one variable *count* of type **integer** that will hold the terminal count value. Another output variable, *ClkMon,* is used to show the clock *input* from the pulse generator on a separate LED.

Often a digital logic system is described in terms of what the system does over time. This approach to program design is called Behavioral Modeling. In the traffic light timer, a clock transition is key to continuing the process and the program will use an **if** statement to wait for the transition before executing alternate instructions. The VHDL keyword **event** causes the program to look for a change on the clock signal such as the transition from a LOW to a HIGH. Examine the following sequential VHDL statement:

$$clock\text{'}\textbf{event and } clock = \text{'}1\text{'}$$

The first part of the statement looks for a change (transition) of the clock signal; the second part indicates the pulse is a 1 immediately after the occurence of the clock event. This causes the triggering to occur on a rising edge.

Pre-lab Questions

1. What is required of all sequential logic?
2. What statement or statements are executed when a Boolean condition evaluates to a 0 in an **if** statement?

VHDL
Procedure

1. Connect the project board to a computer as described in *Project Board Familiarization* and review *VHDL Software Familiarization*.

2. Enter the program entitled *Timer* shown in Figure 14–1 into the text editor.

3. Referring to the section on Software Familiarization, compile and download the program to your project board. Assign input *Enable* to an on-board switch. Assign the input *clock* to a global clock input pin on the PLD and then connect a TTL pulse generator at 1 Hz. (See section 4b of the *Project Board Familiarization* for the method). Assign the integer input *SetCount* to four switches as *Setcount0, Setcount1, Setcount2, Setcount3*. Assign the output *QOut* to an on-board LED. An identifier *Clk-Mon* has been defined as a convenient output to monitor the input from the pulse generator. Assign the output *ClkMon* to an on-board LED.

4. Test your timer program by setting *SetCount* to a binary 0101. The input *SetCount* is treated by the program as a decimal 5. Predict the expected output by sketching the *Enable, Clk,* and *QOut* outputs in plot 1.

5. Set *Enable* to a LOW for at least one second (one clock pulse) to load the value from *SetCount*. Then set Enable to a HIGH to start the count. Observe outputs *QOut* and *ClkMon* at the same time.

6. Change the *SetCount* switches to a count of 1010 and repeat step 5 to verify the program can be reconfigured for a different time count.

7. In this step you will test the timer program's ability to reset the time count while counting. With *SetCount* still set to 1010, move the *Enable* switch to a LOW, then back to a HIGH. Monitor *QOut*. After *ClkMon* has flashed four times, move the *Enable* switch back to a LOW, then back to a HIGH once again. Verify that the counter restarts the count after *Enable* is set back to a HIGH.

8. The timer program can be configured for count values from 0 to 15. Since this counter uses a 1 Hz clock, the maximum time it is active cannot exceed 15 seconds, which is insufficient for the traffic light. The traffic light is required to hold a red light for 25 seconds. Make the appropriate modifications to allow for the 25 second requirement. Show your program changes in the space provided in the report. If directed by your instructor, include a printout of the modified program with your report.

For Further Investigation

As you can see, the timer program starts from 0 and counts up to the count value loaded in *SetCount*. Change the program so that it starts from the value loaded into *SetCount* and counts down to 0. Of course, the *QOut* light would stay on for the same time whether the program is counting up or down, so as a second change, make the *QOut* light turn on when the count has finished instead of turning off.

Report for Experiment 14

Name: _____ Date: _____ Class: _____

Data and Observations:

```vhdl
library IEEE;
use IEEE.std_logic_1164.all;

entity Timer is
  port (Enable, clock: in std_logic;
        ClkMon: out std_logic;
        SetCount: in integer range 0 to 15;
        QOut: inout std_logic);
end entity Timer;

architecture TimerCounter of Timer is
begin
  ClkMon<=clock;
  process (Enable, clock)
  variable count:  integer range 0 to 15;
  begin
    if (clock'event and clock = '1') then
      if Enable = '0' then
        count:= 0;
        Qout <= '1';
      end if;
      if count = SetCount then – Reset the counter and set timeout flag to false;
        count:= 1;
        Qout <= '0';
      else – Increment the count value
        count:= count + 1;
      end if;
    end if;
  end process;
end architecture TimerCounter;
```

CODE TIP
The keyword **range** can be used to limit the variable identifier to the decimal numbers 0 through 15 represented by 4 binary bits.

FIGURE 14–1

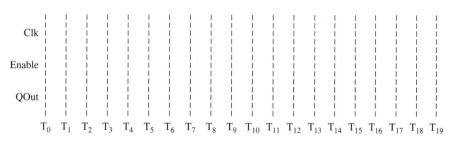

T_0 T_1 T_2 T_3 T_4 T_5 T_6 T_7 T_8 T_9 T_{10} T_{11} T_{12} T_{13} T_{14} T_{15} T_{16} T_{17} T_{18} T_{19}

PLOT 1

Step 8. Program modifications to allow for a minimum of a 25 s time:

Review Questions (VHDL)

1. What would happen to the count sequence if the Enable is toggled while the counter is counting?

2. How could the program be modified to cause the count to increment on the falling edge of the clock instead of the leading edge?

15

The D Latch and D Flip-Flop

Objectives

After completing this experiment, you will be able to
☐ Demonstrate how a latch can debounce an SPDT switch.
☐ Implement and test a gated D latch from four NAND gates and an inverter.
☐ Test a D flip-flop and investigate several application circuits for both the latch and the flip-flop.

Reference Reading

Floyd, *Digital Fundamentals with VHDL,* Chapter 8, "Flip-Flops and Related Devices"

Materials Needed (TTL)

Red LED
Green LED
7486 quad XOR gate
7400 quad NAND gate
7404 hex inverter
7474 dual D flip-flop
Resistors: two 330 Ω, two 1.0 kΩ

Materials Needed (VHDL)

Project Board

Summary of Theory

As you have seen, *combinational* logic circuits are circuits in which the outputs are determined fully by the inputs. *Sequential* logic circuits contain information about previous conditions. The difference is that sequential circuits contain *memory* and combinational circuits do not.

The basic memory unit is the *latch,* which uses feedback to lock onto and hold data. It can be constructed from two inverters, two NAND gates, or two NOR gates. The ability to remember previous conditions is easy to demonstrate with Boolean algebra. For example, Figure 15–1 shows an $\overline{\text{S}}$-$\overline{\text{R}}$ latch made from NAND gates. This circuit is widely used for switch debouncing and is available as an integrated circuit containing four latches (the 74LS279).

A simple modification of the basic latch is the addition of steering gates and an inverter, as shown in Figure 15–2. This circuit is called a gated D (for Data) latch. An enable input allows data present on the D input to be transferred to the output when Enable is asserted. When the enable input is not asserted, the last level—Q and $\overline{Q}$—is latched. This circuit is available in integrated circuit form as the 7475A quad D latch. Although there are four latches in this IC, there are only two shared enable signals.

Design problems are often simplified by having all transitions in a system occur synchronously

FIGURE 15–1
$\overline{S}$-$\overline{R}$ latch.

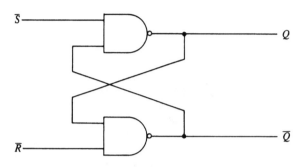

Equation for top NAND gate:

$$Q = \overline{\overline{S} \cdot \overline{Q}}$$

Applying DeMorgan's theorem:

$$Q = S + Q$$

Thus, Q appears on both sides of the equation.
If $\overline{S} = 1$, then $S = 0$ and $Q = 0 + Q$ (Q is previous state)
output is latched.

(at the same time) by using a common source of pulses to cause the change. This common pulse is called a *clock*. The output changes occur only on either the leading or the trailing edge of the clock pulse. Some ICs have inputs that directly set or reset the output any time they are asserted. These inputs are labeled *asynchronous* inputs because no clock pulse is required. The D-type flip-flop with positive edge-triggering and asynchronous inputs is the 7474. In this experiment, you will also test this IC.

It is useful to review oscilloscope timing. If you are using an analog dual-trace oscilloscope, you should trigger the scope from the channel with the *slowest* of two waveforms that are being compared to be sure to see the correct time relationship. A digital scope will show it correctly for either trigger channel.

Pre-lab Questions

1. Explain the difference between *combinational* logic and *sequential* logic.
2. What is meant by the term *asynchronous?*

Procedure

$\overline{S}$-$\overline{R}$ Latch

1. Build the $\overline{S}$-$\overline{R}$ latch shown in Figure 15–3. You can use a wire to simulate the single-pole, double-throw (SPDT) switch. The LEDs will be used in this section as logic monitors. Because TTL logic is much better at sinking current than at sourcing current, the LEDs are arranged to be ON when the output is LOW. To make the LEDs read the HIGH output when they are ON, we read them from the opposite output! This simple trick avoids the use of an inverter.

2. Leave the wire on the *A* terminal and note the logic shown on the LEDs. Now simulate a bouncing switch by removing the *A* end of the wire. Do NOT touch *B* yet! Instead, reconnect the wire to *A* several times.

FIGURE 15–2
Gated D latch.

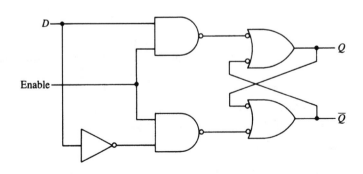

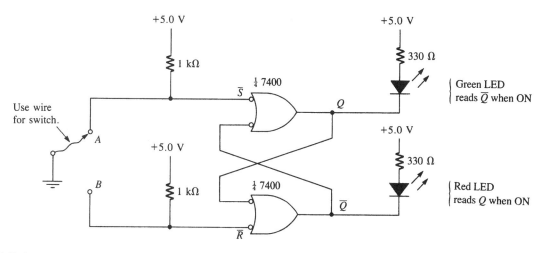

FIGURE 15–3
SPDT switch debounce. The NAND gates are drawn as negative-input OR gates to emphasize the active-LOW.

3. After touching A several times, touch B. Simulate the switch bouncing several times by re-moving and reconnecting B. (Switches never bounce back to the opposite terminal, so you should not touch A). Summarize your observations of the $\overline{S}$-$\overline{R}$ latch used as a switch debounce circuit in the report.

D Latch

4. Modify the basic $\overline{S}$-$\overline{R}$ latch into a D latch by adding the steering gates and the inverter shown in Figure 15–4. Connect the D input to a TTL level pulse generator set for 1 Hz. Connect the enable input to a HIGH (through a 1.0 kΩ resistor). Observe the output; then change the enable to a LOW.

5. Leave the enable LOW and place a momentary short to ground first on one output and then on the other. Summarize your observations of the gated D latch in the report.

6. Now make the simple burglar alarm shown in Figure 15–5. The data input represents switches connected to windows and doors. The enable input is pulled HIGH when the system is activated or LOW for standby. To reset the system, put a momentary ground on the Q output as shown. Summarize your observations in the report.

The D Flip-Flop

7. The 7474 is a dual, positive edge–trig-gered D flip-flop containing two asynchronous in-puts labeled $\overline{PRE}$ (preset) and $\overline{CLR}$ (clear). Construct the test circuit shown in Figure 15–6. Connect the clock through the delay circuit. The purpose of the delay is to allow setup time for the D input. Let's look at this effect first. Observe both the delayed clock signal and the Q output signal on a two-channel oscilloscope. View the delayed clock

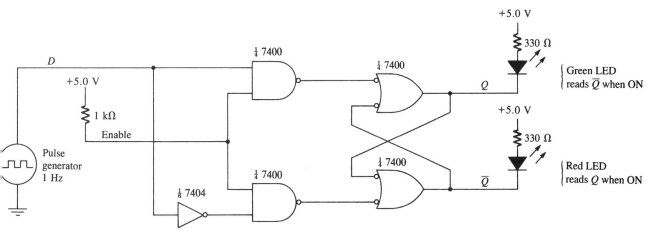

FIGURE 15–4
Gated D latch.

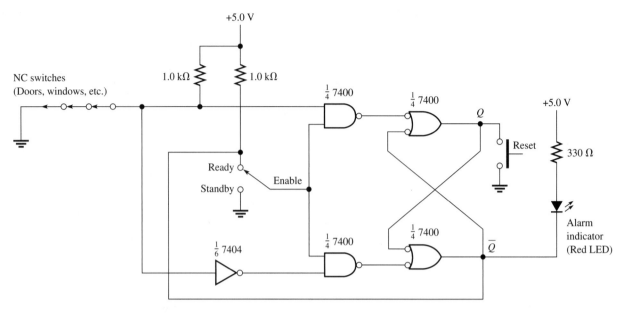

FIGURE 15–5
Simple burglar alarm.

signal on channel 1, and trigger the scope from channel 1. You should observe a dc level on the output (channel 2).

8. Now remove the clock delay by connecting the clock input directly to the pulse generator. The output dc level should have changed because there is insufficient setup time. Explain your observations in the report.

9. Reinstall the clock delay circuit and move the $\overline{PRE}$ input to a LOW and then a HIGH. Then put a LOW on the $\overline{CLR}$ input followed by a HIGH. Next repeat the process with the clock pulse disconnected.

Determine if $\overline{PRE}$ and $\overline{CLR}$ are synchronous or asynchronous inputs.

10. Leave the clock delay circuit in place, but disconnect the D input. Attach a wire from $\overline{Q}$ to the D input. Observe the waveforms on a scope. Normally, for relative timing measurements, you should trigger the scope using the channel that has the *slowest* waveform as the trigger channel, as discussed in the Summary of Theory. Summarize, in the report, your observations of the D flip-flop. Discuss setup time, $\overline{PRE}$ and $\overline{CLR}$ inputs, and your timing observation from this step.

FIGURE 15–6

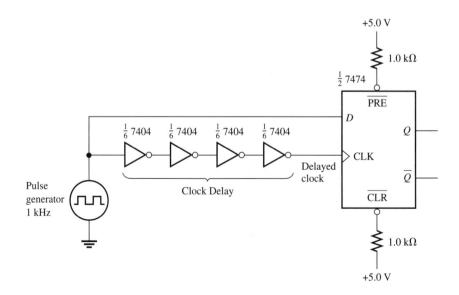

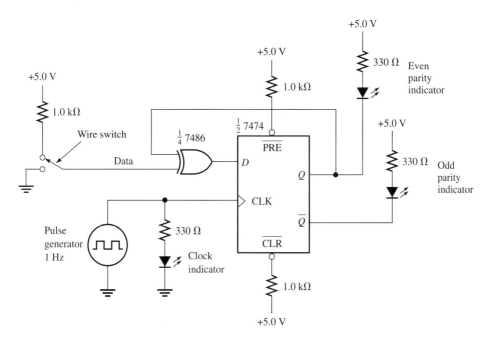

FIGURE 15–7

For Further Investigation

The circuit shown in Figure 15–7 is a practical application of a D flip-flop. It is a parity test circuit that takes serial data (bits arriving one at a time) and performs an exclusive-OR on the previous result (like a running total). The data are synchronous with the clock; that is, for every clock pulse a new data bit is tested. Construct the circuit and set the clock for 1 Hz. Move the data switch to either a HIGH or a LOW prior to the clock pulse, and observe the result. Describe your observations in the report. If a logic 1 is received, what happens to the parity? What happens when a logic 0 is received? Does the circuit have any advantage over the 74LS280 9-bit parity generator/checker?*

*See Figure 6–44 of Floyd's text.

Report for Experiment 15

Name: _____ Date: _____ Class: _____

Data and Observations:

Step 3. Observations for SPDT switch debounce circuit:

Step 5. Observations for D latch circuit:

Step 6. Observations for the simple burglar alarm:

Steps 7 and 8. Observations for setup time:

Step 10. Observations for the D flip-flop:

Results and Conclusion:

Further Investigation Results:

Review Questions (TTL)

1. **a.** Explain why the switch debounce circuit in Figure 15–3 is used only for double-throw switches.

   b. Could NOR gates be used for debouncing a switch? Explain.

2. What advantage does the gated D latch have compared to the $\overline{S}$-$\overline{R}$ latch?

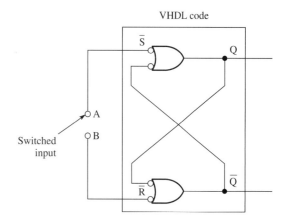

FIGURE 15–9
SPDT switch debounce. The NAND gates are drawn as negative-input OR gates to emphasize the active-LOW input. A and B inputs are the contacts for a single switch but are represented by two SPST switches in this experiment.

Program Overview

Recall that one of the methods of modeling VHDL applications is called structural modeling where blocks of logic are defined such as the function of a common fixed function IC. In this experiment, you will simulate the fixed function logic of a D latch and a D flip-flop in VHDL.

VHDL supports three basic modes within the entity portion of a VHDL application. These modes are **in**, **out**, and **inout**. Mode **in** is used for identifiers that name input signals. Mode **out** is used for identifiers that name output signals. Mode **inout** was first introduced in Experiment 10, where feedback was used to cause a variable to be both an input and an output. Latches and flip-flops use a similar feedback idea, so **inout** will again be used in this experiment to represent bidirectional identifiers.

One of the useful capabilities of a latch is the ability to debounce a SPDT (single-pole double-throw) switch. Unfortunately, most project boards do not have such a switch available. Consequently, to simulate a SPDT switch, two SPST switches will be used. Each of the SPST switches will have one of the throws (contacts) for the simulated SPDT switch. The Procedure section explains how SPDT switches bounce, so you will see the latching action for the simulated switch anyway.

Procedure

1. Connect the project board to a computer as described in *Project Board Familiarization* and review *VHDL Software Familiarization*.

2. Enter the program named *S_RLatch* shown in Figure 15–8 of the report into the text editor. Input identifiers *A* and *B* are shown as mode **in**. Because the output identifiers *Q* and *QNot* provide feedback for the latch, they must be mode **inout**.

3. Assign inputs *A* and *B* to on-board switches and assign outputs *Q* and *QNot* to LEDs. Then compile and download the program to the project board.

4. Test your program using Figure 15–9 as a reference. Set and leave the *A* input switch in the LOW position. Set *B* switch to the HIGH position. This represents the SPDT switch shown in Figure 15–3. Note that the *Q* LED is on and the *QNot* LED is off. Now simulate a bouncing switch by toggling the *A* switch. Do NOT move the *B* switch yet because a bouncing switch will only touch one contact.

5. After toggling *A* several times, set the *A* switch to a logic HIGH position and set *B* to a logic LOW position. Note that the *QNot* LED is on and the *Q* LED is off. Simulate the switch bouncing several times on the *B* contact by toggling the *B* switch. (Switches never bounce back to the opposite terminal, so you should not move the *A* switch again). You should observe latching action. Summarize your observations of the $\overline{S}$-$\overline{R}$ latch used as a switch debounce circuit in the report.

The D Latch as a Reaction Time Tester

6. Enter the program *D_Latch* shown in Figure 15–10 of the report into the text editor. The program changes the S-R latch to a D latch by adding the logic for the steering gates and the inverter shown in Figure 15–11. Identifiers *S1* and *S2* represent internal **signal** identifiers, which are the outputs of the two steering NAND gates. The input identifier *E* represents the enable input to the steering NAND gates.

7. Assign input *D* to an external global input pin where the pulse generator will be applied (see *Project Board Familiarization,* part 4b). Assign the input *E* to a switch. Assign *ClkMon* to an LED. Finally, assign *Q* and *QNot* to LEDs. Compile and download the program to the project board.

8. Connect the *D* input to a TTL level pulse generator set for 1 Hz. Set the enable switch to a HIGH and observe the output; then change the enable to a LOW. You should be able to use the enable switch to "catch" a HIGH or a LOW in the output and latch it. For more challenge, speed up the pulse generator and try to catch a predetermined state.

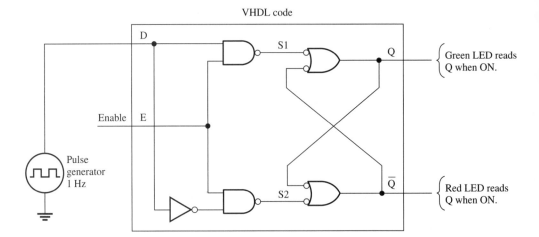

FIGURE 15–11
Gated D latch.

VHDL code

Green LED reads Q when ON.

Red LED reads $\overline{Q}$ when ON.

Summarize your observations in the space provided in the report.

The D Flip-Flop

9. Enter the program *DFlipFlop* given in Figure 15–12 of the report into the text editor. Assign inputs *Pre, Clr,* and *D* to on-board switches. Assign *Clock* to an external global input pin. Assign *Q* and *QNot* to LEDs. Then compile and download the program to the project board.

10. Connect a TTL level pulse generator set for 1 Hz to the *Clock* input as shown in Figure 15–13.

11. Set the *Pre* and *Clr* input switches to HIGH. Set the *D* input switch to LOW and observe the LEDs. *Q* will transition to OFF and *QNot* will transition to ON with the rising edge of the next clock pulse.

12. Now move the *D* input switch to HIGH. Summarize your observations in the report.

13. Set input *D* to a LOW. Now set the *Pre* input to a LOW and then a HIGH. Repeat this several times while the pulse generator supplies the clock pulse. Then set input *D* to a HIGH and put a LOW on the *Clock* input followed by a HIGH. Next repeat the process with the clock pulse disconnected. Determine if *Pre* and *Clr* are synchronous or asynchronous inputs. Summarize your observations in the report.

Serial Parity Application

14. The logic diagram shown in Figure 15–14 is a practical application of a D flip-flop. It is a parity test circuit that takes serial data (bits arriving one at a time) and performs an exclusive-OR on the previous results (like a running total). The data are synchronous with the clock; that is, for every clock pulse a new data bit is tested. Enter the program named *LAB15SPA* in Figure 15–15 (in the report) to the VHDL editor. Assign inputs *Pre, Clr,* and *Data* to switches. Assign input *Clock* to an external global pin. Assign outputs *Q, QNot,* and *ClkMon* to LEDs.

15. Compile and download the program to the project board. Connect the pulse generator to *Clock,* set a clock pulse for 1 Hz, move the data switch to either a HIGH or LOW prior to the clock pulse and observe the result. Describe your observations in the report. If a logic 1 is received, what happens to the parity? What happens when a logic 0 is received?

For Further Investigation

This investigation is a little different than others. A complete program is shown in Figure 15–16. The program is a burglar alarm that works similarly to the one given in Figure 15–5 but is designed differently. For one thing, it does not have the feedback to the Ready signal. Read the code and figure out what the equivalent circuit looks like. Draw the circuit in the space provided in the report.

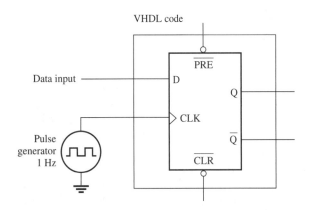

FIGURE 15–13
D flip-flop application.

FIGURE 15–14
D flip-flop application.

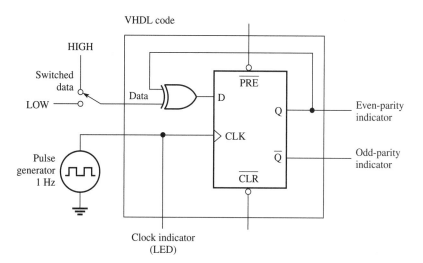

FIGURE 15–16

```
entity Burglar is
  port (Doors, Ready, Reset: in bit;  - - Array of 4 bits
        Alarm: inout bit); - - Array of 5 bits
end entity Burglar;

architecture Behavior of Burglar is
signal S1, High, Low: bit;
component D_Latch is
  port (D, E: in bit; Q, QNot, ClkMon: inout bit);
end component D_Latch;

component DFlipFlop is
   port (D, Clr, Pre, Clock: in bit;
         Q, QNot, ClkMon: inout bit);
end component DFlipFlop;
begin
 High <= '1'; Low <= '0';
 DLatch1: D_Latch port map (D =>Doors,E=>Ready,Q=>S1);
 DFlip : DFlipFLop port map (D=>Low,Clr=>High,Pre=>Reset,clock=>S1,QNot=>Alarm);
end architecture  Behavior;
```

201

Report for Experiment 15

Name: _____ Date: _____ Class: _____

Data and Observations:

```
entity S_RLatch is
    port (A, B: in bit;  Q, QNot: inout bit);
end entity S_RLatch;

architecture Behavior of S_RLatch is
begin
    Q <=  not A or not QNot;
    QNot <=  not B or not Q;
end architecture Behavior;
```

FIGURE 15–8

```
entity D_Latch is
    port (D, E: in bit; Q, QNot: inout bit);
end entity D_Latch;

architecture Behavior of D_Latch is
signal S1, S2: bit;
begin
    S1 <= D nand E;
    S2 <= not D nand E;
    Q  <= not S1 or not QNot;
    QNot <=  not S2 or not Q;
end architecture Behavior;
```

FIGURE 15–10

```
entity DFlipFlop is
    port (D, Clr, Pre, Clock: in bit;
        Q, QNot: inout bit);
end entity DFlipFlop;

architecture DBehavior of DFlipFlop is
signal Temp: std_logic := '0';
begin
    process (D, Clr, Pre, Clock) is
    begin
        if Clr = '0' then Q <= '0'; QNot <= '1';-- Clear
        elsif Pre = '0' then Q <= '1'; QNot <= '0';-- Preset
        elsif Clock = '1' and Clock'event then
            if D = '1' and Clr = '1' and Pre = '1' then
                Q <= '1';
                QNot <= '0';
            else
                Q <= '0';
                QNot<= '1';
            end if;
        end if;
    end process;
end architecture DBehavior ;
```

CODE TIP
This line looks
for a rising edge
of the clock.

FIGURE 15–12

Step 5. Observations for simulated SPDT switch debounce circuit:

Step 8. Observations for the D latch as a reaction time tester:

Steps 12 and 13. Observations for the D flip-flop:

Step 15. Observations for serial parity application:

```
entity LAB15SPA is
    port (Data, Clr, Pre, Clock: in bit;
          Q, QNot, ClkMon: inout bit);
end entity LAB15SPA;

architecture DBehavior of LAB15SPA is
signal D : bit;
begin
  process (D, Clr, Pre, Clock) is
  begin
    -- The following statements for the xor input to the original
    -- D flip-flop logic.
    D <= Data xor Q;
    ClkMon <= Clock;

    if Clr = '0' then Q <= '0'; QNot <= '1';-- Clear
    elsif Pre = '0' then Q <= '1'; QNot <= '0';-- Preset
    elsif Clock = '1' and Clock'event then
      if D = '1' and Clr = '1' and Pre = '1' then
        Q <= '1';
        QNot <= '0';
      else
        Q <= '0';
        QNot<= '1';
      end if;
    end if;
  end process;
end architecture DBehavior;
```

FIGURE 15–15

Results and Conclusion:

Further Investigation Results:

Review Questions (VHDL)

1. How is the VHDL mode **inout** different from the **in** and **out** modes for identifiers in the **entity** section?

2. Explain how the delay circuit in Figure 15–12 could be implemented on the same PLD.

16

The Fallen-Carton Detector

Objectives

After completing this experiment, you will be able to
☐ Design the logic that detects the presence of a tipped-over carton for a food-processing application and rejects it before it reaches the carton-sealing machine.
☐ Decide on a troubleshooting procedure for testing the circuit if it fails.
☐ Write a laboratory report documenting your circuit and a simple test procedure.

Reference Reading

Floyd, *Digital Fundamentals with VHDL*, Chapter 8, "Flip-Flops and Related Devices"

Materials Needed (TTL)

7474 D flip-flop
Two CdS photocells (Jameco 120299 or equivalent)
Resistors as determined by student

Materials Needed (VHDL)

Project Board and Protoboard
Two CdS photocells (Jameco 120299 or equivalent)
Resistors as determined by student

Summary of Theory

A D flip-flop can hold information temporarily, acting as a memory element capable of storing one bit of information. In this experiment, it is necessary to store information temporarily to use after the inputs have changed. The circuit can then take an action even though the originating event has passed.

The event can do the clocking action to assure that the flags are set each time an event occurs. The occurrence of an event (carton passing a detector) is asynchronous—not related to a clock signal. Since the event will do the clocking, it is necessary to use delay in the clock signal to assure that sufficient setup time is given to the D flip-flop.

Pre-lab Questions

1. What is the setup time specification for a 7474 D flip-flop?
2. Which edge (rising or falling) is used to clock the 7474 D flip-flop?

TTL **Procedure**

Design the circuit that implements the fallen carton detector described in the problem statement. Test your circuit and write a report that describes the circuit you designed. The circuit will be in operation when you are not present to help fix it in case of trouble. Your write-up should include a simple troubleshooting guide to technicians so that they can identify a circuit failure using a test procedure that you devise.

FIGURE 16–1

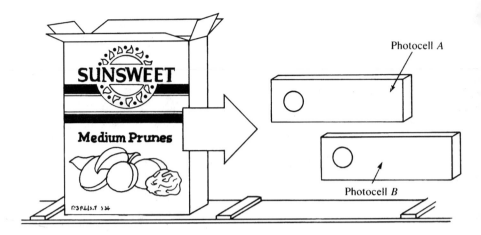

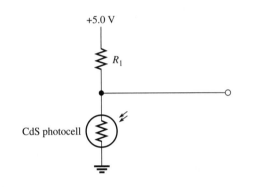

Problem Statement: A food-processing company needs a circuit to detect a fallen carton on a conveyer belt and activate an air solenoid to blow the carton into a reject hopper. The circuit is needed because occasionally a carton will fall and cause a jam to occur at the carton-sealing machine. Mechanics have installed two photocells on the line, as illustrated in Figure 16–1. Notice that the two photocells are offset from each other. The top photocell is labeled *A* and the lower photocell is labeled *B*. An upright carton will cause photocell *A* to be covered first and then photocell *B* to be covered. A fallen carton will cause only photocell *B* to be covered.

You can assume that if both photocells sense the carton, it must be upright and should proceed to the sealing machine. However, if only photocell *B* is covered, a signal needs to be generated that will be sent to the air solenoid (an LED will simulate the solenoid). The solenoid needs to be turned on until the next upright carton is sensed.

For this design problem, you can use the photocell circuit shown in Figure 16–2 to produce logic levels for your circuit. You will need to experiment with the value of R_1 to determine a value that gives TTL logic levels for your particular photocell and room lighting. The resistance of a photocell is lower as the light intensity increases. If the photocell is covered (high resistance), the output should be set for a logic HIGH; when it is uncovered it should be a logic LOW. If photocell *A* is covered, and then photocell *B* is covered, the circuit should *not* trip the solenoid (light the LED). On the other hand, if

FIGURE 16–2
Simplified photocell circuit.

photocell *B* is covered and *A* remains uncovered, the circuit has detected a fallen carton, and the solenoid should be tripped (LED on). The LED should be turned on with a LOW signal. No more than two ICs can be spared for the design.

For Further Investigation

A new improved Model 2 fallen-carton detector is needed. After a single fallen carton, the air solenoid remains on, annoying the line supervisor. To avoid this, the line supervisor has requested that the solenoid be turned off by a photocell that senses the carton going into the reject hopper. Also, a reset button needs to be added to reset the circuit when it is first turned on. No more ICs can be spared for this modification.

Report for Experiment 16

Name: _____ Date: _____ Class: _____

Data and Observations:

Results and Conclusion:

Review Questions (TTL)

1. For the circuit in Figure 16–2, what happens to the logic levels if R_1 is made larger?

2. For the circuit in Figure 16–2, what happens to the logic levels if the incident light is increased?

Introduction

In this part of the experiment you will investigate a PLD in a simple detection circuit using two CdS photocells for light sensors. To accomplish this, you will need to select a resistor that will form a voltage divider with each photocell to produce a TTL HIGH and LOW output. The resistor value depends on the light conditions you have and the specific CdS photocell but will typically be in the 1 kΩ to 10 kΩ range. The photocell circuits will supply the clock and data signals for a simulated D flip-flop that detects if a carton has fallen over or not. The clock input will be connected to a pin designated as a clock input for your particular project board. The data input will be connected to a selected general-purpose I/O pin designated for your particular project board. Refer to *Project Board Familiarization* for access to the clock input and I/O inputs.

Procedure

1. Construct two CdS photocell detection circuits as shown in Figure 16–2 (Jameco 120299 or equivalent). The resistors need to be chosen based on the light conditions and specific photocell you are using. The output should be a valid TTL HIGH when the photocell is covered and a valid TTL LOW when it is uncovered. Example wiring for a protoboard is shown in Figure 16–3.

2. Connect the CdS circuits to your project board. The ground on the protoboard needs to be common with the ground on the project board. Refer to the section entitled *Project Board Familiarization* for the location of the +5.0 V and ground access points on your board.

3. Copy the program called *DFlipFlop* shown in Figure 16–4 of the report to the VHDL editor. The logic for this program will be represented as the logic symbol for the D flip-flop.

4. Compile and download the DFlipFlop program to the project board.

5. On-board switches will be used for the $\overline{PRE}$ and $\overline{CLR}$ inputs. Connect the output of the CdS photocell detection circuits to the project board. One photocell will be connected to a specific PLD pin designated as a clock input; the other to the dedicated I/O pin representing the D input. Use an on-board LED as an output to indicate when a carton has fallen.

6. Test your circuit and write a report. Your report should include a summary of the light sensor input circuit tests that you conducted to assure that TTL levels were met. You should also explain how the VHDL program simulates the D flip-flop. The circuit will be in operation when you are not present to help fix it in case of trouble. Your write-up should include a simple troubleshooting guide for technicians so that they can identify a circuit failure using a test procedure that you devise.

For Further Investigation

A new improved Model 2 fallen-carton detector is needed. A reset button needs to be added to reset the circuit when it is first turned on. Show the required modifications to the schematic. How do these modifications affect the VHDL program?

FIGURE 16–3

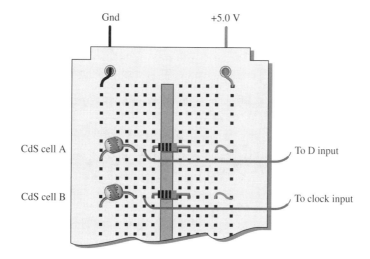

Report for Experiment 16

Name: _____ Date: _____ Class: _____

Data and Observations:

```
library IEEE;
use IEEE.std_logic_1164.all;

entity DFlipFlop is
   port (D, Clr, Pre, Clock: in std_logic;
         Q, QNot: inout std_logic);
end entity DFlipFlop;

architecture DBehavior of DFlipFlop is
signal Temp: std_logic := '0';   ◄───
begin
   process (D, Clr, Pre, Clock) is
   begin
     if Clr = '0' then Q <= '0'; QNot <= '1';-- Clear
     elsif Pre = '0' then Q <= '1'; QNot <= '0';-- Preset
     elsif Clock = '1' and Clock 'event then
       if D = '1' and Clr = '1' and Pre = '1' then
         Q <= '1';
         QNot <= '0';
       else
         Q <= '0';
         QNot<= '1';
       end if;
     end if;
   end process;
end architecture DBehavior ;
```

> **CODE TIP**
> You may see a temporary variable in a program that is used for test purposes. In this program, the **signal** Temp is such a variable.

FIGURE 16–4

Further Investigation Results:

Review Questions (VHDL)

1. What is the purpose of the keyword **event** in the program *DFlipFlop* in Figure 16–4?

2. The fallen-carton detector has been manufactured and the first unit has just come off the assembly line. Due to an error in manufacturing, the location of the photocells in Figure 16–1 have been reversed! There is no time to correct the problem. Show how you could modify the program in Figure 16–4 to save the company.

17

The J-K Flip-Flop

Objectives

After completing this experiment, you will be able to
☐ Test various configurations for a J-K flip-flop, including the asynchronous and synchronous inputs.
☐ Observe frequency division characteristics in the toggle mode.

Reference Reading

Floyd, *Digital Fundamentals with VHDL,* Chapter 8, "Flip-Flops and Related Devices"

Materials Needed (TTL)

74LS76 dual J-K flip-flop
LEDs: one red, one green, one yellow
Resistors: three 390 Ω, four 1.0 kΩ
One 4-position DIP switch

Materials Needed (VHDL)

Project Board

Summary of Theory

The D flip-flop is an edge-triggered device that allows the output to change only during the active clock edge. The D flip-flop can only be set and reset, a limitation for some applications. Furthermore, it cannot be latched unless the clock pulses are removed—a condition that limits applications for this device. The

S-R flip-flop could be latched but one combination of inputs is disallowed ($S = 1$, $R = 1$). A solution to these problems is the J-K flip-flop, which is basically a clocked S-R flip-flop with additional logic to replace the S-R invalid output states with a new mode called *toggle.* Toggle causes the flip-flop to change to the state opposite to its present state. It is similar to the operation of an automatic garage door opener. If the button is pressed when the door is open, the door will close; otherwise, it will open.

The J-K flip-flop is the most versatile of the three basic flip-flops. All applications for flip-flops can be accomplished with either the D or the J-K flip-flop. The clocked S-R flip-flop is seldom used; it is used mostly as an internal component of integrated circuits. (See the 74165 shift register, for example.) The truth tables for all three flip-flops are compared in Figure 17–1. The inputs are labeled J (the set mode) and K (the reset mode) to avoid confusion with the S-R flip-flop.

The need to assure that input data do not affect the output until they are at the correct level led to the concept of edge-triggering, which is the preferred method to assure synchronous transitions. An older method that is sometimes used is *pulse-triggered* or *master-slave* flip-flops. In these flip-flops, the data are clocked into the master on the leading edge of the clock and into the slave on the trailing edge of the clock. It is imperative that the input data not change during the time the clock pulse is HIGH or the data in the master may be changed. J-K flip-flops are available as either edge- or pulse-triggered devices. The older 7476 is a dual pulse-triggered device; the

213

FIGURE 17–1
Comparison of basic flip-flops.

Inputs		Output
S	R	Q
0	0	Latched
0	1	0
1	0	1
1	1	Invalid

Input	Output
D	Q
No equivalent	
0	0
1	1
No equivalent	

Inputs		Output
J	K	Q
0	0	Latched
0	1	0
1	0	1
1	1	Toggle

74LS76 is a dual edge-triggered device that is clocked on the HIGH to LOW transition. Either type will work in the TTL part of this experiment.

Pre-lab Questions

1. a. What is toggle mode?
   b. How is a J-K flip-flop put in toggle mode?
2. What type of clocking is preferred for J-K flip-flops?

Procedure

The J-K Edge-Triggered Flip-Flop

1. Construct the circuit of Figure 17–2(a). The LEDs are logic monitors and are ON when their output is LOW. Select the inactive level (HIGH) for PRE and CLR. Select the "set" mode by connecting J to a logic 1 and K to a logic 0. With the clock LOW (not active), test the effect of PRE and CLR by putting a logic 0 on each, one at a time. Are preset and clear inputs synchronous or asynchronous?

Put CLR on LOW; then pulse the clock by putting a HIGH, then a LOW, on the clock. Observe that the CLR input overrides the J input.

Determine what happens if both PRE and CLR are connected to a 0 at the same time. Summarize your observations from this step in the report.

2. Put both PRE and CLR on a logic 1. Connect a TTL level pulse generator set to 1 Hz on the clock input. Add an LED clock indicator to the pulse generator, as shown in Figure 17–2(b), so that you can observe the clock pulse and the outputs at the same time. Test all four combinations of J and K inputs while observing the LEDs.

Are data transferred to the output on the leading or the trailing edge of the clock?

Observe that the output frequency is not the same as the clock frequency in the toggle mode.

Also note that the output duty cycle in the toggle mode is not the same as the clock duty cycle. This is a good way to obtain a 50% duty cycle pulse. Summarize your observations in the report. Include a discussion of the truth table for the J-K flip-flop.

3. Look at the circuit shown in Figure 17–3. From your knowledge of the truth table, predict what it will do; then test your prediction by building it. Summarize your observations.

4. An application of the toggle mode is found in certain counters. Cascaded flip-flops can be used to perform frequency division in a circuit called a *ripple counter.* Figure 17–4 illustrates a ripple counter using the two flip-flops in the 74LS76. Connect the circuit and sketch the Q_A and Q_B outputs on Plot 1 in the report.

Notice that when an LED is ON, the Q output is HIGH. The red and green LEDs indicate that the pulse generator frequency has been changed by the flip-flops.

For Further Investigation

Measurement of t_{PLH}

NOTE: The measurement of a parameter such as t_{PLH} is done differently for analog and digital scopes. Set up the experiment as in step 1; then if you are using an analog scope, do step 2a. If you are using a digital scope, do step 2b. If both scopes are available, do both steps 2a and 2b.

1. Set up the J-K flip-flop for toggle operation. Set the clock frequency for 100 kHz and view the clock on channel 1 and the Q output on channel 2 of your oscilloscope. Set the scope sweep time for 5 μs/div to observe the complete waveforms of both the clock and the Q output. Set the VOLTS/DIV control on each channel to 2 V/div and center the two waves across the center graticule of the display.

*Ripple counters are covered further in Experiment 19.

214

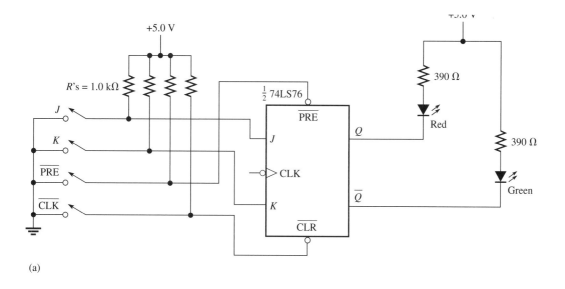

(a)

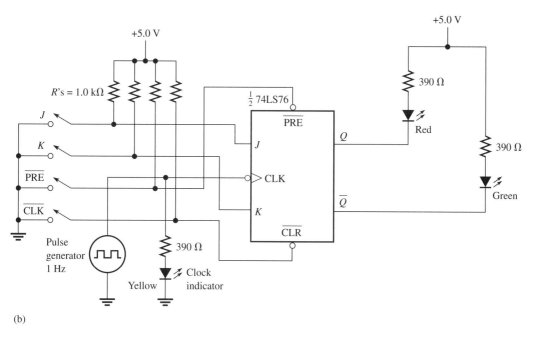

(b)

FIGURE 17–2

2a. With an analog scope, you will need to trigger the scope on the earlier signal (the clock). Trigger the scope using CH1 and select falling-edge triggering from the trigger controls. Then increase the sweep speed to 5 ns/div (or use the fastest available sweep time if 5 ns/div is not possible). You may need to adjust the trigger LEVEL control to see the entire clock waveform. You should see a falling edge of the clock and either a rising or falling edge of the Q output. You can observe the LOW-to-HIGH transition of the output by adjusting the HOLDOFF control. When you have a stable trace, go to step 3.

2b. With a digital scope such as the Tektronix TDS220, you can trigger on the slower waveform (the output) which is on channel 2. This is because the DSO can show signals before the trigger event. From the trigger menu, select CH2 triggering and select SET LEVEL TO 50%. Then increase the sweep speed to 5 ns/div. In the trigger menu, you can choose between RISING SLOPE or FALLING SLOPE to observe t_{PLH} or t_{PHL}, respectively.

3. Measure the time from the 50% level of the falling clock signal to the 50% level on the output signal for both a rising and falling output signal. Record your time in the report and compare it to the manufacturer's specified maximum values from the data sheet.

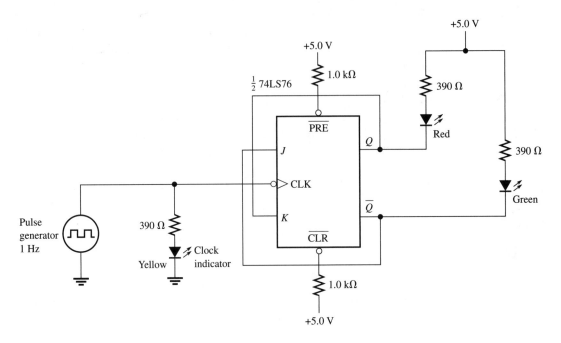

FIGURE 17–3

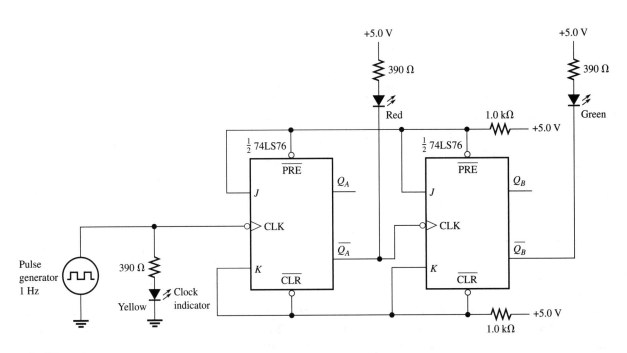

FIGURE 17–4

216

Report for Experiment 17

Name: _____ Date: _____ Class: _____

Data and Observations:

Step 1. Observations for $\overline{PRE}$ and $\overline{CLR}$ inputs:

Step 2. Observations of clocking the J-K flip-flop:

Step 3. Observations of test circuit:

Step 4. Ripple counter:

Clock:

Q_A

Q_B

Plot 1

Results and Conclusion:

Further Investigation Results:

Review Questions (TTL)

1. If both J and K inputs are LOW and $\overline{\text{PRE}}$ and $\overline{\text{CLR}}$ are HIGH, what effect does the clock have on the output of a J-K flip-flop?

2. Assume a student accidently reversed the J and K inputs on the circuit in Figure 17–3. What effect would be observed?

Program Overview

Recall that one of the methods of modeling VHDL applications is called *structural modeling* where blocks of logic are defined such as the function of a common fixed function IC. In this experiment, you will simulate the fixed-function logic of a typical J-K flip-flop in VHDL. One small addition in the VHDL program is that you will add a clock monitor (*ClkMon*) output in order to visually observe the clock pulse when the clock rate is low.

The naming convention for variables is to identify programming variables with names that can easily be associated with the common schematic name. Thus, within the program the variable *ClrNot* represents the input from the switch assigned to the CLR input, as shown on the schematic.

As mentioned in Experiment 15, VHDL supports three basic modes within the **entity** portion of a VHDL application. These modes are **in, out,** and **inout.** Mode **in** is used for identifiers that name in-

put signals. Mode **out** is used for identifiers that name output signals. Mode **inout** is used to represent bidirectional identifiers. Look for the **inout** identifier in the program.

Procedure

1. Connect the project board to a computer as described in *Project Board Familiarization* and review *VHDL Software Familiarization.*

2. Enter the program *JKFlipFlop* shown in Figure 17–5 of the report into the text editor. The program simulates a trailing edge-triggered J-K flip-flop as shown in Figure 17–6. Recall that feedback is provided by *Q* and *QNot;* thus, they are defined as using mode **inout.**

3. Referring to the section on Software Familiarization, compile and download the program to the project board. Use on-board switches to connect the inputs PRE and CLR. Assign the *Q* and $\overline{Q}$ outputs to LEDs to complete the logic circuit. Assign *Clock* to a PLD global clock input pin. Connect a TTL level pulse generator set to 1 Hz on the clock (CLK) input, as shown in Figure 17–7. Assign an LED to *ClkMon*, which is provided as a visual clock monitor.

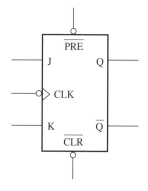

FIGURE 17–6
J-K flip-flop.

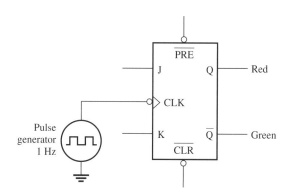

FIGURE 17–7

4. Select the inactive level (HIGH) for $\overline{PRE}$ and $\overline{CLR}$. Select the "set" mode by switching the J input switch to a logic 1 and the K input switch to a logic 0. Put $\overline{CLR}$ to a LOW.

Does the $\overline{CLR}$ input override the J and K SET mode? Is it independent of the CLK? Summarize your observations in the space provided in the report.

5. Leave the TTL pulse generator connected. Put both $\overline{PRE}$ and $\overline{CLR}$ on a logic 1. Observe the clock monitor LED and the Q and $\overline{Q}$ outputs at the same time. Test all four combinations of J and K inputs while observing the LEDs.

Observe that the output frequency is not the same as the clock frequency in the toggle mode, but is divided by 2. Also, note the output duty cycle. Summarize your observations, including the duty cycle, in the space provided in the report. In-

clude a discussion of the truth table for the J-K flip-flop.

6. An application of the toggle mode is found in certain counters. Cascaded flip-flops can be used to perform frequency division in a circuit called a *ripple counter.* Figure 17–8 illustrates a ripple counter using the two flip-flops. Enter the program *Counter* shown in Figure 17–9 using the original flip-flop you constructed in VHDL. Save program *Counter* in the same folder as program *JKFlipFlop,* so the compiler can use it as a **component.** Your program should perform the combined logic of the two cascaded flip-flops in Figure 17–8. Sketch the Q_A and Q_B outputs on Plot 2 in the report. (You can easily verify your sketched result by speeding up the pulse generator to 1 kHz and observing the signals on the LEDs on an oscilloscope).

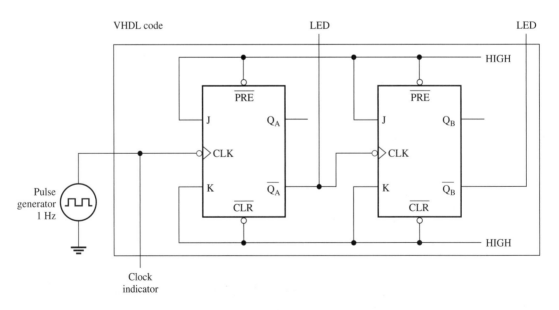

FIGURE 17–8

Report for Experiment 17

Name: _____ Date: _____ Class: _____

Data and Observations:

FIGURE 17–5

```
library IEEE;
use IEEE.std_logic_1164.all;

entity JKFlipFlop is
  port (J, K, Clr, Pre, Clock: in std_logic;
        ClkMon: out std_logic;
        Q, QNot: inout std_logic);
end entity JKFlipFlop;

architecture JKBehavior of JKFlipFlop is
begin
  process (J, K, Clr, Pre, Clock) is
  begin
    ClkMon <= Clock – Output the input clock for monitoring purposes.
    if Clr = '0' then Q <= '0'; QNot <= '1';   -- Clear
    elsif Pre = '0' then Q <= '1'; QNot <= '0'; -- Preset
    elsif Clock = '0' and Clock'event then     -- Clock Driven J-K
      if J = '1' and K = '0' then
        Q <= '1';
        QNot <= '0';
      elsif J = '0' and K = '1' then
        Q <= '0';
        QNot <= '1';
      elsif J = '1' and K = '1' then
        if Q = '1' then
          Q <= '0';
          QNot <= '1';
        else
          Q <= '1';
          QNot<= '0';
        end if;
      end if;
    end if;
  end process;
end architecture JKBehavior ;
```

```
library ieee;
use ieee.std_logic_1164.all;

entity Counter is
  port( Clr, Clk: in std_logic;
                  QA,QB: buffer std_logic);
end entity Counter;

architecture Behavior of Counter is
signal HighVal, QANot, QBNot, High: std_logic;

component JKFlipFlop is
  port (D, Clr, Pre, Clk: in std_logic;
        ClkMon: out std_logic;
        Q,QNot: inout std_logic);
end component JKFlipFlop;

begin
  HighVal <= '1';
  FF0:DFlipFlop port map (J=> HighVal, K<= HighVal, Clr=>Clr, Pre=> HighVal, Clk => Clk, Q=>QA, QNot=>QANot);
  FF1:DFlipFlop port map (J=> HighVal, K<= HighVal, Clr=>Clr, Pre=> HighVal, Clk =>QA,    Q=>QB, QNot=>QBNot);
end architecture Behavior;
```

> **CODE TIP**
> This program uses
> *JKFlipFlop* as a **component**.
> This **component** needs to
> be in the same folder as
> the Counter program that
> calls it.

FIGURE 17–9

Step 4. Observations for $\overline{\text{PRE}}$ and $\overline{\text{CLR}}$ inputs:

Step 5. Observations of clocking the J-K flip-flop:

Step 6. Ripple counter:

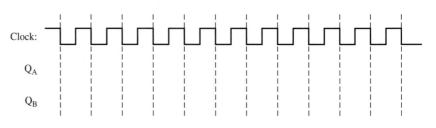

Clock:

Q_A

Q_B

Plot 2

Results and Conclusion:

Further Investigation Results:

Review Questions (VHDL)

1. Explain how you could change the VHDL model of a J-K flip-flop into a D flip-flop without modifying the program.

2. What two changes to the program in Figure 17–9 would allow you to add a third stage to the ripple counter?

18

One-Shots and Astable Multivibrators

Objectives

After completing this experiment, you will be able to
- Specify components and trigger logic for a 74121 one-shot to produce a specified pulse and trigger mode.
- Measure the frequency and duty cycle of a 555 timer configured as an astable multivibrator.
- Specify components for a 555 timer configured as an astable multivibrator and test your design.

Reference Reading

Floyd, *Digital Fundamentals with VHDL,* Chapter 8, "Flip-Flops and Related Devices"

Materials Needed (TTL)

74121 one-shot
7474 dual flip-flop
555 timer
Two 0.01 μF capacitors
Signal diode (1N914 or equivalent)
Resistors: 10 kΩ, 7.5 kΩ
Other components determined by student

Summary of Theory

There are three types of multivibrators: the bistable, the monostable (or *one-shot*), and the astable. The name of each type refers to the number of stable states. The bistable is simply a latch or flip-flop that can be either set or reset and will re-main in either state indefinitely. The one-shot has one stable (or inactive) state and one active state, which requires an input trigger to assert. When triggered, the one-shot enters the active state for a precise length of time and returns to the stable state to await another trigger. Finally, the astable multivibrator has no stable state and alternates (or "flip-flops") between HIGH and LOW by itself. It frequently functions as a clock generator, since its output is a constant stream of pulses. Many systems require one-shot or astable multivibrators. The traffic light control system,* requires two one-shots and an astable multivibrator as a clock. In this experiment, you will specify the components for the astable multivibrator and test the frequency and duty cycle. In the For Further Investigation section, you will design the one-shots.

Most applications for one-shots can be met with either an IC timer or an IC one-shot. A timer is a general-purpose IC that can operate as an astable or as a one-shot. As a one-shot, the timer is limited to pulse widths of not less than about 10 μs or frequencies not greater than 100 kHz. For more stringent applications, the IC one-shot takes over. The 74121, which you will test in this experiment, can provide pulses as short as 30 ns. In addition, integrated circuit one-shots often have special features, such as both leading and trailing edge-triggering and multiple inputs that can allow triggering only

*See Experiments 13, 14, and text "Digital System Application for Chapter 6.

for specific logic combinations. As you will see later, these can be extremely useful features. The logic circuit and function table for the 74121 are shown in Figure 18–1. The circuit is triggered by a rising pulse on the output of the Schmitt AND gate. The purpose of the Schmitt AND gate is to allow slow rise-time signals to trigger the one-shot. In order for B to trigger it, the input must be a rising pulse, and either A_1 or A_2 must be held LOW, as shown in the last two lines of the function table. If B is held HIGH, then a trailing edge trigger on either A_1 or A_2 will trigger the one-shot provided the other A input is HIGH. Other combinations can be used to inhibit triggering.

This experiment includes a more detailed introduction to the 555 timer, the first and still the most popular timer. It is not a TTL device but can operate on +5.0 V (and up to +18 V), so it can be TTL- or CMOS-compatible. This timer is extremely versatile but has limited triggering logic. Some applications include accurate time-delay generation, pulse generation, missing pulse detectors, and voltage-controlled oscillators (VCOs).

Pre-lab Questions

1. What is the advantage of the Schmitt AND gate shown in Figure 18–1?

2. Assume you want to use a rising transition for triggering a 74121. Explain how you would configure the A_1, A_2, and B inputs.

TTL

Procedure

Monostable Multivibrator Using the 74121

1. The 74121 contains an internal timing resistor of 2.0 kΩ. You can select the internal resistor for the timing resistor by connecting R_{INT} to V_{CC}, or you can select an external resistor. To use an external timing resistor, connect it as shown in Figure 18–1 with R_{INT} (pin 9) left open. The capacitor is an external component but can be eliminated for very short pulses. (See the manufacturer's data sheet.)

The equation that gives the approximate pulse width t_W is

$$t_W = 0.7 C_{EXT} R_T$$

where R_T is the appropriate timing resistor, either internal or external. C_{EXT} is in pF, R_T is in kΩ, and t_W is in ns. Using a 0.01 μF capacitor, calculate the required timing resistor to obtain a 50 μs pulse width. Obtain a resistor near the calculated value. Measure its resistance and measure the capacitance C_{EXT}. Record the computed R_T and the measured values of R_T and C_{EXT} in Table 18–1 of the report.

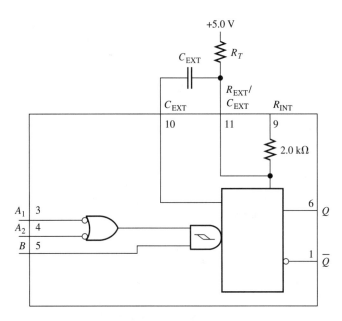

Inputs			Outputs	
A_1	A_2	B	Q	$\bar{Q}$
L	X	H	L	H
X	L	H	L	H
X	X	L	L	H
H	H	X	L	H
H	↓	H	⊓	⊔
↓	H	H	⊓	⊔
↓	↓	H	⊓	⊔
L	X	↑	⊓	⊔
X	L	↑	⊓	⊔

H = high logic level
L = low logic level
X = can be either low or high
↑ = positive going transition
↓ = negative going transition
⊓ = a positive pulse
⊔ = a negative pulse

FIGURE 18–1

2. Using the measured values of R_T and C_{EXT}, compute the expected pulse width, t_W. Record the computed value in Table 18–1.

3. Assume that you need to trigger the one-shot using a leading-edge trigger from the pulse generator. Determine the required connections for A_1, A_2, and B. List the input logic levels and the generator connection in your report. Build the circuit. One-shots are susceptible to noise pickup, so you should install a 0.01 μF bypass capacitor from V_{CC} to ground as close as possible to the 74121.

4. Apply a 10 kHz TTL-compatible signal from the pulse generator to the selected trigger input. Look at the pulse from the generator on channel 1 of a two-channel oscilloscope and the Q output on channel 2. Measure the pulse width and compare it with the expected pulse width from Step 1. (You may need to adjust R.) Record the measured pulse width in Table 18–1.

5. Increase the frequency slowly to 50 kHz while viewing the output on the scope. What evidence do you see that the 74121 is not retriggerable? Describe your observations.

The 555 Timer as an Astable Multivibrator

6. One of the requirements for many circuits is a clock, a series of pulses used to synchronize the various circuit elements of a digital system. In the astable mode, a 555 timer can serve as a clock generator.

A basic astable circuit is shown in Figure 18–2. There are two timing resistors. The capacitor is charged through both but is discharged only through R_2. The duty cycle, which is the ratio of the output HIGH time t_H divided by the total time T, and the frequency f are found by the following equations:

$$\text{Duty cycle} = \frac{t_H}{T} = \frac{R_1 + R_2}{R_1 + 2R_2}$$

$$f = \frac{1.44}{(R_1 + 2R_2)C_1}$$

Measure the value of two resistors R_1 and R_2 and capacitor C_1 with listed values as shown in Table 18–2. Record the measured values of the compo-

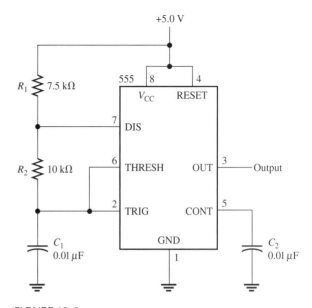

FIGURE 18–2

nents in Table 18–2. Using the equations, compute the expected frequency and duty cycle for the 555 astable multivibrator circuit shown in Figure 18–2. Enter the computed frequency and duty cycle in Table 18–2.

7. Construct the astable multivibrator circuit shown in Figure 18–2. Using an oscilloscope, measure the frequency and duty cycle of the circuit and record it in Table 18–2.

8. With the oscilloscope, observe the waveforms across capacitor C_1 and the output waveform at the same time. On Plot 1, sketch the observed waveforms.

9. While observing the waveforms from Step 8, try placing a short across R_2. Remove the short and write your observations in space provided in the report.

10. A clock oscillator signal, generated from an astable multivibrator, is required for the traffic-light control system. The specified oscillator frequency is 10 kHz. The circuit in Figure 18–2 oscillates at too low a frequency. Modify the design of this circuit so that it oscillates at 10 kHz (the duty cycle is not critical). Show the circuit in the space provided in the report.

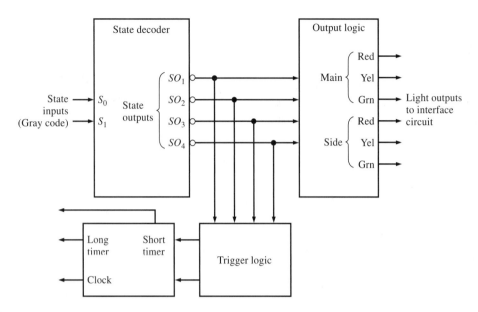

FIGURE 18–3
Block diagram of the state decoding and output logic.

For Further Investigation

The traffic light control system requires two one-shots, shown in the system as the *short timer* and the *long timer* (Figure 18–3). When the state decoder changes from LOW to HIGH, it causes the trigger logic to change from HIGH to LOW (trailing edge). It is this HIGH-to-LOW transition (trailing edge) that is used to trigger the timers. The short timer must have a 4 s positive pulse and the long timer must have a 25 s positive pulse. Check the manufacturer's maximum values of R_T and C_{EXT} for the 74121. Then design and build the circuits. An LED (with 330 Ω current-limiting resistor) can be used as an indicator. Test your design to see that the pulse width is approximately correct. Draw the circuits in the report and indicate your test results.

Report for Experiment 18

Name: _____ Date: _____ Class: _____

Data and Observations:

TABLE 18–1
Data for 74121 monostable multivibrator.

Quantity	Computed Value	Measured Value
Timing Resistor, R_T		
External Capacitor, C_{EXT}	0.01 μF	
Pulse Width, t_W		

Step 3. Input logic levels and generator connection:

Step 5. Observations as frequency is raised to 50 kHz:

TABLE 18–2
Data for 555 timer as an astable multivibrator.

Quantity	Computed Value	Measured Value
Resistor, R_1	7.5 kΩ	
Resistor, R_2	10.0 kΩ	
Capacitor, C_1	0.01 μF	
Frequency		
Duty Cycle		

Step 8.

Capacitor waveform:

Output waveform:

Plot 1

Step 9. Observations with a short across R_2:

Step 10. Circuit for a 10 kHz oscillator for traffic light controller:

Results and Conclusion:

Further Investigation Results:

Review Questions (TTL)

1. What does the term *nonretriggerable* mean for a monostable multivibrator?

2. a.   For the 74121 monostable multivibrator circuit, compute the value of the capacitor for a pulse width of 50 μs using the internal resistor.

   b. What change to the circuit is required to cause the output to be variable from 50 μs to 250 μs?

3. Compute the duty cycle and frequency for a 555 astable multivibrator if $R_1 = 1.0$ kΩ, $R_2 = 180$ kΩ, and $C_1 = 0.01$ μF.

19

Asynchronous Counters

Objectives

After completing this experiment, you will be able to
☐ Implement and analyze asynchronous up and down counters.
☐ Change the modulus of a counter.
☐ Implement a reduced count sequence for a 4-bit counter.

Reference Reading

Floyd, *Digital Fundamentals with VHDL,* Chapter 9, "Counters"

Materials Needed (TTL)

7400 quad NAND gates
7474 dual D flip-flop
7493A binary counter
Two LEDs
Resistors: two 330 Ω, two 1.0 kΩ

For Further Investigation:
   7486 quad XOR gate

Materials Needed (VHDL)

Project Board

Summary of Theory

Digital counters are classified as either *synchronous* or *asynchronous,* depending on how they are clocked. Synchronous counters are made from a series of flip-flops that are clocked together. By contrast, asynchronous counters are a series of flip-flops, each clocked by the previous stage, one after the other. Since all stages of the counter are not clocked together, a "ripple" effect propagates as various flip-flops are clocked. For this reason, asynchronous counters are called *ripple counters.* You can easily make a ripple counter from D or J-K flip-flops by connecting them in a toggle mode.

The *modulus* of a counter is the number of different output states the counter may take. The counters you will test in the first four steps of this experiment can represent the numbers 0, 1, 2, and 3; therefore, they have a modulus of 4. You can change the modulus of a ripple counter by decoding any output state and using the decoded state to asynchronously preset or clear the current count. Ripple counters can be made to count either up or down. (They can be made to count both up and down, but usually it is easier to use a synchronous counter for an up/down counter.)

Two methods for changing a counter from up to down or vice versa are illustrated in this experiment. The first method involves moving the logical "true" output of the counter to the other side (as illustrated in Figures 19–2 and 19–3). The second method changes the manner in which the counter is triggered.

If we tabulate a binary count sequence, we note that the LSB (least significant bit) changes at the fastest rate and the rate of change is divided by 2 as we look at succeeding columns. A typical 3-stage counter might have output waveforms as shown in

229

FIGURE 19–1

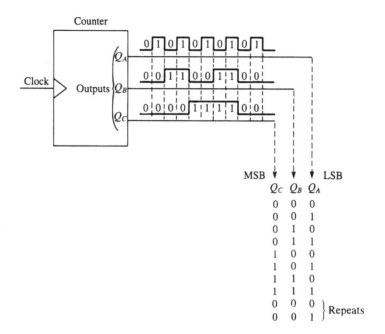

Q_C	Q_B	Q_A	
0	0	0	
0	0	1	
0	1	0	
0	1	1	
1	0	0	
1	0	1	
1	1	0	
1	1	1	
0	0	0	} Repeats
0	0	1	

Figure 19–1. For this counter, we can assign each output with a "weight" equal to the column value that would be assigned to binary numbers. Output Q_A has a weight of 1, output Q_B has a weight of 2, and output Q_C has a weight of 4. For the counter shown, the count sequence is for an up counter.

Because each stage of a ripple counter changes state at a slightly different time, the counter has a tendency to produce "glitches"—spikes of short duration—when the outputs are decoded owing to the short time delays when the flip-flops are changing states. Glitches are a disadvantage of ripple counters for many applications. Another disadvantage is the limited speed owing to the cumulative delays through the counter. For some applications, such as digital clocks, the slower speed is not a problem.

For most applications requiring a counter, MSI counters are available. The 7493A is an example of an asynchronous counter containing four J-K flip-flops, with the J and K inputs internally wired HIGH, putting them in the toggle mode. Three of the flip-flops are connected together as a 3-bit counter. The fourth flip-flop is separate, including its own clock input. To form a 4-bit counter, connect the Q_A output of a single J-K flip-flop to the clock B input of the 3-bit counter. A common reset line goes to all flip-flops. This reset line is controlled by an internal 2-input NAND gate. You can select any count sequence up to 16 by choosing the internal counter, detecting the desired count, and using it to reset the counter. In the For Further Investigation section, you will be introduced to an idea for changing the up/down count sequence using a control signal.

In this experiment and subsequent experiments, it is necessary to determine the time relationships between various digital signals. If your laboratory is equipped with a logic analyzer*, you may want to use it to capture data from the counters. The basic logic analyzer is a versatile digital instrument that allows you to capture multiple channels of digital data, store them, manipulate them, and view them. A basic logic analyzer converts the input data on each channel to a series of 1's and 0's of digital information and stores them in a digital memory. The data can be stored using an internal or external clock to sample the data at specific time intervals, or the signals can be sampled using an asynchronous signal, such as might be found in an asynchronous data transmission system. After the data are sampled, they can be viewed in several modes, depending on the analyzer. The primary viewing mode is either a set of reconstructed digital waveforms or a state listing of the data in memory. This list can be presented in various formats. More complex analyzers include a digital storage oscilloscope (DSO).

Other important features make logic analyzers important instruments for testing and troubleshooting digital circuits. Because logic analyzers differ in features and capabilities, it is not possible in this summary to explain detailed operation. Refer to the operator's manual for your analyzer for operating instructions.

*The logic analyzer is introduced in Section 1–9 of the text.

230

Pre-lab Questions

1. What are two disadvantages of a ripple counter?
2. Explain how the count sequence of 7493A counter can be truncated and reset to zero.

Procedure

Two-Bit Asynchronous Counters

NOTE: The LED indicators in this experiment are connected through NAND inverters to form the display portion of the circuit. Although not strictly necessary, this method enables you to more easily visualize the ideas presented in the experiment without violating the I_O specification for the 7474. Also, in this experiment, it is necessary to show the difference between the *electrical* output, Q, and the *logic* output. Accordingly, the logic output is labeled with the letter A or B. It is possible for the electrical and logic outputs to have opposite meanings, as will be seen.

1. Construct the 2-bit asynchronous counter shown in Figure 19–2. Clock flip-flop A using a 1 Hz TTL pulse from the function generator to the clock input, and watch the sequence on the LEDs. Then speed up the generator to 1 kHz, and view the A and B output waveforms on a dual-channel oscilloscope. Trigger the oscilloscope from channel 1 while viewing the B signal on channel 1 and the A signal or the clock on channel 2. Triggering on the slower B signal will give a stable trace and assures there is no ambiguity in determining the timing diagram (possible on analog scopes). Sketch the output timing diagram in Plot 1 of the report.

Notice that the frequency of the B output is one-half that of the A output. As explained in the Summary of Theory section, the column weight of flip-flop B is twice that of flip-flop A, and thus it can be thought of as the MSB of the counter. By observation of your waveforms, determine whether this is an up counter or a down counter, and record your answer.

2. Now we will change the way we take the "true" output from the counter and see what happens. If logic "truth" is taken from the other side of each flip-flop, then we have the circuit shown in Figure 19–3. Modify your circuit and view the output waveform from each stage. Sketch the timing diagram on Plot 2 of the report.

3. Next we will change the manner in which flip-flop B is clocked. Change the circuit to that of Figure 19–4. The "true" output of the counter remains on the $\overline{Q}$ side of the flip-flops. View the outputs as before, and sketch the waveforms on Plot 3.

4. Now change the logic "true" side of the counter, but do not change the clock, as illustrated in Figure 19–5. Again, sketch the outputs of each flip-flop on Plot 4.

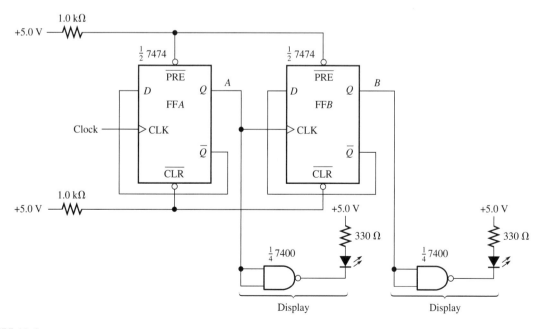

FIGURE 19–2
Ripple counter with D flip-flops.

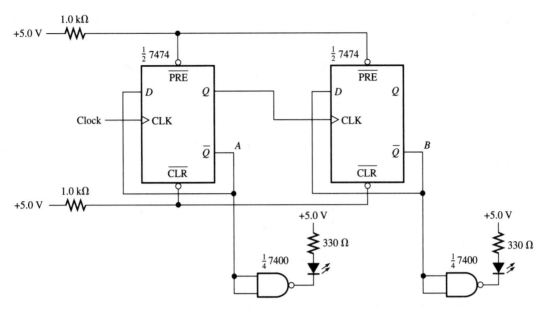

FIGURE 19–3
Ripple counter with D flip-flops. Note that the "true" output is shown on the $\bar{Q}$ output.

5. You can change the modulus of the counter by taking advantage of the asynchronous clear ($\overline{\text{CLR}}$) and asynchronous preset ($\overline{\text{PRE}}$) inputs of the 7474. Look at the circuit of Figure 19–6, a modification of the circuit in Figure 19–5. Predict the behavior of this circuit, and then build the circuit. Sketch the output waveforms of each flip-flop on Plot 5. Set the generator clock frequency at 500 kHz and look for the very short spike that causes the count sequence to be truncated.

6. The very short spike, called a *glitch*, on the A output is necessary to cause the counter to reset. While this signal serves a purpose, glitches in digital systems are often troublesome. Let's look at an undesired glitch caused by two flip-flops changing states at nearly the same time.

Add a 2-input NAND gate to the circuit of Figure 19–6, which decodes state 0. (Connect the inputs of the NAND gate to $\bar{A}$ and $\bar{B}$.) Leave the generator frequency at 500 kHz. Look carefully at

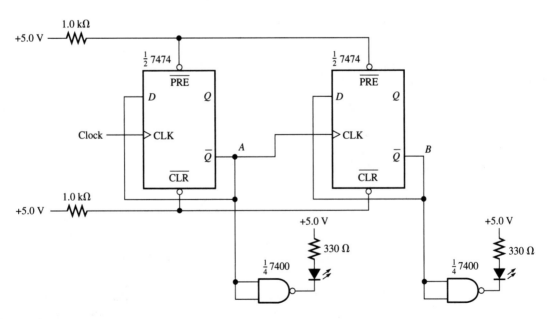

FIGURE 19–4
Ripple counter with D flip-flops. Note that the B counter is triggered from the $\bar{Q}$ output.

232

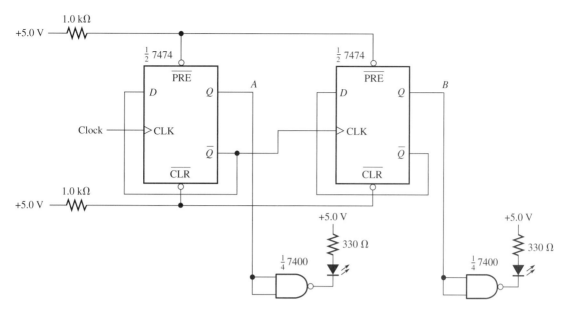

FIGURE 19–5

Ripple counter with D flip-flops. Note that the "true" output is on the Q outputs.

the output of the NAND gate. Sketch the observed waveforms on Plot 6.

The 7493A Asynchronous Counter

7. You can configure the 7493A 4-bit binary counter to count from 0 to 15 by connecting the output of the single flip-flop (Q_A) to the clock B input.

Connect the output of a TTL-level pulse from the function generator to the clock A input. From the data sheet, determine the necessary connections for the reset inputs.

Set the input frequency for 400 kHz. Trigger a two-channel oscilloscope from the lowest-frequency symmetrical waveform (Q_D), and observe, in turn, each output on the second channel. (If you have a

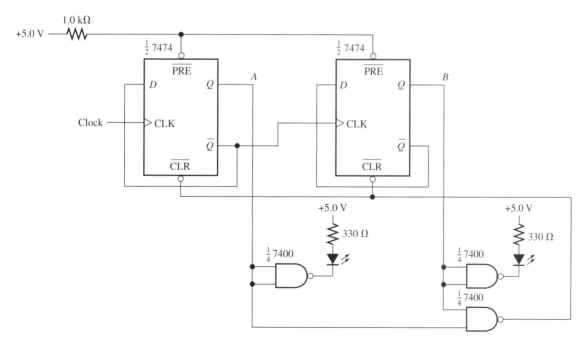

FIGURE 19–6

Ripple counter with D flip-flops and truncated count.

233

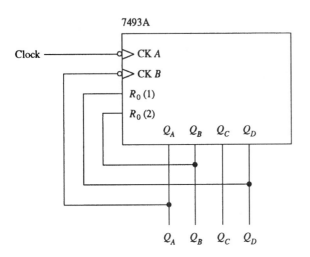

FIGURE 19–7
7493A with truncated count sequence.

logic analyzer, you can observe all four outputs together.) Sketch the timing diagram on Plot 7.

8. Figure 19–7 shows a 7493A counter configured with a truncated count sequence. Modify your previous circuit and observe the output waveforms on an oscilloscope or logic analyzer. Again, trigger the oscilloscope on the lowest-frequency symmetrical waveform, and observe each output on the second channel. Sketch the timing diagram on Plot 8.

For Further Investigation

Adding the UP/DOWN Function to the 7493A

The methods you have investigated so far involve hardware changes to the circuit to change the counter function. A more useful circuit enables the up/down function to be controlled by a separate control line. The line could be controlled by a switch or even from a computer using a software command.

You have seen how reversing the bits causes the count sequence to reverse. This occurs for any nontruncated binary counting sequence, no matter how long. You can take advantage of this idea by either passing the output bits on unchanged or reversing them. The 7486 XOR gate allows you to do this. Each output from the 7493A can be connected to one input of an XOR gate. The other input is connected to an up/down control line. This enables the counter to count either up or down; but when the sequence is reversed, it causes the output number to change immediately, a disadvantage to this technique.

Design the circuit using the 7493A as a 4-bit (0 to 15) counter. Add the up/down control using an SPST switch to select between up or down counting. Draw your circuit in the report and test its operation. Be sure to show all connections to the 7493A, including the reset and clock lines. Summarize your findings in your report.

Report for Experiment 19

Name: _____ Date: _____ Class: _____

Data and Observations:

Waveforms from Step 1:

Clock:

A:

B:

Plot 1

Is this an up counter or a down counter? _____

Waveforms from Step 2:

Clock:

A:

B:

Plot 2

Is this an up counter or a down counter? _____

Waveforms from Step 3:

Clock:

A:

B:

Plot 3

Is this an up counter or a down counter? _____

Waveforms from Step 4:

Clock:

A:

B:

Plot 4

Is this an up counter or a down counter? _____

Waveforms from Step 5:

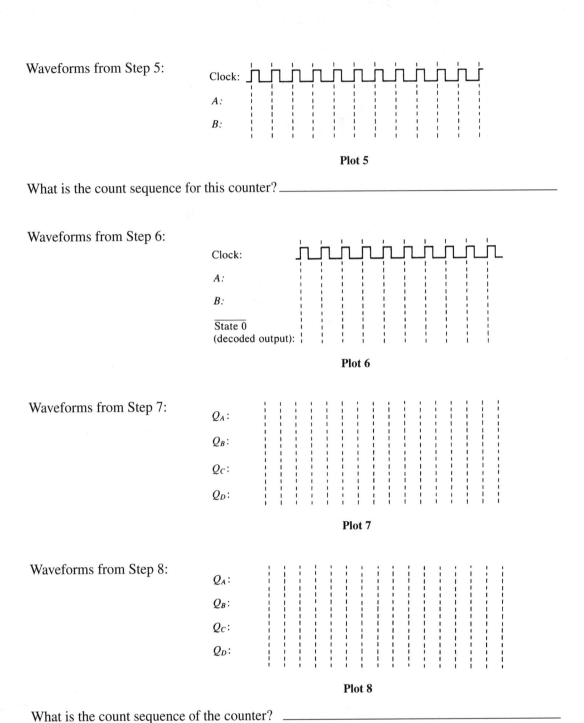

Clock:

A:

B:

Plot 5

What is the count sequence for this counter? _____

Waveforms from Step 6:

Clock:

A:

B:

$\overline{\text{State 0}}$
(decoded output):

Plot 6

Waveforms from Step 7:

Q_A:

Q_B:

Q_C:

Q_D:

Plot 7

Waveforms from Step 8:

Q_A:

Q_B:

Q_C:

Q_D:

Plot 8

What is the count sequence of the counter? _____

Results and Conclusion:

Further Investigation Results:

Review Questions (TTL)

1. Suppose the counter in Figure 19–2 has both LEDs on at the same time. The clock is checked and found to be present. What possible faults would cause this condition?

2. Explain why the Q_A output in Figure 19–7 is connected to the CK B input. (Hint: See the internal schematic for the 7493A.)

3. Assume the 7493A in Figure 19–7 were replaced with a 7492A and wired the same way. Referring to the count sequence shown on the data sheet,* determine the modulus and count sequence of the circuit.

*See Appendix A.

Program Overview

In Experiment 15, a small VHDL program named *DFlipFlop* was used that simulated the behavior of a D flip-flop. The simulation used only a fraction of the capability of the PLD. Many useful devices, such as the asynchronous counters you will see in this experiment, need two or more D flip-flops. To simulate this, it is not necessary to rewrite the program for a D flip-flop each time you need one; instead the original program is used over again for each flip-flop required. A small program that is used within a larger one is called a *subprogram*. Subprograms are commonly used in most high-level computer languages. In this experiment, the program *DFlipFlop* will be considered to be a subprogram to the main counter program. Recall in Experiment 17 that by using the VHDL keyword **component**, external programs such as *DFlipFlop* can be available any time a D flip-flop is needed. It is a much more efficient method for writing VHDL code, as you will see.

Starting in step 12, a different technique for programming a counter is introduced. The method uses a programming structure called a register mode to perform the counting and does not have an equivalent component structure (like the D flip-flop). The programmer cannot directly determine when the register mode is used. Instead, the VHDL compiler analyzes the program and selects the register mode when required. In the counter, the program chooses a register mode in order to store the count; then, on the selected clock edge, it changes the count using a **when** statement to overwrite a new value in the register. Notice that this structure implies memory, which is basic to all counters. It also is a simple way of defining an arbitrary count sequence, as you will see.

Procedure

1. Connect the project board to a computer as described in *Project Board Familiarization* and review *VHDL Software Familiarization*.

2. Enter the program *DFlipFlop* shown in Figure 19–8 (in the report) into the VHDL editor. This is the same program you used in Experiment 15 to describe the gate logic of a D flip-flop. The main counter program in this experiment will treat the D flip-flop as an entity.

3. Assign the *D* and *Clock* inputs to on-board switches. Now assign the *Q* and *QNot* outputs to on-board LEDs. (Note that *QNot* is the variable name that stands for the $\overline{Q}$ output of the flip-flop.)

4. Compile and download the D flip-flop program to the project board. This program will be used as a VHDL **component** (or subprogram) as discussed in the Program Overview.

5. In this step, you will do a quick verification that the program *DFlipFlop* is functioning correctly. Put the Clock on a LOW and the *D* input on a HIGH and move the clock switch from the LOW position to the HIGH position, simulating a leading-edge triggering. The *Q* output should be HIGH after the clock input is moved. Repeat the process but with the *D* input LOW. The *Q* output should change to a LOW.

6. Enter the counter program, *Lab19a*, shown in Figure 19–9 (in the report) into the text editor. This program represents the 2-bit asynchronous counter shown in Figure 19–10. It uses the D flip-flop as a VHDL **component;** therefore, you will want to save *Lab19a* in the same folder as program *DFlipFlop*. Notice that the original program *DflipFlop* is now a subprogram of *Lab19a*.

7. Assign the input *Clr* to an on-board switch and assign *Clock* to an external pulse generator input (see *Project Board Familiarization*, part 4b). Assign the outputs *QA* and *QB* to LEDs. Then compile and download the program to the project board.

8. Test the counter program by clocking flip-flop A using a 1 Hz TTL pulse from the function generator to the clock input on your project board, and watch the sequence on the LEDs. Then speed up the generator to 1 kHz, and view the *QA* and *QB* output waveforms on a dual-channel oscilloscope. The schematic shows the "true" output as *A* and *B,* which are equivalent to the program variables *QA* and *QB*. Trigger the oscilloscope from channel 1 while viewing the *B* signal in channel 1 and the *A* signal on channel 2. Triggering on the slower *B* signal will give a stable trace and assures there is no ambiguity in determining the timing diagram (possible on analog scopes). Sketch the output timing diagram in Plot 9 of the report.

Notice that the frequency of the *B* output is one-half that of the *A* output. As explained in the Summary of Theory section, the column weight of flip-flop B is twice that of flip-flop A, and thus it can be thought of as the MSB of the counter. By observation of your waveforms, determine whether this is an up counter or a down counter, and record your answer.

VHDL code

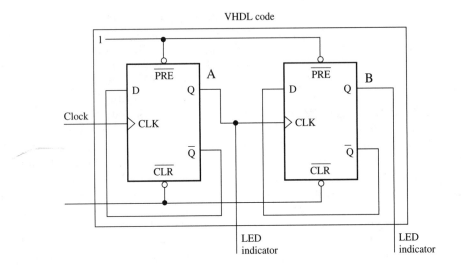

FIGURE 19–10
Ripple counter with D flip-flops.

9. Enter the program *Lab19b* in Figure 19–11 (in the report) into the text editor. This program changes the way we take the "true" output from the counter. If logic "truth" is taken from the other side of each flip-flop, then the counter is equivalent to the one shown in Figure 19–12.

10. Assign the input *Clr* to an on-board switch and assign *Clock* to an external pulse generator input (see *Project Board Familiarization,* part 4b). Assign the outputs *QANot* and *QBNot* to LEDs.

Then compile and download the program to the project board.

11. View the output waveforms, *A* and *B,* as before on an oscilloscope. Notice that *A* and *B* are now defined on the schematic as the "true" output of the counter but are internally assigned to the program variables *QANot* and *QBNot*. Sketch the timing diagram on Plot 10 of the report.

12. Enter the program *Lab19c* in Figure 19–13 (in the report) into the text editor. This program is a

VHDL code

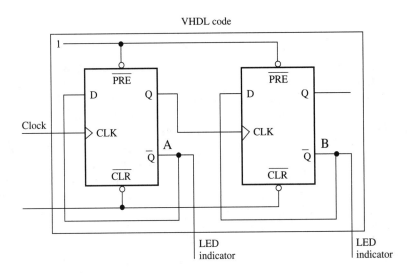

FIGURE 19–12

240

counter that does not have an equivalent **component** circuit. VHDL makes it particularly easy to define an arbitrary sequence as you will see.

13. Assign the input *Clr* to an on-board switch (Altera users: Assign *Clr* to PLD pin 1). Assign *Clock* to an external pulse generator input. Assign the outputs *Q0*, *Q1*, and *Q2* to LEDs. Compile and download the program to the project board.

14. Set the pulse generator to a 1 Hz clock and observe the sequence of lights. From your observations, draw a state diagram in the space provided in the report.

For Further Investigation

1. Copy the program *Lab19d* for the modified counter in Figure 19–14 (in the report) to the VHDL editor. You will change the manner in which flip-flop *B* is clocked in this program. The program simulates the counter shown in Figure 19–15.

2. Assign pins as required by the program. Compile and download your program. Then view the outputs as before, and sketch the waveforms on Plot 11.

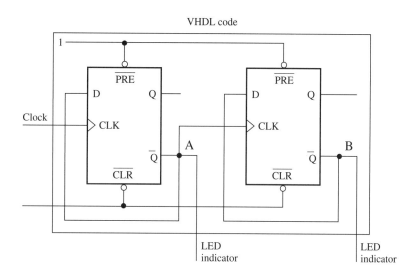

FIGURE 19–15

Report for Experiment 19

Name: _____ Date: _____ Class: _____

Data and Observations:

```
library IEEE;
use IEEE.std_logic_1164.all;

entity DFlipFlop is
   port (D, Clr, Pre, Clock: in std_logic;
         Q, QNot: inout std_logic);
end entity DFlipFlop;

architecture DBehavior of DFlipFlop is
signal Temp: std_logic := '0';
begin
   process (D, Clr, Pre, Clock) is
   begin
     if Clr = '0' then Q <= '0'; QNot <= '1';-- Clear
     elsif Pre = '0' then Q <= '1'; QNot <= '0';-- Preset
     elsif Clock = '1' and Clock'event then
       if D = '1' and Clr = '1' and Pre = '1' then
         Q <= '1';
         QNot <= '0';
       else
         Q <= '0';
         QNot<= '1';
       end if;
     end if;
   end process;
end architecture DBehavior ;
```

FIGURE 19–8

```
library IEEE;
use IEEE.std_logic_1164.all;

entity Lab19a is
   port (Clr, Clock: in std_logic;
         QA, QB: inout std_logic);
end entity Lab19a;

architecture Counter of Lab19a is
signal Pre, QANot, QBNot: std_logic;
component DFlipFlop is
   port  (D, Clr, Pre, Clock: in std_logic;
         Q, QNot: inout std_logic);
end component DFlipFlop;

begin
   Pre <= '1';
   FF0:DFlipFlop port map (D=>QANot,Clr=>Clr,Pre=>Pre,Clock=>Clock,Q=>QA, QNot=>QANot);
   FF1:DFlipFlop port map (D=>QBNot,Clr=>Clr,Pre=>Pre,Clock=>QA,Q=>QB, QNot=>QBNot);
end architecture Counter;
```

FIGURE 19–9

```vhdl
library IEEE;
use IEEE.std_logic_1164.all;

entity Lab19b is
  port (Clr, Clock: in std_logic;
        QANot, QBNot: inout std_logic);
end entity Lab19b;

architecture Counter of Lab19b is
signal Pre, QA, QB, High: std_logic;

component DFlipFlop is
  port (D, Clr, Pre, Clock: in std_logic;
        Q, QNot: inout std_logic);
end component DFlipFlop;

begin
  Pre <= '1';
  FF0:DFlipFlop port map (D=>QANot,Clr=>Clr,Pre=>Pre,Clock=>Clock,Q=>QA, QNot=>QANot);
  FF1:DFlipFlop port map (D=>QBNot,Clr=>Clr,Pre=>Pre,Clock=>QA,Q=>QB, QNot=>QBNot);
end architecture Counter;
```

FIGURE 19–11

```vhdl
library IEEE;
use IEEE.std_logic_1164.all;

entity Lab19c is
  port (Clock, Clr: in std_logic;
        Q: buffer std_logic_vector (2 downto 0));
end entity Lab19c;

architecture Counter of Lab19c is
begin
  process (clock)
  begin
    if Clr = '0' then Q <= "000";
      elsif clock = '1' and clock'event then
        case Q is
          when "000" => Q <= "010";
          when "010" => Q <= "011";
          when "011" => Q <= "001";
          when "001" => Q <= "101";
          when "101" => Q <= "100";
          when "100" => Q <= "000";
          when others => Q <= "000";
        end case;
      end if;
  end process;
end architecture Counter;
```

FIGURE 19–13

244

Step 8.

Plot 9

Is this an up counter or a down counter? _____

Step 11.

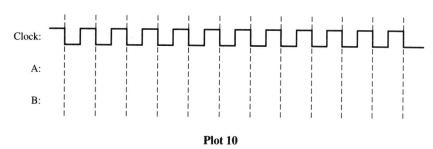

Plot 10

Is this an up counter or a down counter? _____

Step 14. State diagram:

Results and Conclusion:

Further Investigation Results:

```vhdl
library IEEE;
use IEEE.std_logic_1164.all;

entity Lab19d is
   port (Clr, Clock: in std_logic;
         QANot, QBNot: inout std_logic);
end entity Lab19d;

architecture Counter of Lab19d is
signal Pre, QA, QB, High: std_logic;

component DFlipFlop is
   port (D, Clr, Pre, Clock: in std_logic;
         Q, QNot: inout std_logic);
end component DFlipFlop;

begin
   Pre <= '1';
   FF0:DFlipFlop port map (D=>QANot,Clr=>Clr,Pre=>Pre,Clock=>Clock,Q=>QA, QNot=>QANot);
   FF1:DFlipFlop port map (D=>QBNot,Clr=>Clr,Pre=>Pre,Clock=>QANot,Q=>QB, QNot=>QBNot);
end architecture Counter;
```

FIGURE 19–14

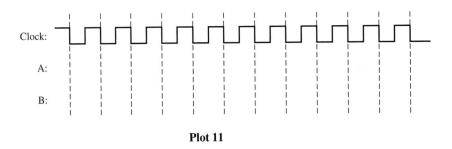

Plot 11

Is this an up counter or a down counter? _____

Review Questions (VHDL)

1. Most VHDL programmers work in a team consisting of several people. Many times a programmer will write a subprogram that other programmers will use. Explain the advantages of being able to share subprograms in this way and why documentation is important.

2. Show how the counter in Figure 19–10 could be modified to include a manual reset feature.

3. Explain how to change the sequence of the counter in the program *Lab19c*.

246

20

Analysis of Synchronous Counters with Decoding

Objectives

After completing this experiment, you will be able to
☐ Analyze the count sequence of synchronous counters using a tabulation method.
☐ Construct and analyze a synchronous counter with decoding. Draw the state diagram.
☐ Use an oscilloscope to measure the time relationship between the flip-flops and the decoded outputs.

Reference Reading

Floyd, *Digital Fundamentals with VHDL,* Chapter 9, "Counters"

Materials Needed (TTL)

Two 74LS76 dual J-K flip-flops
7400 quad NAND gates
Two SPST N.O. pushbuttons
Four LEDs
Resistors: four 330 Ω, two 1.0 kΩ

For Further Investigation:
One MAN-72 seven-segment display
Seven 470 Ω resistors

Materials Needed (VHDL)

Project Board

Summary of Theory

Synchronous counters have all clock lines tied to a common clock, causing all flip-flops to change at the same time. For this reason, the time from the clock pulse until the next count transition is much faster than in a ripple counter. This greater speed reduces the problem of glitches (short, unwanted signals due to nonsynchronous transitions) in the decoded outputs. However, glitches are not always eliminated, because stages with slightly different propagation delays can still have short intermediate states. One way to eliminate glitches is to choose a Gray code count sequence (only one flip-flop transition per clock pulse).

Decoding is the "detecting" of a specific number. A counter with full decoding has a separate output for each state in its sequence. The decoded output can be used to implement some logic that performs a task. The decoded outputs are also useful for developing counters with irregular count sequences. This experiment will also introduce you to *partial* decoding, a technique that allows you to decode the output with less than all of the bits.

A number of MSI counters are available with features on one chip, such as synchronous and asynchronous preset or clear, up/down counting, parallel loading, display drivers, and so on. If it is possible to use an MSI counter for an application, this choice is generally the most economical. If it is not possible, then you must design the counter to meet the requirement. In this experiment you will analyze already designed synchronous counters step by step.

In the next experiment, you will design a counter to meet a specific requirement.

Analysis of Synchronous Counters

The method for analyzing a synchronous counter is a systematic tabulation technique. This method is illustrated for the counter shown in Figure 20–1. Begin by setting up Table 20–1(a). The table lists the outputs and inputs for each flip-flop in the counter.

Step 1. Write the equations for J and K inputs of each counter using the schematic.

Step 2. Assume the counter is in some state; in this example, it is arbitrarily placed in state 0000_2.

Step 3. Complete first row by determining each J and K input. The equations and the inputs 0000_2 are used to compute the binary value of J and K.

Step 4. Use the J-K truth table to determine the next state of each flip-flop. In this example, $J_D = K_D = 0$ means Q_D will not change; Q_C and Q_B also will not change, but $J_A = 1$, $K_A = 0$ means that $Q_A = 1$ after the next clock pulse. Write the next state under the present state that was originally assumed.

Step 5. Continue until all possible inputs are accounted for. This is done in Table 20–1(b). The sequence can now be shown on a state diagram, as in Figure 20–2.

The analysis continues along these lines until all possible (2^N) states have been taken into account, including states that are not in the main count sequence. The completed table is shown as Table 20–1(b). Using the information from the table, the complete state diagram can then be drawn as illustrated in Figure 20–2. This completely describes the operation of the counter. This particular counter has an interesting and somewhat unusual application. It is used to develop the proper sequence of signals necessary to half-step a stepper motor.

Pre-lab Questions

1. Looking at a counter, how could you identify whether it is synchronous or asynchronous?
2. What is one way to assure there will be no glitches in the outputs of a synchronous counter?
3. How many possible states are in a counter with N flip-flops?

Procedure

Analysis of Synchronous Counters

1. Examine the counter shown in Figure 20–3. Since there are two flip-flops, there are four possible output states. Analyze the sequence by the method illustrated in the Summary of Theory section. Complete Table 20–2 in the report. From the table, draw the predicted state diagram in the space provided in the report.

2. Build the circuit. Use a TTL-level pulse generator at 10 kHz for the clock signal. The NAND gates serve as state decoders with an active-LOW output for each state. To avoid confusion, the lines from the counter to the decoders are not shown on the schematic. If you have a logic analyzer available, look at the outputs of the two flip-flops and the four decoders at the same time. If you do not have a logic

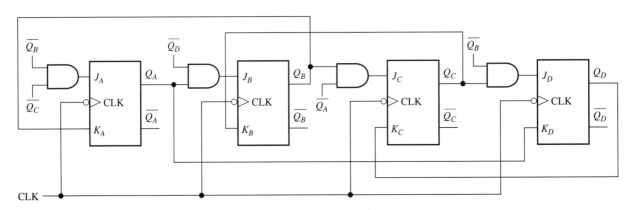

FIGURE 20–1
Synchronous counter with irregular sequence used for half-stepping a stepper motor.

TABLE 20–1

Analysis of synchronous counter shown in Figure 20–1.

Outputs				Inputs								
Q_D	Q_C	Q_B	Q_A	$J_D = \overline{Q}_B \cdot Q_C$	$K_D = Q_A$	$J_C = \overline{Q}_A \cdot Q_B$	$K_C = Q_D$	$J_B = Q_A \cdot \overline{Q}_D$	$K_B = Q_C$	$J_A = \overline{Q}_B \cdot \overline{Q}_C$	$K_A = Q_B$	
0	0	0	0	0	0	0	0	0	0	1	0	
0	0	0	1									

Step 2 → (row 0 0 0 0)
Step 4 → (row 0 0 0 1, Q column)
Step 3 (under J_D / K_D)
Step 1 (under J_B / J_A)

(a) Steps in filling out the table

Outputs				Inputs							
Q_D	Q_C	Q_B	Q_A	$J_D = \overline{Q}_B \cdot Q_C$	$K_D = Q_A$	$J_C = \overline{Q}_A \cdot Q_B$	$K_C = Q_D$	$J_B = Q_A \cdot \overline{Q}_D$	$K_B = Q_C$	$J_A = \overline{Q}_B \cdot \overline{Q}_C$	$K_A = Q_B$
0	0	0	0	0	0	0	0	0	0	1	0
0	0	0	1	0	1	0	0	1	0	1	0
0	0	1	1	0	1	0	0	1	0	0	1
0	0	1	0	0	0	1	0	0	0	0	1
0	1	1	0	0	0	1	0	0	1	0	1
0	1	0	0	1	0	0	0	0	1	0	0
1	1	0	0	1	0	0	1	0	1	0	0
1	0	0	0	0	0	0	1	0	0	1	0
1	0	0	1	0	1	0	1	0	0	1	0
0	0	0	1	At this step, a repeated pattern is noted.							
1	1	0	1	1	1	0	1	0	1	0	0
0	0	0	1	Returns to main sequence							
0	1	0	1	1	1	0	0	1	1	0	0
1	1	1	1	0	1	0	1	0	1	0	1
0	0	0	0	Returns to previously tested state (0000)							
0	1	1	1	0	1	0	0	1	1	0	1
0	1	0	1	Returns to previously tested state (0101)							
1	0	1	0	0	0	1	1	0	0	0	1
1	1	1	0	0	0	1	1	0	1	0	1
1	0	0	0	Returns to main sequence							
1	0	1	1	0	1	0	1	0	0	0	1
0	0	1	0	Returns to main sequence							

Main sequence (rows 1–9)

Account for all other states (remaining rows)

(b) Completed table

analyzer, you can establish the relative time between signals using a two-channel oscilloscope. The following procedure will guide you:

a. Set up the scope to trigger on channel 1 with the Q_B signal (the slowest signal) viewed on that channel. If you are using an analog scope, do not use composite or vertical-mode triggering.

b. View the pulse generator (clock) on channel 2. Adjust the frequency or SEC/DIV control so that each clock pulse coincides with a major division on the horizontal axis.

c. Do not change the triggering or the Q_B signal on the triggering channel. Probe the circuit with channel 2. The observed signals will be in the proper relationships to the Q_B signal.

d. You can move channel 2 to each of the decoder outputs and see the relationship to the Q_B signal.

249

FIGURE 20–2

Analysis of synchronous counter shown in Figure 20–1 gives this state diagram. Analysis procedure is shown in Table 20–1(b).

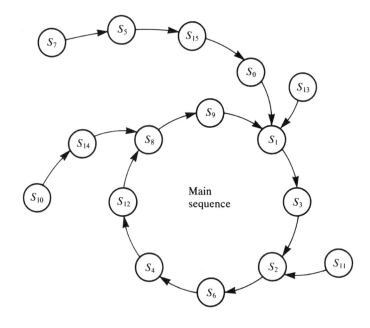

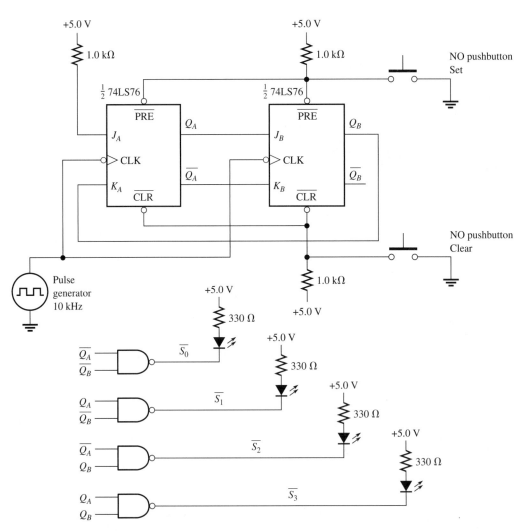

FIGURE 20–3

Synchronous counter with state decoding.

Now on Plot 1 in the report, sketch the outputs of the flip-flops and decoders in the proper time relationship to each other.

3. Looking at the waveforms you have drawn, check that your predicted state diagram is correct. As an extra check, you can slow the clock to 1 Hz and verify the sequence with the LEDs.

4. Assume that a failure has occurred in the circuit. The wire from the Q_B output to K_A has become open. What effect does this open have on the output? Look at the signals and determine the new state diagram.

Draw the predicted state diagram in your report. Test your prediction by opening the K_A input and observing the result. You can put the counter into state 0 by pressing the clear pushbutton and into state 3 by pressing the set pushbutton.

5. Modify the circuit by adding another flip-flop and changing the inputs to J_A, K_A, and J_B, as shown in Figure 20–4. Leave the 7400 decoder circuit, but remove the set and clear switches. The decoder circuit will form an example of *partial* decoding—a technique frequently employed in computers.

6. Analyze the counter by completing Table 20–3 in the report. Account for all possible states, including unused states. If you correctly account for the unused states, you will see that all unused states return to state 2. Draw the state diagram.

7. Set the pulse generator for 1 Hz and observe the LEDs connected to the state decoders. Notice that state 4 is *not* in the main sequence but state 0 *is* in the main sequence of the counter. This means that every time the state 0 LED turns ON, the counter is actually in state 0. This is an example of partial decoding; the MSB was not connected to the decoder, yet there is no ambiguity for state 0 because state 4 is not possible. Likewise, there is no ambiguity for state 0 or state 7, but partial decoding is not adequate to uniquely define states 2 and 6.

EWB/MSM Troubleshooting

The synchronous counter in Figure 20–3 is simulated in Electronics Workbench and Multisim on the CD packaged with this lab manual. There are three files associated with this circuit. The file Exp-20nf uses the simulated logic analyzer and has no faults. You may want to view the logic analyzer outputs first and test the C (Clear) and S (Set) switches to verify the circuit performs the same way as your laboratory circuit. Then open the files Exp-20f1 and Exp-20f2. These files contain faults. Analyze the circuits and indicate the most likely problem and how you would isolate the problem.

For Further Investigation

A unique circuit is shown in Figure 20–5. The output is connected in a rather unusual way directly to a seven-segment display. You are challenged to figure out the sequence of letters that will be on the display. Here is your only clue: It is an English word that has something to do with detective work. (You get the other clue when you build the circuit.) If you give up, build the circuit and find the answer.

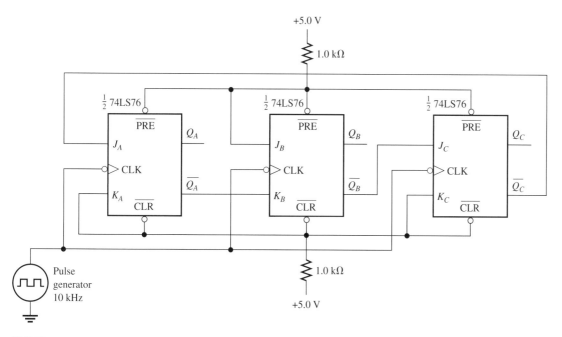

FIGURE 20–4

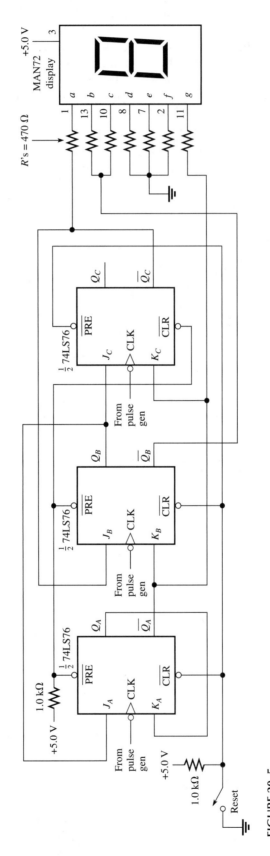

FIGURE 20–5

A synchronous counter with "mystery" output.

Report for Experiment 20

Name: _____ Date: _____ Class: _____

Data and Observations:

TABLE 20–2

Analysis of synchronous counter shown in Figure 20–3.

Outputs		Inputs			
Q_B	Q_A	$J_B =$	$K_B =$	$J_A =$	$K_A =$

Step 1. State diagram:

Step 4. State diagram:

Q_A:

Q_B:

$\overline{S_0}$:

$\overline{S_1}$:

$\overline{S_2}$:

$\overline{S_3}$:

Plot 1

TABLE 20–3

Analysis of synchronous counter shown in Figure 20–4.

Outputs			Inputs					
Q_C	Q_B	Q_A	$J_C =$	$K_C =$	$J_B =$	$K_B =$	$J_A =$	$K_A =$

Step 6. State diagram:

Results and Conclusion:

EWB/MSM Troubleshooting:

Exp-20f1 Most likely problem: _____

Exp-20f2 Most likely problem: _____

Further Investigation Results:

Review Questions (TTL)

1. The counter used for half-stepping a motor in the example of Figure 20–1 has a state diagram sequence that is shown in Figure 20–2. Beginning with state 1, sketch the Q_D, Q_C, Q_B, and Q_A outputs on Plot 2. (HINT: An easy way to start is to write the binary number vertically where the waveform begins. This procedure is started as an example.)

Plot 2

2. How could you incorporate full decoding into the counter circuit shown in Figure 20–4?

3. Assume a problem exists with the counter shown in Figure 20–3. The counter is "locked-up" in state 3. What are two faults that can account for this problem?

Program Overview

Asynchronous counters require an external clock driving only the first flip-flop. Each successive flip-flop is clocked by the output of the preceding flip-flop. Synchronous counters require an external clock that drives all of the flip-flops simultaneously. In this VHDL implementation of a synchronous counter, notice in particular the clock signal description and how it differs from the asynchronous version.

The program for the counter will include decoders. In the VHDL implementation of the decoders, they will produce a high output when they are active (opposite of the TTL logic).

Procedure

Analysis of Synchronous Counters

1. Connect the project board to a computer as described in *Project Board Familiarization* and *VHDL Software Familiarization.*

2. Enter the program for the *JKFlipFlop* program shown in Figure 20–6 into the text editor. This is the same program you used in Experiment 17 to describe the gate logic of a J-K flip-flop. The counters you will investigate in this experiment treat the flip-flop as a VHDL **component.**

3. Save the program *JKFlipFlop* in a folder that you can access for later use in step 6. Compile the *JKFlipFlop* program to make sure there are no errors.

4. Examine the synchronous counter shown in Figure 20–3. Since there are two flip-flops, there are four possible output states. Analyze the sequence by the method illustrated in the Summary of Theory. Complete Table 20–4 in the report. From the table, draw the predicted state diagram in the space provided in the report.

5. In this step, you will implement the JK-CounterA program, which simulates the synchronous counter in Figure 20–3 except the decoders are AND gates in the VHDL program instead of NAND gates. Notice that the JKFlipFlop program is a subprogram for *JKCounterA.* Complete the program shown in Figure 20–7 of the report by entering the equations for the *J* and *K* inputs for flip-flops *FF0* and *FF1.*

6. Enter your completed program in the text editor. Because program *JKCounterA* uses *JK-FlipFlop* as a **component,** save it to the same folder as *JKFlipFlop.* Assign on-board switches and LEDs for *JKCounterA* as required, based on the inputs and outputs listed in the **entity** section of the program. The decoder outputs are S0, S1, etc.

7. Compile and download the *JKCounterA* program to the project board.

8. Test the program using a TTL-level pulse generator set to 10 kHz for the clock signal. If you have a logic analyzer available, it is a handy way to see the relative timing between the counter and state decoder outputs. If not, you can observe the outputs with a two-channel oscilloscope and establish the correct time relationship between all signals. The following procedure will guide you.

 a. Set up the scope to trigger on channel 1 with the Q_B signal (the slowest signal) viewed on that channel. If you are using an analog scope, do not use composite or vertical-mode triggering.
 b. View the pulse generator (clock) on channel 2. Adjust the frequency or SEC/DIV control so that each clock pulse coincides with a major division on the horizontal axis.
 c. Do not change the triggering on the Q_B signal on the triggering channel. Probe the Q_A output with channel 2. The observed signal will be in the proper relationship to the Q_B signal.
 d. You can move channel 2 to each of the decoder outputs and see the relationship to the Q_B signal.

Now on Plot 3 in the report, sketch the outputs of the flip-flops and decoders in the proper time relationship to each other.

9. Looking at the waveforms you have drawn in step 8, check that your predicted state diagram is correct. As an extra check, you can slow the clock to 1 Hz and verify the sequence with the LEDs.

10. Figure 20–8 shows a VHDL program entitled *JKCounterB.* From the program, read and enter the logic for the J-K inputs in Table 20–5 in the report. Using the method described in the Summary of Theory, complete the table.

11. From the data in Table 20–5, draw the state diagram for the counter. Account for all possible states, including unused states. If you correctly account for the unused states, you will see that all unused states return to state 2.

12. Enter the program *JKCounterB* into the text editor. Assign pins for the inputs and outputs required, based on the inputs and outputs listed in the **entity** section of the program. Compile and download your program to verify your predicted state diagram.

For Further Investigation

A unique TTL logic circuit is shown in Figure 20–5. The VHDL implementation of this circuit is shown in Figure 20–9. The output is connected in a rather unusual way directly to a seven-segment display. You are challenged to figure out the sequence of letters that will be on the display. Here is your clue: It is an English word that has something to do with detective work. (You get the other clue when you build the circuit.) If you give up, enter the VHDL program and use the on-board seven-segment display to find the answer. Notice that the Reset input on the circuit is equivalent to *Clr* in the program. Good Luck!

Report for Experiment 20

Name: _____ Date: _____ Class: _____

Data and Observations:

FIGURE 20–6

```
library IEEE;
use IEEE.std_logic_1164.all;

entity JKFlipFlop is
  port (J, K, Clr, Pre, Clock: in std_logic;
        Q, QNot: inout std_logic);
end entity JKFlipFlop;

architecture JKBehavior of JKFlipFlop is
begin
  process (J, K, Clr, Pre, Clock) is
  begin
    if Clr = '0' then Q <= '0'; QNot <= '1';   -- Clear
    elsif Pre = '0' then Q <= '1'; QNot <= '0'; -- Preset
    elsif clock = '0' and clock'event then      -- Clock Driven J-K
      if J = '1' and K = '0' then
        Q <= '1';
        QNot <= '0';
      elsif J = '0' and K = '1' then
        Q <= '0';
        QNot <= '1';
      elsif J = '1' and K = '1' then
        if Q = '1' then
          Q <= '0';
          QNot <= '1';
        else
          Q <= '1';
          QNot<= '0';
        end if;
      end if;
    end if;
  end process;
end architecture JKBehavior ;
```

FIGURE 20–7

```
library IEEE;
use IEEE.std_logic_1164.all;

entity JKCounterA is
  port( Clr, Pre, Clock: in std_logic;
        QA, QB, S0, S1, S2, S3: inout std_logic);
end entity JKCounterA;

architecture Counter of JKCounterA is
signal QANot, QBNot, High: std_logic;

component JKFlipFlop is
  port( J,K,Clr,Pre,Clock: in std_logic;
        Q,QNot: inout std_logic);
end component JKFlipFlop2;

begin
  High <= '1';
  FF0: JKFlipFlop port map (J=>      ,K=>      ,Clr=>Clr,Pre=>Pre,Clock=>Clock,Q=>QA, QNot=>QANot);
  FF1: JKFlipFlop port map (J=>      ,K=>      ,Clr=>Clr,Pre=>Pre,Clock=>Clock,Q=>QB, QNot=>QBNot);
  S0 <= QANot and QBNot;
  S1 <= QA and QBNot;
  S2 <= QANot and QB;
  S3 <= QA and QB;
end architecture Counter;
```

> Complete the J and K assignments
> for flip-flop for FF0 and FF1.

TABLE 20–4
Analysis of synchronous counter.

Outputs		Inputs			
Q_B	Q_A	$J_B =$	$K_B =$	$J_A =$	$K_A =$

Step 4. State diagram:

Q_A:

Q_B:

S_0:

S_1:

S_2:

S_3:

Plot 3

```
library IEEE;
use IEEE.std_logic_1164.all;

entity JKCounterB is
   port (Clr, Pre, Clock: in std_logic;
         QA, QB, QC, S0, S1, S2, S3: inout std_logic);
end entity JKCounterB;

architecture Counter of JKCounterB is
signal QANot, QBNot, QCNot, High: std_logic;

component JKFlipFlop is
   port (J, K, Clr, Pre, Clock: in std_logic;
         Q, QNot: inout std_logic);
end component JKFlipFlop;

begin
   High <= '1';
   FF0: JKFlipFlop port map (J=>QCNot,K=>Clr,Clr=>Clr,Pre=>Pre,Clock=>Clock,Q=>QA, QNot=>QANot);
   FF1: JKFlipFlop port map (J=>Pre,K=>QANot,Clr=>Clr,Pre=>Pre,Clock=>Clock,Q=>QB, QNot=>QBNot);
   FF2: JKFlipFlop port map (J=>QBNot,K=>Clr,Clr=>Clr,Pre=>Pre,Clock=>Clock,Q=>QC, QNot=>QCNot);
   S0 <= QANot and QBNot;
   S1 <= QA and QBNot;
   S2 <= QANot and QB;
   S3 <= QA and QB;
end architecture Counter;
```

FIGURE 20–8

TABLE 20–5
Analysis of synchronous counter shown in Figure 20–5.

Outputs	Inputs					
Q_C Q_B Q_A	$J_C =$	$K_C =$	$J_B =$	$K_B =$	$J_A =$	$K_A =$

Step 11. State diagram:

Results and Conclusion:

For Further Investigation:

```vhdl
library IEEE;
use IEEE.std_logic_1164.all;

entity MysteryCounter is
  port (Clr, Clock: in std_logic;
        a, b, c, d, e, f, g : out std_logic);
end entity MysteryCounter;

architecture Behavior of MysteryCounter is
signal QA, QB, QC, QANot, QBNot, QCNot, High, NPre, NClr: std_logic;
component JKFlipFlop is
  port (J,K,Clr,Pre,Clock: in std_logic;
        Q,QNot: inout std_logic);
end component JKFlipFlop;

begin
  High <= '1';
  FF0: JKFlipFlop port map (J=>QB,    K=>QA    ,Clr=>Clr  ,Pre=>High,Clock=>Clock,Q=>QA, QNot=>QANot);
  FF1: JKFlipFlop port map (J=>QCNot,K=>QANot,Clr=>Clr  ,Pre=>High,Clock=>Clock,Q=>QB, QNot=>QBNot);
  FF2: JKFlipFlop port map (J=>QB,    K=>QANot,Clr=>High,Pre=>Clr  ,Clock=>Clock,Q=>Qc, QNot=>QCNot);
  a <= not Clr or (QA and QC);
  b <= not QBNot;
  c <= not QBNot;
  d <= '1'; e <= '1'; f <= '1';
  g <= not QANot;
end architecture Behavior;
```

FIGURE 20–9

Review Questions (VHDL)

1. What hardware changes are required to change an asynchronous counter application in VHDL to a synchronous version?

2. Assume you have an application that requires three identical stepper motors, driven by a PLD. Looking at the logic in Figure 20–1, how would you go about implementing the design?

21

Design of Synchronous Counters

Objectives

After completing this experiment, you will be able to
- ☐ Design a synchronous counter with up to 16 states in any selected order.
- ☐ Implement and test the counter. Determine the state diagram of the counter.
- ☐ Implement logic for a decoder.

Reference Reading

Floyd, *Digital Fundamentals with VHDL,* Chapter 9, "Counters"

Materials Needed (TTL)

Two 74LS76 dual J-K flip-flops
7408 quad AND gate or other SSI ICs determined by student

For Further Investigation:
74LS139A dual 2-to-4 line decoder Six LEDs

Materials Needed (VHDL)

Project Board

Summary of Theory

The design of a synchronous counter begins with a description of the state diagram that specifies the required sequence. All states in the main sequence should be shown; states that are not in the main sequence should be shown only if the design requires these unused states to return to the main sequence in a specified way. If the sequence can be obtained from an already existing IC, this is almost always more economical and simpler than designing a special sequence.

From the state diagram, a next-state table is constructed. This procedure is illustrated with the example in Figure 21–1 for a simple counter and again in Figure 21–3 for a more complicated design. Notice in Figure 21–1 that the next state table is just another way of showing the information contained in the state diagram. The advantage of the table is that the changes made by each flip-flop going from one state to the next state are clearly seen.

The third step is to observe the transitions (changes) in each state. The required logic to force these changes will be mapped onto a Karnaugh map. In this case, the Karnaugh map takes on a different meaning than it did in combinational logic but it is read the same way.* Each square on the map represents a state of the counter. In effect, the counter sequence is just moving from square to square on the Karnaugh map at each clock pulse. To find the logic that will force the necessary change in the flip-flop outputs, look at the transition table for the J-K flip-flop, shown as Table 21–1. Notice that all possible output *transitions* are listed first; then the inputs that cause these changes are given. The transition table contains a number of X's (don't cares) because of the

*This type of Karnaugh map may be more properly termed a Karnaugh state map.

Assume you need to design a counter that counts 0–1–3–2 and stays in state 2 until a reset button is pressed. Two flip-flops are required. Let Q_B = MSB and Q_A = LSB. Use a J-K flip-flop.

Step 1: Draw a state diagram.

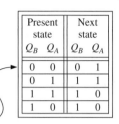

Step 2: Draw next-state table.

Present state		Next state	
Q_B	Q_A	Q_B	Q_A
0	0	0	1
0	1	1	1
1	1	1	0
1	0	1	0

Step 3: Determine inputs required for each flip-flop.
  (a) Read present state 00 on next-state table.
  (b) Note that Q_B does not change $0 \rightarrow 0$ (present to next state) and Q_A changes from $0 \rightarrow 1$.
  (c) Read the required inputs to cause these results from transition Table 21-1.
  (d) Map each input from transition table onto Karnaugh map.

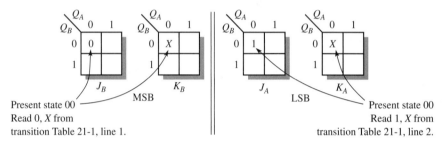

Present state 00
Read 0, X from
transition Table 21-1, line 1.

MSB   LSB

Present state 00
Read 1, X from
transition Table 21-1, line 2.

  (e) Complete maps.

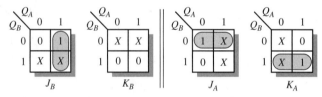

  (f) Read minimum logic from each map.

$$J_B = Q_A, \qquad K_B = 0, \qquad J_A = \overline{Q_B}, \qquad K_A = Q_B$$

Step 4: Draw circuit and check.

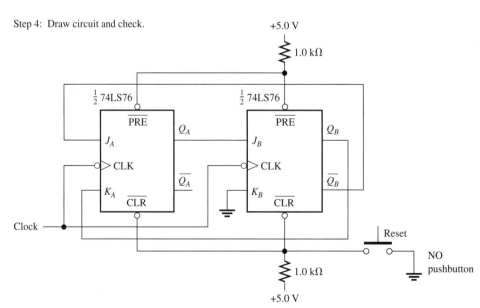

FIGURE 21–1

TABLE 21–1

Transition table for J-K flip-flop.

Output Transitions		Inputs	
Q_N	Q_{N+1}	J_N	K_N
0 $\rightarrow$ 0		0	X
0 $\rightarrow$ 1		1	X
1 $\rightarrow$ 0		X	1
1 $\rightarrow$ 1		X	0

Q_N = output before clock
Q_{N+1} = output after clock
J_N, K_N = inputs required to cause transition
X = don't care

versatility of the J-K flip-flop, as explained in the text. The data from the transition table are entered onto the Karnaugh maps as illustrated.

When the maps are completed, the logic can be read from the map. This logic is then used to set up the circuit as shown in Step 4. It is a good idea to check the design by verifying that the count sequence is correct and that there are no lock-up states. (A lock-up state is one that does not return to the main sequence of the counter.) The design check can be done by completing a table such as Table 20–1 in the last experiment.

The design procedure just described can be extended to more complicated designs. In Experiment 20 a counter was shown (Figure 20–1) that generates the required waveforms for half-stepping a stepper motor. This counter produces the state sequence shown in Figure 21–2(a). This sequence can be drawn as a series of four waveforms required by the stepper motor as shown in Figure 21–2(b).

The design method described here is not the only way to obtain the desired sequence, but it does lead to a fairly straightforward design. Figure 21–3 illustrates the detailed procedure for designing this circuit. Note that only the main sequence is shown in the state diagram and on the next-state table. The reason for this is that the unused states will show up as extra "don't cares" in the logic, making the design simpler. All unused states are entered on the maps as "don't cares." After reading the logic equations for the inputs to each flip-flop, the design is checked for lock-up problems. Corrections are made to prevent lock up by examining the "don't-care" logic and changing it if required. The maps for the A and B flip-flops are not shown in Figure 21–3, but left as a student exercise in Question 1 of the Review Questions.

As you can see in Figure 21–3, the steps for the more complicated counter are basically the same as those used in Figure 21–1. The unused states allow the counter to be designed with a minimum of additional logic. The completed design is shown in Figure 20–1; it is the same circuit that was analyzed in Experiment 20.

Pre-lab Questions

1. **a.** When a Karnaugh map is used to design a counter, what does each square on the map represent?
   b. When are X's entered in these squares?
2. Why is it important to find out where unused states go in a counter design?

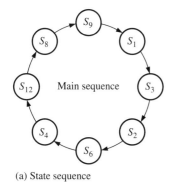

(a) State sequence

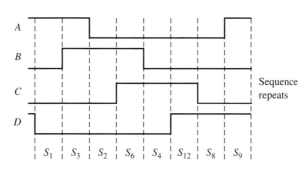

(b) Waveform representation of state sequence

FIGURE 21–2

Step 1: Draw the required state diagram. (Note that only the main sequence is shown as the unused states are not important in this problem.)

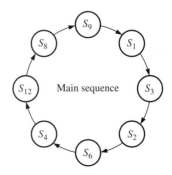

Step 2: Draw the next-state table. Four flip-flops are required because of the number of bits used in the sequence.

Present state				Next state			
Q_D	Q_C	Q_B	Q_A	Q_D	Q_C	Q_B	Q_A
0	0	0	1	0	0	1	1
0	0	1	1	0	0	1	0
0	0	1	0	0	1	1	0
0	1	1	0	0	1	0	0
0	1	0	0	1	1	0	0
1	1	0	0	1	0	0	0
1	0	0	0	1	0	0	1
1	0	0	1	0	0	0	1

Step 3: Using the next-state and transition tables, draw the Karnaugh maps for each flip-flop. For example, in state 1, note that Q_D and Q_C do not change in going to the next state. The transition is $0 \rightarrow 0$. From the transition table, a $0 \rightarrow 0$ transition requires $J = 0$ and $K = X$. These values are entered onto the maps for the D and C counters in the square that represents state 1. Unused states are mapped as Xs. Only the D and C maps are shown in this example.

(Note: Q_B and Q_A are positioned to make the map below easier to read.)

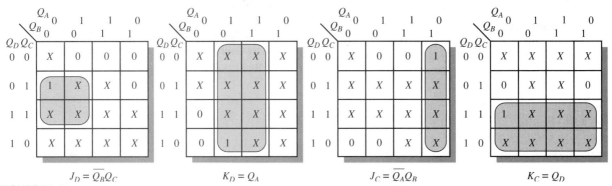

FIGURE 21–3

TTL

Procedure

1. A Gray code synchronous counter is often used in state machine design. This problem requires a six-state Gray code counter. The usual Gray code sequence is not used because the sixth state would not be "Gray" when the counter returns to zero. Instead, the sequence shown in Figure 21–4 is required. There are two unused states: state 5 and state

7. For the initial design, these states are not shown. Complete the next-state table (Table 21–2) in the report for the main sequence shown here.

2. Using the transition table for the J-K flip-flop, complete the Karnaugh maps shown in the report. The J-K transition table (Table 21–1) is repeated in the report as Table 21–3 for convenience.

3. Read the required logic expressions from each map that you completed in step 2. Check that the unused states return to the main sequence. If they do not, modify the design to assure that they do

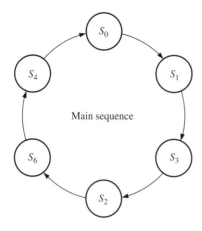

FIGURE 21–4
Required sequence for Gray code counter.

return. Then, construct and test your circuit. You can check the state sequence with an oscilloscope or a logic analyzer. Summarize the results of your test in your report.

For Further Investigation

A decoded output is needed for the counter you designed. Unfortunately, the only decoder IC that engineering has available for decoding is a 2-line to 4-line 74LS139A decoder! Show how you could connect this IC to obtain full decoding of the output. Then construct the circuit and put a separate LED on each output so that only one LED lights as the counter goes around. (*Hint:* Consider how you could use the enable inputs of the 74LS139A.)

TTL

Report for Experiment 21

Name: _____ Date: _____ Class: _____

Data and Observations:

TABLE 21–2

Present State			Next State		
Q_C	Q_B	Q_A	Q_C	Q_B	Q_A
0	0	0			
0	0	1			
0	1	1			
0	1	0			
1	1	0			
1	0	0			

TABLE 21–3
Transition table for J-K flip-flop (repeated for reference).

Output Transitions			Inputs	
Q_N		Q_{N+1}	J_N	K_N
0	$\rightarrow$	0	0	X
0	$\rightarrow$	1	1	X
1	$\rightarrow$	0	X	1
1	$\rightarrow$	1	X	0

Q_N = output before clock

Q_{N+1} = output after clock

J_N, K_N = inputs required to cause transition

X = don't care

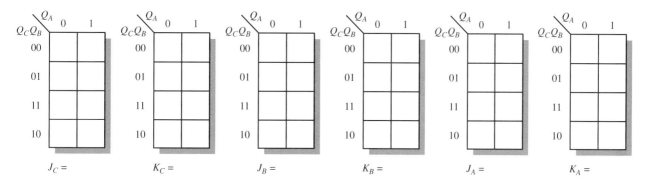

$J_C =$ $K_C =$ $J_B =$ $K_B =$ $J_A =$ $K_A =$

Circuit Design:

Results and Conclusion:

Further Investigation Results:

Review Questions (TTL)

1. Complete the design of the sequential counter in Figure 21–3 by constructing Karnaugh maps for the *B* and *A* flip-flops. Read the maps. As a check, you can compare your result with the circuit drawn in Figure 20–1.

2. Assume you wanted to change the circuit from this experiment to be able to reverse the sequence. How would you go about this?

3. Assume you wanted to trigger a one-shot (74121) whenever the circuit you designed went into state 2 or state 4. Explain how you could do this.

Program Overview

The program in this experiment is a six-state Gray code synchronous counter. Both asynchronous and synchronous counters can be directly implemented in VHDL using a common flip-flop description from a subprogram. An advantage to VHDL counters is that they can easily be modified for a different sequence or new feature without having to physically rewire a circuit. In the Further Investigation section, you will make a simple modification of the counter in this experiment by adding a decoder with an interesting output.

Procedure

1. Connect the project board to a computer as described in *Project Board Familiarization.*

2. A Gray code synchronous counter is often used in a state machine design. This problem requires a six-state Gray code counter. The usual Gray code sequence is not used because the sixth state would not be "Gray" when the counter returns to zero. Instead, the sequence shown in Figure 21–4 is required. There are two unused states: state 5 and state 7. For the initial design, these states are not shown. Complete the next-state table in the report (Table 21–4) for the main sequence shown in Figure 21–4.

3. Using the transition table for the J-K flip-flop, complete the Karnaugh maps shown in the report. The J-K transition table (Table 21–5) is repeated in the report for convenience.

4. Read the required logic expressions from each map that you complete in step 3. Check that the unused states return to the main sequence. If they do not, modify the design to assure that they do return.

The Gray Code Program

5. Enter the program *JKFlipFlop* as shown in the program listing in Figure 21–5 into the text editor. This is essentially the same program* you used in Experiment 17 to describe the gate logic of a J-K flip-flop and is used as a **component** in the program in step 7. Compile the program to assure there are no errors. Recall that to use a program as a **component** you must save it to the same folder as the program that calls it.

6. Using the J and K expressions obtained from the Karnaugh maps in the report, complete the equations for the program titled *GrayCode* shown in Figure 21–6 and enter your program into the text editor. The A flip-flop (FF0) has been completed as an example.

7. Assign a global clock input for the *clock* signal, which will be furnished by a TTL pulse generator. Set the generator to a frequency of 1 Hz. Use a switch to control the *clr* input. Assign the program outputs listed in the **entity** section of the program to LEDs for monitoring.

8. Compile and download your GrayCode program to the project board.

9. Test your program by observing the output LEDs. The Gray-code sequence should be observed. Summarize the results of your test in the report.

For Further Investigation

This investigation adds a decoder feature to your GrayCode program. Using combinational logic, complete the decoding logic in the program shown in Figure 21–7 to light separate LEDs A through F as the counter goes through its sequence. Modify your existing program by adding this new feature.

---

*The *ClkMon* is not needed here.

Report for Experiment 21

Name: _____ Date: _____ Class: _____

Data and Observations:

TABLE 21–4

Present State			Next State		
Q_C	Q_B	Q_A	Q_C	Q_B	Q_A
0	0	0			
0	0	1			
0	1	1			
0	1	0			
1	1	0			
1	0	0			

TABLE 21–5

Transition table for J-K flip-flop (repeated for reference).

Output Transitions			Inputs	
Q_N		Q_{N+1}	J_N	K_N
0	→	0	0	X
0	→	1	1	X
1	→	0	X	1
1	→	1	X	0

Q_N = output before clock

Q_{N+1} = output after clock

J_N, K_N = inputs required to cause transition

X = don't care

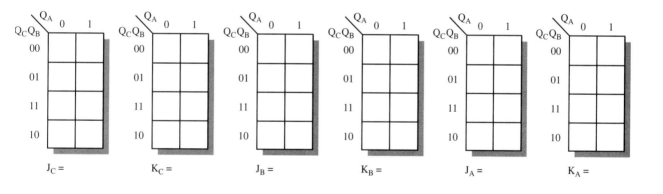

J_C =   K_C =   J_B =   K_B =   J_A =   K_A =

```
library IEEE;
use IEEE.std_logic_1164.all;

entity JKFlipFlop is
  port (J, K, Clr, Pre, Clock: in std_logic;
        Q, QNot: inout std_logic);
end entity JKFlipFlop;

architecture JKBehavior of JKFlipFlop is
begin
  process (J, K, Clr, Pre, Clock) is
  begin
    if Clr = '0' then Q <= '0'; QNot <= '1';   -- Clear
    elsif Pre = '0' then Q <= '1'; QNot <= '0'; -- Preset
    elsif clock = '0' and clock'event then     -- Clock Driven J-K
      if J = '1' and K = '0' then
        Q <= '1';
        QNot <= '0';
      elsif J = '0' and K = '1' then
        Q <= '0';
        QNot <= '1';
      elsif J = '1' and K = '1' then
        if Q = '1' then
          Q <= '0';
          QNot <= '1';
        else
          Q <= '1';
          QNot<= '0';
        end if;
      end if;
    end if;
  end process;
end architecture JKBehavior ;
```

FIGURE 21–5

```
library IEEE;
use IEEE.std_logic_1164.all;

entity GrayCode is
  port (clock, clr: in std_logic;
        QA, QB, QC: inout std_logic);
end entity GrayCode;

architecture GrayCodeBehavior of GrayCode is
signal QANot, QBNot, QCNot, Pre : std_logic;
signal JC, JB, JA, KC, KB, KA: std_logic;

component JKFlipFlop is
  port (J, K, Clr, Pre, Clock: in std_logic;
        Q, QNot: inout std_logic);
end component JKFlipFlop;
begin
  Pre <= '0';
  JA <= QBNot and QCNot;    KA <= QB;      ┐
  JB <=                     KB <=          ├  ⌐ Complete the equations ⌐
  JC <=              ;      KC <=          ┘
  FF0: JKFlipFlop port map (J=>JA,K=>KA, Clr=>Clr,Pre=>Pre,Clock=>clock,Q=>QA, QNot=>QANot);
  FF1: JKFlipFlop port map (J=>JB,K=>KB, Clr=>Clr,Pre=>Pre,Clock=>clock,Q=>QB, QNot=>QBNot);
  FF2: JKFlipFlop port map (J=>JC,K=>KC, Clr=>Clr,Pre=>Pre,Clock=>clock,Q=>QC, QNot=>QCNot);
end architecture GrayCodeBehavior;
```

FIGURE 21–6

272

Results and Conclusion:

Further Investigation Results:

```
library IEEE;
use IEEE.std_logic_1164.all;

entity Lab21Fl is
  port (clock,clr: in std_logic;
        QA, QB, QC, A, B, C, D, E, F: inout std_logic);
end entity Lab21Fl;

architecture GrayCode of Lab21Fl is
signal QANot, QBNot, QCNot, Pre: std_logic;
signal JC, JB, JA, KC, KB, KA: std_logic;

component JKFlipFlop is
  port (J, K, Clr, Pre, Clock: in std_logic;
        Q, QNot: inout std_logic);
end component JKFlipFlop;
begin
  Pre <= '0';
  JA <= QBNot and QCNot;   KA <= QB;
  JB <=                    KB <=
  JC <=            ;       KC <=
  FF0: JKFlipFlop2 port map (J=>JA,K=>KA, Clr=>Clr, Pre=>Pre, Clock=>clock, Q=>QA, QNot=>QANot);
  FF1: JKFlipFlop2 port map (J=>JB,K=>KB, Clr=>Clr, Pre=>Pre, Clock=>clock, Q=>QB, QNot=>QBNot);
  FF2: JKFlipFlop2 port map (J=>JC,K=>KC, Clr=>Clr, Pre=>Pre, Clock=>clock, Q=>QC, QNot=>QCNot);

  A <= QANot and QBNot and QCNot;
  B <=
  C <=
  D <=
  E <=
  F <=
end architecture GrayCode;
```

FIGURE 21–7

Review Questions (VHDL)

1. In the VHDL experiment, the flip-flop subprogram used signal definitions for the interconnection of flip-flop stages. Compare VHDL **signals** for connecting the virtual flip-flops to the methods you would use on a protoboard.

2. Does the process for designing a VHDL synchronous counter differ from the TTL design methods?

3. What are the advantages of implementing a counter using VHDL?

22

The Traffic Light Controller

Objectives

After completing this experiment, you will be able to
☐ Complete the design of a sequential counter that is controlled by input variables.
☐ Construct and test the circuit from the first objective.

Reference Reading

Floyd, *Digital Fundamentals with VHDL,* Chapter 9, "Counters"

Materials Needed (TTL)

7408 quad AND gate
7474 dual D flip-flop
74121 one-shot
74LS153 dual data selector
One 150 μF capacitor
Two LEDs
Resistors: two 330 Ω, six 1.0 kΩ, one to be determined by student

Materials Needed (VHDL)

Project Board

Summary of Theory

A synchronous counter forms the heart of many small digital systems. The traffic light controller that was introduced in Experiments 13 and 18 uses a small synchronous counter to represent each of the four possible "states" that the output can take. The block diagram of the system was given in Figure 13–4. Unlike the counters in Experiment 21, the state of the counter in the traffic light controller is determined by three input variables and two state variables. When certain conditions of these variables are met, the counter advances to the next state. The three input variables are defined as follows:

> Vehicle on side street = V_s
> 25 s timer (long timer) is on = T_L
> 4 s timer (short timer) is on = T_S

A complemented variable indicates the opposite condition. A state diagram, introduced in the text, is repeated in Figure 22–1 for reference. Based on this state diagram, the sequential operation is described as follows:

1st state: The counter shows the Gray code 00, representing main-green, side-red. It will stay in the first state if the long timer is on *or* if there is no vehicle on the side street $(T_L + \overline{V}_s)$. It will go to the second state if the long timer is off *and* there is a vehicle on the side street $(\overline{T}_L V_s)$.

2nd state: The counter shows 01, representing main-yellow, side-red. It will stay in the second state if the short timer is on (T_S). It will go to the third state if the short timer is off $(\overline{T}_S)$.

3rd state: The counter shows 11, representing main-red, side-green. It will stay in the third

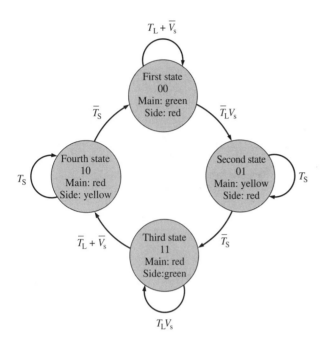

FIGURE 22–1
State diagram.

state if the long timer is on *and* there is a vehicle on the side street ($T_L V_s$). It will go to the fourth state if the long timer is off *or* there is no vehicle on the side street ($\overline{T}_L + \overline{V}_s$).

4th state: The counter shows 10, representing main-red, side-yellow. It will stay in the fourth state if the short timer is on (T_S). It will go to first state if the short timer is off ($\overline{T}_S$).

The block diagram in Figure 22–2 further defines the sequential logic. The input logic block consists of two data selectors to route the three input variables (V_s, T_L, and T_S) to the flip-flops. This is shown in more detail in the partially completed schematic shown in the report as Figure 22–4. The data selectors (DS-0 and DS-1) are the 74LS153

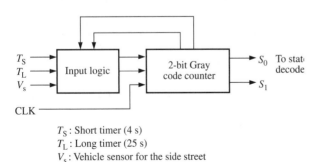

T_S: Short timer (4 s)
T_L: Long timer (25 s)
V_s: Vehicle sensor for the side street

FIGURE 22–2
Block diagram of the sequential logic.

276

chips. The line selected (C_0 through C_3) is determined by the present state (because the flip-flop outputs are connected to the select inputs). Notice the similarity of this idea to that shown in Experiment 12 for implementing combinational logic with a MUX.

In this experiment, you will expand on the traffic light system investigated earlier. To make our simulation more realistic, it will be helpful to have the short timer working either as hardware from Experiment 18 (TTL) or as software from Experiment 14 (VHDL). From the next-state table, it can be seen that the short timer should be ON in the second and fourth states (Gray codes 01 and 10). Triggering will be set up so that the short timer will trigger on the trailing edge of the clock, causing it to start in any state. The trailing edge is used for triggering the short timer because the outputs change on the leading edge. This avoids a "race" condition where the clock and states change together. The triggering for this experiment is shown in Figure 22–3.

The present state–next state table with input conditions is shown in Table 22–1 of the report. Each pair of lines in Table 22–1 represents the two possible states that the counter could assume. For example, on the first pair of lines, the counter is in the first state (Gray code 00) and could either stay in the first state (Gray code 00) or go to the second state (Gray

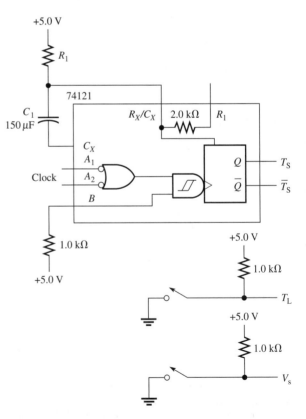

FIGURE 22–3

code 01), depending on the long timer and vehicle sensor inputs. Notice that in the first state (Gray code 00), the next state for Q_1 requires that it remain a 0 *no matter what the inputs do,* so a 0 is entered for the product term for data selector-1 (DS-1). On the other hand, Q_0 will be a 1 *only* if the long timer is LOW (timed out) *and* the vehicle sensor is HIGH (vehicle waiting). Thus, the input product term for DS-0 is $T_L V_s$. As one more example, notice that in the second state (Gray code 01), the next state for Q_0 will be a 1 *no matter what the inputs do,* so a 1 is entered in the table.

Pre-lab Questions

1. a. What two conditions are required for the counter to stay in the first state (Gray code 00)?
   b. Explain why a 0 is entered on Table 22–1 for the input product term for Data Selector-1 for the first state (Gray code 00).
2. Why was Gray code used for the counter?

TTL

Procedure

1. Review the Summary of Theory to be sure you understand the idea for the circuit. The present state–next state table with input conditions is shown in Table 22–1 of the report. Three of the inputs for the data selectors are completed as an example. Decide what to do with the remaining inputs and complete the remaining five inputs in Table 22–1.

2. From the inputs determined in Step 1, complete the schematic shown in Figure 22–4 of the report. Show the inputs to each data selector and the enable. Note that the select lines of the data selectors are connected to the outputs of the flip-flops.

3. To simulate the inputs, you *could* construct the one-shots and the oscillator from Experiment 18. However, to save time and board space, construct only the short timer shown in Figure 22–3. You will need to compute the value of R_1 in order to make a 4 s timer. Notice that the triggering of the short timer is different than in the full system for reasons of simplicity. The long timer and vehicle sensor are made

from SPST switches as shown in Figure 22–3. A "NOTed" variable, such as $\overline{T_L}$, is asserted when the switch is closed.

4. On the same protoboard as the short timer and the switches representing the long timer and vehicle sensor, add the sequential logic in Figure 22–4. The LEDs serve as state indicators. Connect all inputs in accordance with your design in Step 1. Set the pulse generator to 10 kHz.

5. The state diagram (Figure 22–1) will guide you through the inputs required for the sequence in order to test the circuit. Start by opening the long timer and vehicle sensor switches (both HIGH). Place the counter in the first state (Gray code 00) by placing a momentary ground on the $\overline{CLR}$ inputs. In this condition, a vehicle is assumed to be on the side street (because V_s is HIGH) but the long timer has not finished the cycle on the main street. Close the long timer switch. This should immediately cause the circuit to go into the second state (Gray code 01), and the 4 s short timer should take over. While the 4 s timer is on, open the long timer switch again. The circuit should switch by itself (after 4 s) to the third state (Gray code 11).

6. If you successfully arrived in the fourth state (Gray code 10), look at the state diagram and decide what steps need to be taken to return to the first state and remain there. Then, use the switches to move back to the first state. Summarize your results in the report.

For Further Investigation

Assume your boss wonders, "Can you simplify the traffic light controller if you eliminate the short timer and make the clock (pulse generator) operate at a period of 4 s? Does this have any advantages? Also, as a second idea, I noticed you triggered the short timer without using trigger logic, just the clock. Could you also trigger the long timer this way?"

Consider both of these ideas (after all, you shouldn't ignore the boss). Indicate the circuit modifications you would suggest in order to accomplish each. Try putting the first idea into effect by modifying the circuit and testing it again. Then write a short summary to the boss stating what you think of her idea.

Report for Experiment 22

Name: _____ Date: _____ Class: _____

Data and Observations:

TABLE 22–1

Present State		Next State		Input Conditions	Input Product Term for Data Selector-1	Input Product Term for Data Selector-0
Q_1	Q_0	Q_1	Q_0			
0	0	0	0	$T_L + \overline{V}_s$		
0	0	0	1	$\overline{T}_L V_s$	0	$\overline{T}_L V_s$
0	1	0	1	T_s		
0	1	1	1	$\overline{T}_s$		1
1	1	1	1	$T_L V_s$		
1	1	1	0	$\overline{T}_L + \overline{V}_s$		
1	0	1	0	T_s		
1	0	0	0	$\overline{T}_s$		

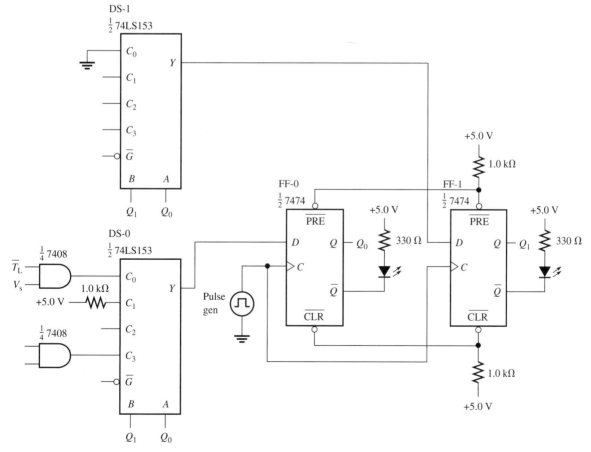

FIGURE 22–4

Results and Conclusion:

Further Investigation Results:

Review Questions (TTL)

1. Explain what modifications would be needed to make the traffic light controller cycle through eight states instead of four states.

2. The *B* input of the 74121 (Figure 22–3) was connected to a HIGH. Explain.

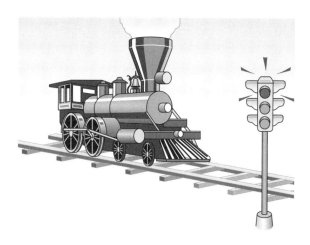

VHDL

Program Overview

The sequential logic for a traffic light consists of a 2-bit Gray code counter and associated logic for light delay timers and vehicle sensors. In this VHDL experiment, the use of a VHDL **case** statement will be used to implement the 2-bit Gray code instead of the flip-flops used in the TTL section. In the Further Investigation, a variable timer will be used, taking advantage of the flexibility of VHDL to allow for changes to the program timing. Finally, both the sequential logic and timer programs are combined as **components** in a complete traffic light system.

Procedure

1. Review the Summary of Theory to be sure you understand the idea for the logic. The present state/next state table with input conditions is shown in Table 22–2 of the report. Three of the inputs for the data selectors are completed as an example. Complete the remaining five inputs on Table 22–2.

2. From the inputs determined in Step 1, complete the program entitled *LightSequence* in Figure 22–5 for each input *S* for Gray code states 00, 01, 11, and 10 in the **case** statement portion of the code.

3. Connect the project board to a computer as described in the *Project Board Familiarization.*

4. Enter your completed program entitled *LightSequence* into the text editor. Assign on-board switches for the inputs *VS, TL,* and *TS.* Assign *Clock* to a global clock input pin. Assign *S* to two LEDs for logic monitoring.

5. Compile and download your program to the project board.

6. Test program *LightSequence* by entering each state from Table 22–2 and verify that the appropriate next state appears on the LEDs.

7. In this step, you will test the program *LightSequence.* The state diagram (Figure 22–1) will guide you through the inputs required for the sequence in order to test the circuit. Place the counter in the first state (Gray code 00) by setting the vehicle switch, *VS,* to HIGH and setting both *TL* and *TS* to a LOW. Press the *Clock* pushbutton repeatedly to cycle your program to the 00 state.

8. Set the short timer switch, *TS,* to a HIGH and press the *Clock* pushbutton. Pressing the *Clock* pushbutton will cause the circuit to go into the second state (Gray code 01) because *TL* is LOW and *VS*

is HIGH. The short timer *TS* should take over. Set *TS* to a LOW and press the *Clock* pushbutton again. The circuit should switch to the third state (Gray code 11).

9. Press the *Clock* pushbutton again. If you successfully arrive in the fourth state (Gray code 10), look at the state diagram and decide what steps need to be taken to return to the first state. Then, use the switches to move back to the first state. Summarize your results in the report.

10. In the remaining steps of this experiment, you will put together the complete traffic light system in a program called *TrafficLight,* modified from Experiment 13 and shown in Figure 22–6. *TrafficLight* will call the program *LightSequence* (from this experiment) and *Timer* (modified from Experiment 14) as **components**, so all three programs will need to be in the same folder before compiling them. The listing for *Timer* is repeated in Figure 22–7 for convenience.

11. Assign an on-board switch for the input *Vehicle.* Use a global clock input for a TTL pulse generator. Set the generator to a frequency of 10 Hz. (The frequency is not critical in this application). Assign two groups of three LEDs for the lights in *Main* and *Side.*

12. Compile and download your traffic light program.

13. Test your program by pressing the *Vehicle* pushbutton and observe that all light transitions occur properly. The traffic light is now ready for use on your model railroad!

For Further Investigation

In this investigation, you can implement the flashing feature that was introduced in Experiment 13. Modify your program by incorporating the boldface statements shown in Figure 22–8 into your program in the appropriate locations.

Report for Experiment 22

Name: _____ Date: _____ Class: _____

Data and Observations:

TABLE 22–2

Present State		Next State		Input Conditions	Input Product Term for Data Selector-1	Input Product Term for Data Selector-0
Q_1	Q_0	Q_1	Q_0			
0	0	0	0	$T_L + \overline{V}_s$	0	$\overline{T}_L V_s$
0	0	0	1	$\overline{T}_L V_s$		
0	1	0	1	T_S		1
0	1	1	1	$\overline{T}_S$		
1	1	1	1	$T_L V_s$		
1	1	1	0	$\overline{T}_L + \overline{V}_s$		
1	0	1	0	T_S		
1	0	0	0	$\overline{T}_S$		

```
library IEEE;
use IEEE.std_logic_1164.all;

entity LightSequence is
  port (VS, TL, Clock, TS: in std_logic;
  S : buffer std_logic_vector (1 downto 0));
end entity LightSequence;

architecture ControlBehavior of LightSequence is
begin
  process (VS, TL, Clock, TS)
  begin
    if Clock = '1' and Clock'event then
      case S is
        when "00" => if (TL = '1' or VS = '0')    then S <= "00"; elsif
                        (TL = '0' and VS = '1')  then S <= "01"; end if;
        when "01" => if (TS = '1')                then S <= "01"; elsif
                        (TS = '0')               then S <= "11"; end if;
        when "11" => if

        when "10" => if

        when others => S <= "00";
      end case;
    end if;
  end process;
end architecture ControlBehavior;
```

FIGURE 22–5

```vhdl
library IEEE;
use IEEE.std_logic_1164.all;

entity TrafficLight is
  port (clock, Vehicle: in std_logic;
        Main, Side: out std_logic_vector (0 to 2));
end entity TrafficLight;

architecture Behavior of TrafficLight is
type StatesType is (FirstState, SecondState, ThirdState, FourthState );
signal State, NextState: StatesType:= FirstState;
signal LongTime, ShortTime, Long, Short, Fout : std_logic;
signal SetCount: integer range 0 to 256;
signal S: std_logic_vector (1 downto 0);

component timer is
  port (Enable, clock: in std_logic;
        SetCount: in integer range 0 to 256;
        QOut: buffer std_logic);

end component timer;
component LightSequence is
  port (VS, TL, Clock, TS: in std_logic;
        S: out std_logic_vector (1 downto 0));
end component LightSequence;

begin
  clock1: process (S) is
  begin
    case S is
      when "00" => state <= FirstState;
      when "01" => state <= SecondState;
      when "11" => state <= ThirdState;
      when "10" => state <= FourthState;
      when others => state <= FirstStateZero;
    end case;
  end process clock1;

  StateDiag: process (state, clock) is
  begin
    case state is
      when FirstState =>
        Main <= "001";
        Side <= "100";
        SetCount <= 250;-- 25 Second Timer
        LongTime <= '1';
        ShortTime <= '0';
      when SecondState =>
        Main <= "010";
        Side <= "100";
        SetCount <= 40;-- 4 Second Timer
        LongTime <= '0';
        ShortTime <= '1';
      when ThirdState =>
        Main <= "100";
        Side <= "001";
        SetCount <= 250;-- 25 Second Timer
        LongTime <= '1';
        ShortTime <= '0';
      when FourthState =>
        Main <= "100";
        Side <= "010";
        SetCount <= 40;-- 4 Second Timer
        LongTime <= '0';
        ShortTime <= '1';
      end case;
    end process StateDiag;
  SQ: LightSequence port map (VS=>Vehicle, TL=>Long,Clock=>clock, TS=>Short, S=>S);
  TL: timer port map (Enable=>LongTime, clock=>clock, SetCount=>SetCount, QOut=>Long);
  TS: timer port map (Enable=>ShortTime, clock=>clock, SetCount=>SetCount, QOut=>Short);
 end architecture Behavior;
```

FIGURE 22–6

```
library IEEE;
use IEEE.std_logic_1164.all;

entity timer is
  port (Enable, clock: in std_logic;
        SetCount: in integer range 0 to 256;
        QOut: buffer std_logic);
end entity timer;

architecture TimerCounter of timer is
begin
  process (Enable, clock)
  variable cnt: integer range 0 to 256;
  variable flag: boolean;
  begin
    flag := true;
    if (clock'event and clock = '1') then
      if Enable = '0' then
        flag := false; cnt := 0; Qout <= '1';
      end if;
      if cnt = SetCount then
        Qout <= '0'; flag := false;
        cnt := 1;
      else
        cnt := cnt + 1;
      end if;
    end if;
  end process;
end architecture TimerCounter;
```

FIGURE 22–7

Further Investigation Results:

```
entity TrafficLight is
  port ( clock, Vehicle, Flash : in std_logic;
         Main, Side: out std_logic_vector (0 to 2));
end entity TrafficLight;

clock1: process (S) is
begin
  if Flash = '1' then
    State <= SecondState;
  else
    case S is
      when "00" => State <= FirstState;
      when "01" => State <= SecondState;
      when "11" => State <= ThirdState;
      when "10" => State <= FourthState;
      when others => state <= FirstState;
    end case;
  end if;
end process clock1;

when SecondState =>
  SetCount <= 40;-- 4 Second Timer
  if Flash = '1' then
    LongTime <= '0'; -- Set Long Timer off
    ShortTime <= '0'; -- Set Short Timer off
    if Clock = '1' then
      Main <= "010";
      Side <= "100";
    else
      Main <= "000";
      Side <= "000";
    end if;
  else
    Main <= "010";
    Side <= "100";
    LongTime <= '0'; -- Set Long Timer off
    ShortTime <= '1'; -- Set Short Timer on
  end if;
```

FIGURE 22–8

285

Review Questions (VHDL)

1. In the VHDL program *LightSequence,* a **case** statement was used to sequence the program from one state to the next using the 2-bit input S. Explain the modifications required to allow the program to sequence through 8 states instead of 4.

2. What would be the advantage of a variable count timer in the traffic light application?

23

Shift Register Counters

Objectives

After completing this experiment, you will be able to
- ☐ Test two recirculating shift register counters.
- ☐ From oscilloscope measurements, draw the timing diagram for the two shift register counters.

Reference Reading

Floyd, *Digital Fundamentals with VHDL,* Chapter 10, "Shift Registers"

Materials Needed (TTL)

74195 4-bit shift register
7400 quad NAND gate
7493A counter
7474 D flip-flop
7486 quad exclusive OR
Four-position DIP switch
Four LEDs
Resistors: four 330 Ω, six 1.0 kΩ
Two N.O. pushbuttons (optional)

Materials Needed (VHDL)

Project Board

Summary of Theory

A *shift register* is a series of flip-flops connected so that data can be transferred to a neighbor each time the clock pulse is active. An example is the display on your calculator. As numbers are entered on the keypad, the previously entered numbers are shifted to the left. Shift registers can be made to shift data to the left, to the right, or in either direction (bidirectional), using a control signal. They can be made from either D or J-K flip-flops. An example of a simple shift register made from D flip-flops is shown in Figure 23–1(a). The data are entered serially at the left and may be removed in either parallel or serial fashion. With some additional logic, the data may also be entered in parallel, as shown in Figure 23–1(b).

Shift registers are available in IC form with various bit lengths, loading methods, and shift directions. They are widely used to change data from serial form to parallel form, and vice versa. Other applications for shift registers include arithmetic operations in computers. To multiply any number by its base, you simply move the radix point one position to the left. To multiply a binary number by 2, the number is shifted to the left. For example, $7 \times 2 = 14$ in binary is $0111 \times 10 = 1110$. Note that the original number 0111 is shifted by one position to the left. Conversely, division by 2 is represented by a right shift.

Another application of the shift register is as a digital waveform generator. Generally, a waveform generator requires feedback—that is, the output of the register is returned to the input and recirculated. Two important waveform generators are the Johnson (or "twisted-ring") counter and the ring counter. The names can be easily associated with the correct circuit if the circuits are drawn in the manner shown in Figure 23–2. In this experiment, you will construct both of these counters using a 74195 4-bit shift register.

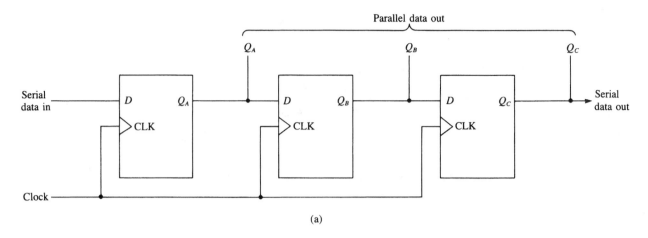

(a)

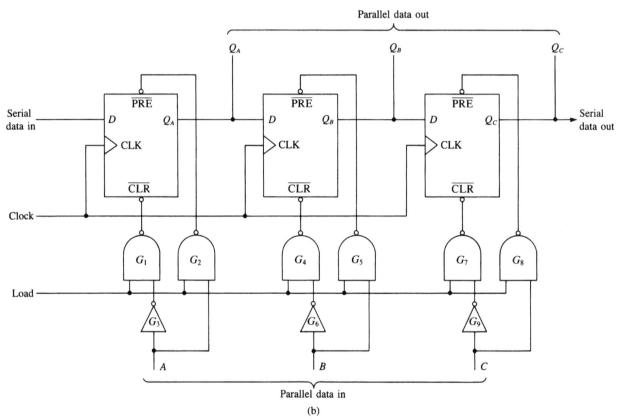

(b)

FIGURE 23–1
Shift registers made from D flip-flops.

The ring counter will then be used to generate a bit stream that can be used for various applications.

The 74195 function table is in the manufacturer's data sheet and is reproduced in Table 23–1 for convenience. The first input listed on the table is an asynchronous $\overline{\text{CLEAR}}$. Next is a parallel SHIFT/ $\overline{\text{LOAD}}$ function on one pin. Assertion level logic is shown to define that a HIGH causes the register to SHIFT from Q_A toward Q_D at the next clock edge,

and a LOW causes the register to $\overline{\text{LOAD}}$ at the next clock edge. The inputs A through D are used only when the register is loaded in parallel (also called a *broadside load*). Notice that the internal register portion of the 74195 is shown with S-R flip-flops, but the serial inputs to the leftmost flip-flop are labeled as J and $\overline{K}$. These inputs function the same as the inputs to an ordinary J-K flip-flop, except the K input is inverted.

288

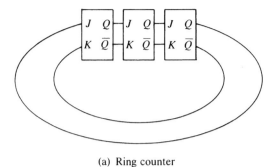
(a) Ring counter

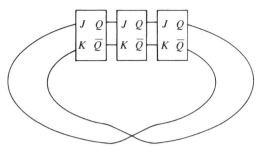
(b) Twisted-ring counter (Johnson counter)

FIGURE 23–2
Shift register counters drawn to emphasize their names. These circuits were drawn with J-K flip-flops but can be constructed from other flip-flops as well. The CLK, $\overline{PRE}$, and $\overline{CLR}$ inputs are not shown.

TABLE 23–1
Function table for 74195 4-bit shift register.

Inputs									Outputs				
	SHIFT/		SERIAL		PARALLEL								
CLEAR	LOAD	CLOCK	J	$\overline{K}$	A	B	C	D	Q_A	Q_B	Q_C	Q_D	$\overline{Q}_D$
L	X	X	X	X	X	X	X	X	L	L	L	L	H
H	L	↑	X	X	a	b	c	d	a	b	c	d	$\overline{d}$
H	H	L	X	X	X	X	X	X	Q_{A0}	Q_{B0}	Q_{C0}	Q_{D0}	$\overline{Q}_{D0}$
H	H	↑	L	H	X	X	X	X	Q_{A0}	Q_{A0}	Q_{Bn}	Q_{Cn}	$\overline{Q}_{Cn}$
H	H	↑	L	L	X	X	X	X	L	Q_{An}	Q_{Bn}	Q_{Cn}	$\overline{Q}_{Cn}$
H	H	↑	H	H	X	X	X	X	H	Q_{An}	Q_{Bn}	Q_{Cn}	$\overline{Q}_{Cn}$
H	H	↑	H	L	X	X	X	X	$\overline{Q}_{An}$	Q_{An}	Q_{Bn}	Q_{Cn}	$\overline{Q}_{Cn}$

H = high level (steady state)

L = low level (steady state)

X = irrelevant (any input, including transitions)

↑ = transition from low to high level

a, b, c, d = the level of steady state input at A, B, C, or D, respectively

Q_{A0}, Q_{B0}, Q_{C0}, Q_{D0} = the level of Q_A, Q_B, Q_C, or Q_D, respectively, before the indicated steady-state input conditions were established

Q_{An}, Q_{Bn}, Q_{Cn} = the level of Q_A, Q_B, or Q_C, respectively, before the most recent transition of the clock

Pre-lab Questions

1. **a.** A 3-state ring counter is loaded with the binary number 101. What are the next three states of the counter?
   b. Repeat a. for a Johnson counter.
2. How can a shift register be used to change data from parallel to serial form?

Procedure

Johnson and Ring Counters

   1. The circuit shown in Figure 23–3 is a partially completed schematic for a shift register counter. It could be connected as either a Johnson (twisted-ring) or as a ring counter. Refer to Figure 23–2 and the function table for the 74195 (Table 23–1) and determine how to complete the feedback loop for a twisted-ring counter. Show the completed schematic in your report.
   2. Connect your circuit. (The $\overline{CLEAR}$ and SHIFT/LOAD pushbuttons can be made with pieces

FIGURE 23–3
Partially completed schematic for
twisted-ring or ring counter.

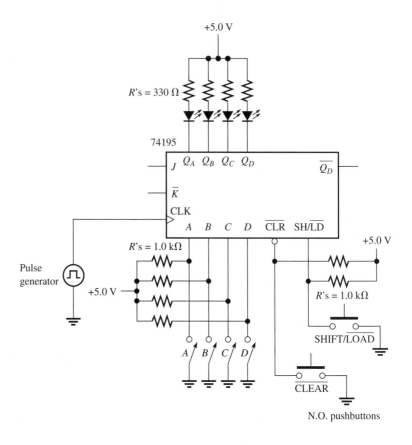

of hook-up wire.) Set the pulse generator for a TTL pulse at 1 Hz. Momentarily close the CLEAR switch. One useful feature of the counter is that when the sequence begins in state 0, it forms a Gray code sequence. Although you could load a pattern other than all zeros, this is a typical starting point for a Johnson counter.

3. Observe the pattern in the LEDs. (The LEDs are ON with a zero.) Then speed up the pulse generator to 1 kHz and develop a timing diagram for the Johnson counter outputs. Draw your timing diagram in the space provided in the report.

4. Referring to Figure 23–2 and the function table for the 74195, change the schematic to that of a ring counter. The partially completed schematic is shown in the report. A ring counter does not invert the bits that are fed back, so the desired bit pattern must be preset through the parallel load feature of the shift register. A common pattern is to have either a single 1 or a single 0 recirculate. Set the load switches for 1110_2 and press the SHIFT/LOAD pushbutton. From the function table, note that this is a synchronous load, so loading will take place only if a clock is present.

5. Reset the pulse generator for 1 Hz and observe the pattern in the LEDs.* After observing the pattern in the LEDs, speed up the pulse generator to 1 kHz and develop a timing diagram for the ring counter outputs. Draw your timing diagram in the space provided in the report.

For Further Investigation

This investigation is a bit different than previous ones. In this investigation, it is not necessary to build the circuit; rather you should try to figure out timing details (of course you could build it if you choose). The circuit is an automated IC tester for 2-input gates shown in Figure 23–4. It uses a 74195 shift register to generate a serial data train that represents the predicted data for a device under test (D.U.T.). The way it works is that a 2-input gate receives four states from the 7493A counter and produces a logical one or zero depending on the type of gate that is tested. If the data

---

*This pattern is essentially the same pattern used in the ring counter for the keyboard encoder shown in Figure 10–30 of Floyd's text.

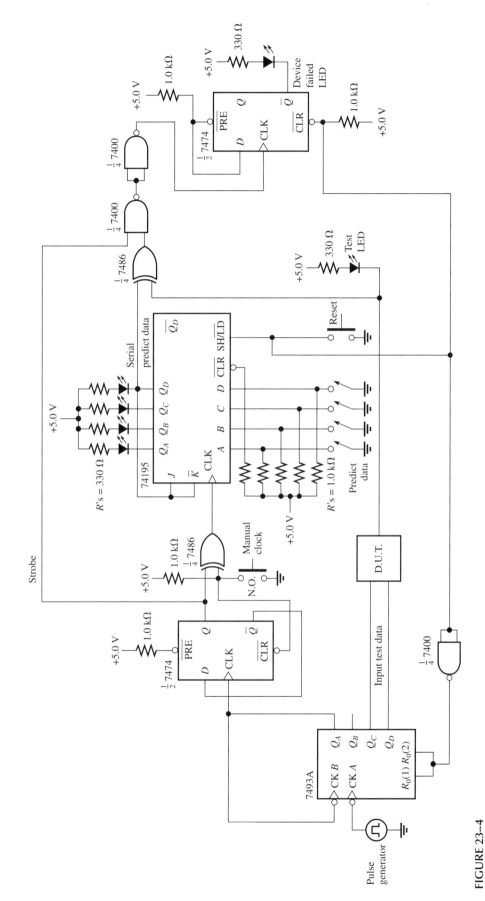

FIGURE 23–4
Automated IC tester.

from the D.U.T. matches the shift register data, the test continues; otherwise the *Device failed LED* will come on. Timing for this simple system is not trivial but by carefully drawing the waveforms for each stage, you can figure out how it works. Start by drawing the waveforms for the 7493A. Assume a 2-input NAND gate is the D.U.T. and the predict data is set for $A = 0$, and $B = C = D = 1$. Show the time relationship between the counter and the Strobe, Input test data, and the Serial predict data. Summarize in a short report how the circuit works and what happens if the Input test data doesn't match the Serial predict data.

Report for Experiment 23

Name: _____ Date: _____ Class: _____

Data and Observations:

Schematic for Johnson counter:

Schematic for ring counter:

Timing diagram for Johnson counter:

CLK
Q_A
Q_B
Q_C
Q_D

Timing diagram for ring counter loaded with 1110:

CLK
Q_A
Q_B
Q_C
Q_D

Results and Conclusion:

Further Investigation Results:

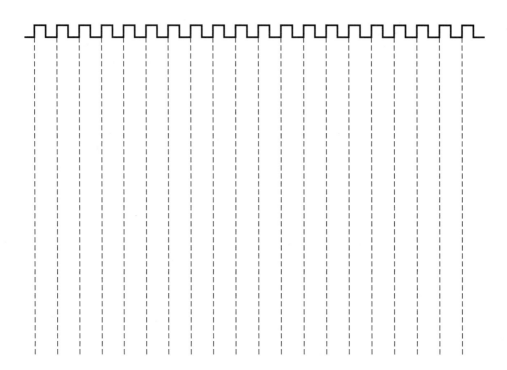

Review Questions (TTL)

1. Explain why it is necessary to use an edge-triggered device for a shift register.

2. Assume the outputs of the Johnson counter that you drew in the report were decoded to show a series of unique codes. Draw the expected waveforms you would observe on a logic analyzer.

component. Compile the program to assure there are no errors. Recall that *JKFlipFlop* will need to be in the same folder as the Counter program used next.

Program Overview

Shift registers are created using sequential logic in a similar manner to the counters studied earlier. In this experiment, the ring and Johnson counters will be studied using *shift registers* constructed with flip-flops modeled in VHDL. In this experiment, you will complete a program that simulates a general-purpose counter with four flip-flops. This program will then be used to implement the Johnson and ring counters.

Procedure

1. Connect the project board to a computer as described in *Project Board Familiarization.*

2. The logic diagram shown in Figure 23–5 in the report is a partially completed logic diagram for a shift register counter. It could be completed as either a Johnson (twisted-ring) or as a ring counter. Refer to Figure 23–2 and determine how to complete the feedback loop for a *twisted-ring* (Johnson) counter. Show the completed logic diagram in your report.

3. Enter the program *JKFlipFlop* shown in Figure 23–6 into the text editor. This is the same program that you used in Experiment 17 to describe a J-K flip-flop except in this experiment it is a leading-edge triggered flip-flop. The ring and Johnson counters in this experiment will treat the flip-flop as a

The Johnson Counter

4. Enter the incomplete program *Counter* in Figure 23–7 into the text editor. Figure 23–8 shows the logic required to add the SHIFT/$\overline{\text{LOAD}}$ to a J-K flip-flop. Write the lines for Clr1, Clr2, and Clr3. Clr0 has been completed as an example.

5. Finish the Counter program by adding the J-K logic equations for each flip-flop. The first two equations have been completed as an example.

6. Assign the inputs and outputs listed in the **entity** section of the program to on-board switches and LEDs. Assign SHIFT/$\overline{\text{LOAD}}$ to a pushbutton. Then compile and download your program to the project board.

7. Set the pulse generator for a TTL pulse at 1 Hz. Press the SHIFT/$\overline{\text{LOAD}}$ pushbutton. One useful feature of the counter is that when the sequence begins at 0, it forms a Gray code sequence. Although you could load a pattern other than all zeros, this is a typical starting point for a Johnson counter.

8. Observe the pattern on the LEDs. Then speed up the pulse generator to 1 kHz and observe the outputs to the LEDs on an oscilloscope. Develop a timing diagram for the Johnson counter outputs. Draw your timing diagram in the space provided in the report.

FIGURE 23–8
Combination logic for parallel in/serial out shift register.

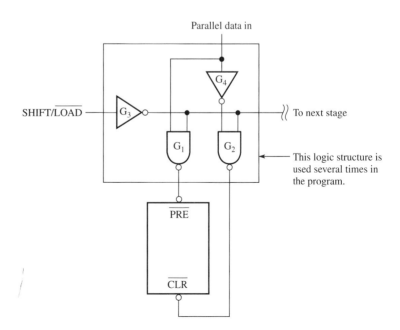

The Ring Counter

9. A ring counter does not invert the bits that are fed back, so the desired bit pattern must be preset through the parallel load feature of the shift register. The logic diagram shown in Figure 23–9 (in the report) is a partially completed logic diagram for a generic shift register counter. Refer to Figure 23–2 and determine how to complete the feedback loop for a ring counter. Show the completed logic diagram in your report.

10. Modify the J-K logic inputs in the program *Counter* to become a ring counter. The pin assignments from the Johnson counter will work for the ring counter.

11. A common pattern is to have either a single 1 or a single 0 recirculate. Test your Counter program by setting the load switches for 1110_2 and press the SHIFT/LOAD pushbutton.

12. Reset the pulse generator for 1 Hz and observe the pattern in the LEDs. After observing the pattern in the LEDs, speed up the pulse generator to 1 kHz and develop a timing diagram for the ring counter outputs. Draw your timing diagram in the space provided in the report.

For Further Investigation

Figure 23–10 is the schematic for a ring counter that was developed with the VHDL graphical design tool. The graphical design tool is a code generator that allows you to bring in a VHDL subprogram that is drawn as a component symbol. The process of creating a system is to "glue" the symbols together within the graphic editor, much like creating a schematic in MultiSim. You simply draw connecting lines between the symbols to create a schematic and

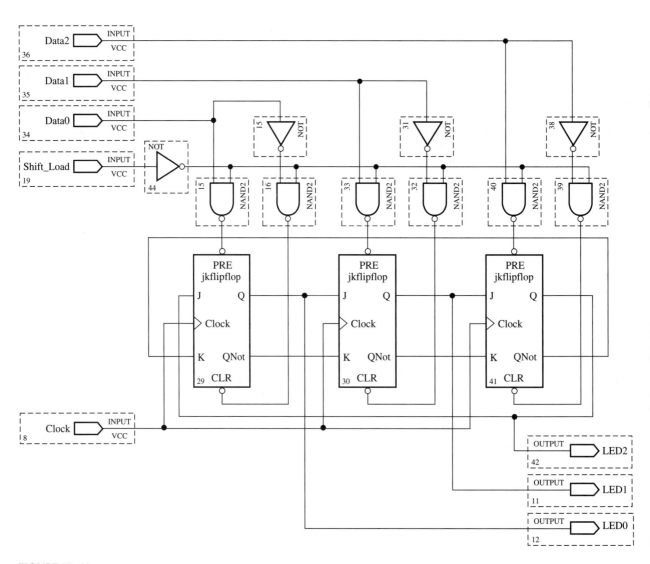

FIGURE 23–10

the graphic editor completes the underlying VHDL program. This is a useful tool for creating simple programs, but it is limited to structural modeling and is only as efficient as the code generator.

The J-K flip-flops that make up the ring counter have been defined as components that have been inserted into the graphic editor. The graphic ed-itor defined internal connections automatically just as you did with the keyword **signal.** Complete the VHDL program in Figure 23–11 from the illustration by completing the logic for FF1 and FF2. FF0 is completed as an example. Test your program and verify its operation.

Report for Experiment 23

Name: ——————————————————— Date: ——————————— Class: ———————————————————

Data and Observations:

Logic Diagram for Johnson Counter:

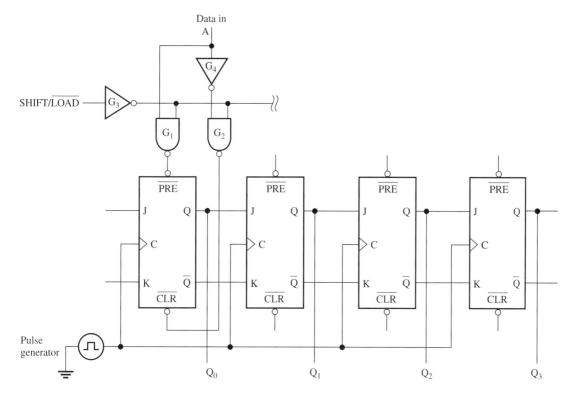

FIGURE 23–5

```vhdl
library IEEE;
use IEEE.std_logic_1164.all;

entity JKFlipFlop is
  port (J, K, Clr, Pre, Clock: in std_logic;
        Q, QNot: inout std_logic);
end entity JKFlipFlop

architecture JKBehavior of JKFlipFlop is
begin
  process (J,K,Clr,Pre,Clock) is
  begin
    if Clr = '0' then Q <= '0'; QNot <= '1';      -- Clear
    elsif Pre = '0' then Q <= '1'; QNot <= '0';  -- Preset
    elsif clock = '1' and clock'event then      -- Clock Driven J-K
      if J = '1' and K = '0' then
        Q <= '1';
        QNot <= '0';
      elsif J = '0' and K = '1' then
        Q <= '0';
        QNot <= '1';
      elsif J = '1' and K = '1' then
        if Q = '1' then
          Q <= '0';
          QNot <= '1';
        else
          Q <= '1';
          QNot<= '0';
        end if;
      end if;
    end if;
  end process;
end architecture JKBehavior;
```

> **CODE TIP**
> Notice that the **"elseif clock = '1' and clock event then"** statement causes the flip-flop to change on the leading edge of the clock.

FIGURE 23–6

```vhdl
library IEEE;
use IEEE.std_logic_1164.all;

entity Counter is
  port (clock, ShiftLoad, A, B, C, D: in std_logic;
        QA, QB, QC, QD: inout std_logic);
end entity Counter;

architecture CounterBehavior of Counter is
signal QANot, QBNot, QCNot, QDNot: std_logic;
signal Pre0, Pre1, Pre2, Pre3, Clr0, Clr1, Clr2, Clr3 : std_logic;

component JKFlipFlop is
  port (J, K, Clr, Pre, Clock: in std_logic;
        Q, QNot: inout std_logic);
end component JKFlipFlop;
begin
  Pre0 <= A nand not ShiftLoad; Clr0 <= not A nand not ShiftLoad;
  Pre1 <= B nand not ShiftLoad; Clr1 <=
  Pre2 <= C nand not ShiftLoad; Clr2 <=
  Pre3 <= D nand not ShiftLoad; Clr3 <=
  -- J and K are reversed for FF0
  FF0:JKFlipFlop port map (J=>QDNot,K=>QD,Clr=>Clr0,Pre=>Pre0,Clock=>clock,Q=>QA, QNot=>QANot);
  FF1:JKFlipFlop port map (J=>QA,K=>QANot,Clr=>Clr1,Pre=>Pre1,Clock=>clock,Q=>QB, QNot=>QBNot);
  FF2:JKFlipFlop port map (J=>  ,K=>    ,Clr=>Clr2,Pre=>Pre2,Clock=>clock,Q=>QC, QNot=>QCNot);
  FF3:JKFlipFlop port map (J=>  ,K=>    ,Clr=>Clr3,Pre=>Pre3,Clock=>clock,Q=>QD, QNot=>QDNot);
end architecture CounterBehavior;
```

> **CODE TIP**
> Occasionally two statements are placed on the same line for readability, such as in this case.

FIGURE 23–7

300

Timing diagram
forJohnson
Counter:

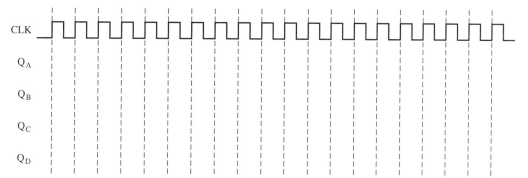

Logic diagram for Ring Counter:

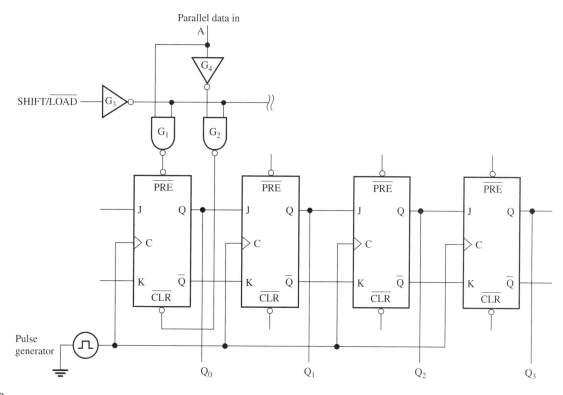

FIGURE 23–9

Timing diagram
for ring counter
loaded with 1110:

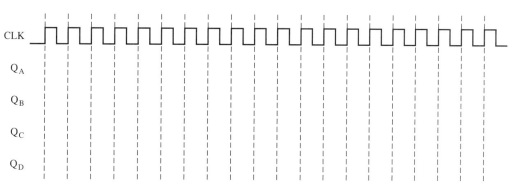

Results and Conclusion:

Further Investigation Results:

```
ibrary ieee;
use ieee.std_logic_1164.all;
entity JKCounter is
  port (Clock, Shift_Load, Data0, Data1, Data2: in std_logic;
       QA, QB, QC: buffer std_logic);
end entity JKCounter;

architecture CounterBehavior of JKCounter is
signal QANot, QBNot, QCNot: std_logic;
signal Pre0, Pre1, Pre2, Clr0, Clr1, Clr2 : std_logic;

component JKFlipFlop is
  port (J, K, Clr, Pre, Clock: in std_logic;
       Q, QNot: inout std_logic);
end component JKFlipFlop;
begin
  Pre0 <= Data0 nand not Shift_Load; Clr0 <= not Data0 nand Shift_Load;
  Pre1 <=                                    ;
  Pre2 <=                                    ;
  FF0:JKFlipFlop port map (J=>QCNot,K=>QC,Clr=>Clr0,Pre=>Pre0,Clock=>Clock,Q=>QA,QNot=>QANot);
  FF1:JKFlipFlop port map (                                                               );
  FF2:JKFlipFlop port map (                                                               );
end architecture CounterBehavior;
```

FIGURE 23–11

Review Questions (VHDL)

1. Draw the waveform for the Johnson counter if the counter is parallel loaded with the binary value 1100.

2. The logic block shown in the box of Figure 23–8 was used several times in the program. An alternate way of coding this block is to use a Procedure as described in the text. What is at least one more way to code this block?

24

The Baseball Scoreboard

Objectives

After completing this experiment, you will be able to
- ☐ Design and implement a logic circuit for part of a baseball scoreboard using shift registers or counters.
- ☐ Write a laboratory report describing the circuit and results.

Reference Reading

Floyd, *Digital Fundamentals with VHDL,* Chapter 10, "Shift Registers"

Materials Needed (TTL)

Five LEDs (two red, three green)
Two N.O. pushbuttons
One 555 timer
Resistors: one 1.0 kΩ, one 10 kΩ, one 22 kΩ, one 1.0 MΩ
Capacitors: one 0.01 μF, one 0.1 μF
Other materials as determined by student

Materials Needed (VHDL)

Project Board

Summary of Theory

A counter uses flip-flops to "remember" the last count until the clock pulse occurs. A shift register can store several events in series depending on the length of the register. A shift register, such as a Johnson counter, can be set with a characteristic sequence like a counter and can be used in applications requiring a counter.

In this experiment, we require two count sequences. Either sequence may be completed first. The sequence completed first must clear both counting devices. One approach might be to use two separate decoders, either of which can clear the counters. The method of solution is entirely up to you. The counting devices are "clocked" by manual pushbuttons. The pushbuttons will need to be debounced to prevent multiple triggers. One method of doing this is shown in Figure 24–1.

Pre-lab Questions

1. A four-bit Johnson counter starts with 0000. List the complete sequence of the counter.
2. What is meant by a "debounced" pushbutton?

Procedure

The Baseball Scoreboard

1. Design a circuit that solves the baseball scoreboard problem stated next. There are two inputs, controlled by pushbutton switches (normally open contacts). There are five outputs represented by

FIGURE 24–1
Circuit to debounce a pushbutton.

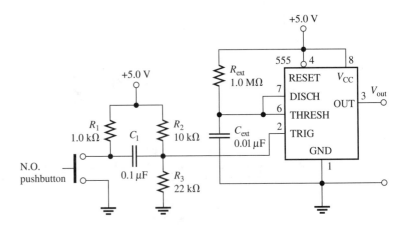

LEDs. Build the circuit. Summarize your design steps and results in a lab report.

Problem Statement: The Latchville Little League needs a new baseball scoreboard (see Figure 24–2.) Your assignment is to do the logic for the strikes-and-balls display. The scoreboard will have two lights (LEDs) for strikes and three lights for balls. The scoreboard operator will have two pushbuttons: one for strikes and the other for balls. Each press of the strike pushbutton turns on one more of the strike lights unless two are already on. If two are on, all lights, including strikes and balls, are cleared. (Note that the count sequence for the strike lights is a binary 00-01-11-00.) The balls pushbutton works in a similar manner. Each press causes one more light to come on unless three are already on. If three lights are already on, then all lights, including strikes, are cleared.

Design Hint: Consider using a 74175 IC for the counting device. The complete circuit can be designed to fit on a single 47-row protoboard.

For Further Investigation

Design the logic circuits needed to complete the scoreboard as illustrated in Figure 24–2. The inning is indicated by a single light (show this as an LED), which corresponds to the inning number. The inning

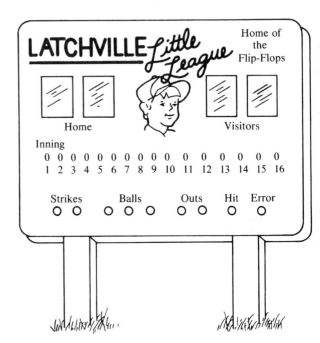

FIGURE 24–2

display is controlled by a single pushbutton to advance the light. The outs display is indicated by two lights, which are controlled by a single pushbutton. When the third out is pressed, all lights on the lower row of the scoreboard are cleared.

Report for Experiment 24

Name: _____ Date: _____ Class: _____

Data and Observations:

Circuit:

Results and Conclusion:

Review Questions (TTL)

1. a. Figure 24–3 shows how shift registers can be connected with a single full-adder to form a serial adder. Analyze the circuit and explain how it operates.

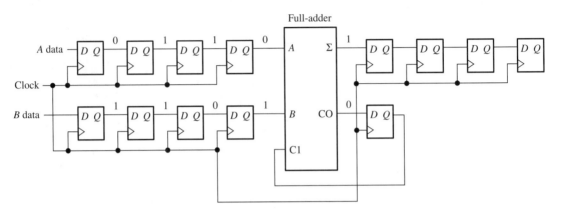

FIGURE 24–3

b. Assume the input shift registers contain the data as shown. What are the contents of the output shift register and the carry-out flip-flop after four clock pulses?

2. Using a 4-bit shift register, design a circuit that produces the two-phase clock signals shown in Figure 24–4.

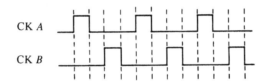

FIGURE 24–4

Program Overview

The program in this experiment is a baseball scoreboard that will use the *DFlipFlop* subprogram introduced in Experiment 15. Recall that the VHDL **component** reserved word was introduced as a convenient way to define the logic of a fixed-function device in the form of a subprogram. D flip-flops will be used to construct two shift registers. A shift register is composed of multiple flip-flops that are used to track or "remember" a series of input binary numbers. You will see how a shift register can be simulated in VHDL to create a new scoreboard for the Latchville Little League (home of the Flip-Flops).

The strikes and balls display on the scoreboard will be controlled by pushbuttons—one for strikes and one for balls. The pushbuttons can be assigned to on-board pushbuttons except for the PLDT-1 project board. If you are using the PLDT-1 board, you can assign one of the DIP switches to control the input.

Procedure

Problem statement: The Latchville Little League needs a new baseball scoreboard. (See Figure 24–2.) Your assignment is to create the logic for the strikes-and-balls display. The scoreboard will have two lights (LEDs) for strikes and three lights for balls. The scoreboard operator will have two pushbuttons: one for strikes and the other for balls. Each press of the strike pushbutton turns on one more of the strike lights unless two are already on. If two are on, all lights, including strikes and balls, are cleared. (Note that the binary sequence for the strike lights is a binary 00-01-11-00.) The balls pushbutton works in a

similar manner. Each press causes one more light to come on unless three are already on. If three lights are already on, then all lights, including strikes and balls, are cleared.

Creating the Scoreboard program

1. Connect the project board to a computer as described in *Project Board Familiarization* and review *VHDL Software Familiarization*.

2. Copy the program *DFlipFlop* shown in Figure 24–5 in the report into the text editor. This is the same program you used in Experiment 15 to describe the gate logic of a D flip-flop. The scoreboard program in this experiment will treat the DFlipFlop as a **component** as was done in Experiment 19.

3. Compile the DFlipFlop program to check for errors.

4. Read over the program *Scoreboard* as shown in Figure 24–6. Complete Table 24–1 by supplying the equation required for the identifier *ResetStrike*. Add this equation to the program where indicated in the **architecture** portion of the program. See the *ResetBall* equation in Table 24–1 for an example.

5. Enter your completed program *ScoreBoard* into the text editor. There are two inputs *StrikeIn* and *BallIn*. Assign these inputs to pushbutton switches. There are five outputs. *BOut* and *SOut* represent standard logic vectors (**std_logic_vector**) that represent balls and strikes. Assign these outputs to LEDs.

6. Compile and download the Scoreboard program to the project board.

7. Test your program and record your observations in a report. Your report should include a summary of theory for the scoreboard, switch and LED designations, and any other information required to reconstruct the project.

Report for Experiment 25

Name: _____ Date: _____ Class: _____

```
library IEEE;
use IEEE.std_logic_1164.all;

entity DFlipFlop is
  port (D, Clr, Pre, Clock: in std_logic;
        Q, QNot: inout std_logic);
end entity DFlipFlop;

architecture DBehavior of DFlipFlop is
signal Temp: std_logic:= '0';
begin
  process (D, Clr, Pre, Clock) is
  begin
    if Clr = '0' then Q <= '0'; QNot <= '1';-- Clear
    elsif Pre = '0' then Q <= '1'; QNot <= '0';-- Preset
    elsif Clock = '1' and Clock'event then
      if D = '1' and Clr = '1' and Pre = '1' then
        Q <= '1';
        QNot <= '0';
      else
        Q <= '0';
        QNot<= '1';
      end if;
    end if;
  end process;
end architecture DBehavior ;
```

TABLE 24–1

Reset Expressions
Ball
ResetBall $<=$ not ((SOut2 and StrikeIn) or (BOut3 and BallIn));
Strike
ResetStrike$=$

FIGURE 24–5

```
library IEEE;
    use IEEE.std_logic_1164.all;

    entity ScoreBoard is
      port (StrikeIn, BallIn: in std_logic;
            BOut: inout std_logic_vector (0 to 2);
            SOut: inout std_logic_vector (0 to 1));
    end entity ScoreBoard;

    architecture StrikeBall of ScoreBoard is
    signal I, Pre, S0, SOut2, BOut3, ResetBall, ResetStrike: std_logic;
    component DFlipFlop is
      port  (D, Clr, Pre, Clock: in std_logic;
             Q, QNot: inout std_logic);
    end component DFlipFlop;

    begin
      I <= '1'; Pre <= '1';
      ResetBall <= not((SOut2 and StrikeIn) or (BOut3 and BallIn));
      FF0: DKFlipFlop port map (D=>I        , Clr=>ResetStrike,Pre =>Pre,Clock=>StrikeIn,Q=>SOut(0));
      FF1: DKFlipFlop port map (D=> SOut(0) , Clr=>ResetStrike,Pre =>Pre,Clock=>StrikeIn,Q=>SOut(1));
      FF2: DKFlipFlop port map (D=> SOut(1) , Clr=>ResetStrike,Pre =>Pre,Clock=>StrikeIn,Q=>SOut2);

      ResetStrike <=
      FF3: DKFlipFlop port map (D=>I        , Clr=>ResetBall,Pre =>Pre,Clock=>BallIn,Q=>BOut(0));
      FF4: DKFlipFlop port map (D=> BOut(0), Clr=>ResetBall,Pre =>Pre,Clock=>BallIn,Q=>BOut(1));
      FF5: DKFlipFlop port map (D=> BOut(1), Clr=>ResetBall,Pre =>Pre,Clock=>BallIn,Q=>BOut(2));
      FF6: DKFlipFlop port map (D=> BOut(2), Clr=>ResetBall,Pre =>Pre,Clock=>BallIn,Q=>BOut3);
    end architecture StrikeBall;
```

FIGURE 24–6

CODE TIP
Signal definitions Sout2 and
Bout3 are used to clear the display
only. Because they are not used as
light indicators, they are defined as
internal signals.

Review Questions (VHDL)

1. Explain how the *ResetBall* identifier clears both the strike and ball sections on the scoreboard at the same time.

2. The baseball program *ScoreBoard* was created using D flip-flops in a shift register. What steps would be needed to implement the scoreboard using J-K flip-flops?

25

Semiconductor Memories

Objectives

After completing this experiment, you will be able to
- □ Complete the design of a memory that stores a series of BCD numbers.
- □ Store and read data from the memory.
- □ Design a counter to sequence automatically through specified addresses.

Reference Reading

Floyd, *Digital Fundamentals with VHDL,* Chapter 11, "Memory and Storage"

Materials Needed

7447A BCD/decimal decodor
MAN72 seven-segment display
74121 one-shot
74LS189 (16 × 4) tristate RAM
Two 4-position DIP switches
One N.O. pushbutton
Resistors: ten 1.0 kΩ, seven 330 Ω
Other materials as determined by student

Summary of Theory

Memories are circuits that can store binary information either temporarily or long term. Memory types include magnetic, optical (CDs), and various types of integrated circuits. IC memories are a form of memory that are particularly useful because of their great speed. Semiconductor memories can be ac-cessed in a few tens of nanoseconds. IC memory types include memory that is programmed into the memory and can only be read, called read-only memory (ROM), and memory that can be read or written to, which is commonly called random-access memory (RAM). The term *RAM* goes back many years and was used to indicate that any location could be accessed in the same time as any other lo-cation. A better term for RAM is *read/write* memory (RWM), to show that data can be both read from and written to any location.

The basic cell in a static RAM is a flip-flop; it can be set or reset for writing operations or tested without changing its state for read operations. In ad-dition, the RAM contains logic gates to control the read and write functions and decoding circuitry. A RAM is organized as an array containing the mem-ory cells in rows and columns, as illustrated in Fig-ure 25–1. In memories, the number of bits treated as one entity is considered the word size. A word is the number of bits that are accessed at one time and can vary from as little as 1 bit to as many as 64 bits. Keep in mind that for computer applications, a word gen-erally means exactly 16 bits; however, this definition is different for memories. In Figure 25–1, the word size is 4 bits because this is the minimum number of bits that are written to or read from the memory.

Each word in a read/write memory is accessed by a set of address lines, representing the location of the word within the matrix. To access a specific word, the address is decoded; this decoded address is used to select the proper row in memory. Depending on the organization of the matrix, column information

FIGURE 25–1

Logic diagram for a small RAM
R/W memory.

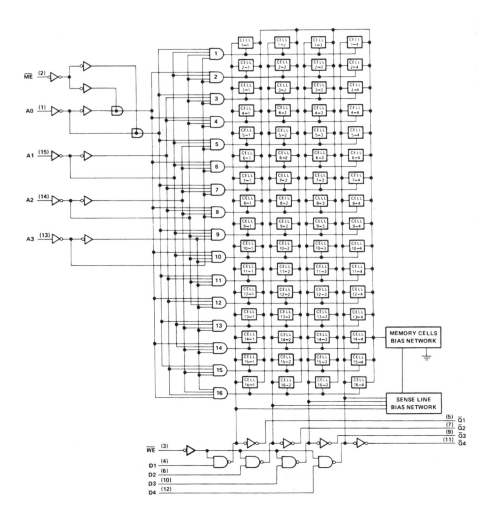

may also be required. There are also one or more control lines, which are used to select the read/write option, control the output, or enable the IC. The enable lines allow expansion of memory by allowing other memories to have different external addresses. Figure 25–2 shows how two small memories can be expanded.

The outputs of memory and other devices are frequently connected to a common set of wires known as a *bus*. In order for more than one output to be connected to a bus, the outputs of each device are either tristate or open-collector types. Essentially, tristate or open-collector devices can be electrically disconnected from the bus when not active. Open-collector devices require a single pull-up resistor on each output line. This pull-up resistor is common to all devices that are connected to that same line. Tristate devices do not require a pull-up resistor.

In this experiment, you will provide an enhancement to the security entry system shown in Figure 25–3. The enhancement is to provide the owner of the system with a readout of the entry se-

quence. Naturally, this will be housed in a locked box and be available only to the owner, as an aid to reprogramming the combination. The memory and associated logic is shown in Figure 25–4. The highlighted portion is the simplified circuit for the experiment. A partially completed schematic of the enhancement is shown in the report section as Figure 25–5. (The counter is constructed in the For Further Investigation section.) You will simulate the output of the encoder with switches. The memory is a 74LS189 tristate static RAM, a 64-bit memory organized as sixteen 4-bit words. An advantage of the static RAM (SRAM) is that it does not require refresh circuitry. There are four address lines (labeled as SELECT inputs), four data inputs, and four output lines (labeled Y_1 through Y_4) plus chip enable ($\overline{CE}$) and a read/write ($R/\overline{W}$) control line. The output lines are shown with inverting bubbles, hence the *complement* of the input data is present at the output when reading the data. The tristate outputs are in the high impedance state when the $R/\overline{W}$ line is LOW. Read and write functions for the 74LS189 are sum-

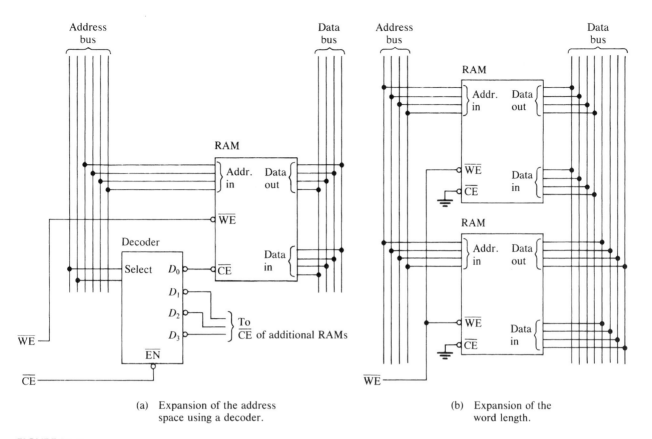

(a) Expansion of the address
space using a decoder.

(b) Expansion of the
word length.

FIGURE 25–2
Expansion of address space or word length with a small memory (partial schematic).

marized in the function table shown as Table 25–1. To write data, the address is placed on the address bus, data are placed on the data bus, and $\overline{CE}$ is asserted LOW. Then the R/$\overline{W}$ line is pulsed LOW to WRITE. Data are written at the end of this pulse. To read data, the address is placed on the address bus, $\overline{CE}$ is asserted LOW, and the R/$\overline{W}$ line is left HIGH to READ.

Pre-lab Questions

1. A memory has 8 address lines and 10 data lines.
   a. How many different locations can be addressed?
   b. What is the word length?
2. Most TTL circuits should not have their outputs connected together. Why is it okay to connect the outputs of the 74LS189 static memory together on a common bus?

Procedure

1. Figure 25–5 in the report shows a partially completed schematic for the enhancement to the security entry system described in the Summary of Theory. The 74121 one-shot provides a 50 ms LOW pulse to the R/$\overline{W}$ line of the memory when the owner wishes to $\overline{STORE}$ the combination. Complete the schematic by showing what to do with all of the inputs and how to connect the output to generate an approximate 50 ms pulse. In particular, show how the trigger lines (A_1, A_2, and B) should be connected for a leading-edge trigger, and show what to do with R_X/C_X, C_X, and R_{INT} inputs. You may use the internal 2 kΩ resistor. Draw the output from the correct side of the 74121 to the R/$\overline{W}$ line of the memory.

2. Construct the circuit from Step 1. The data switches represent the encoder output. The $\overline{STORE}$ pushbutton is simplified from the text but serves the same function. *Note:* The memory shown for this experiment is an 74LS189 that uses tristate outputs. A 74LS289 (with open-collector output) may be substituted by adding 1.0 kΩ pull-up resistors to +5.0 V to the $Y_1 - Y_4$ outputs.

313

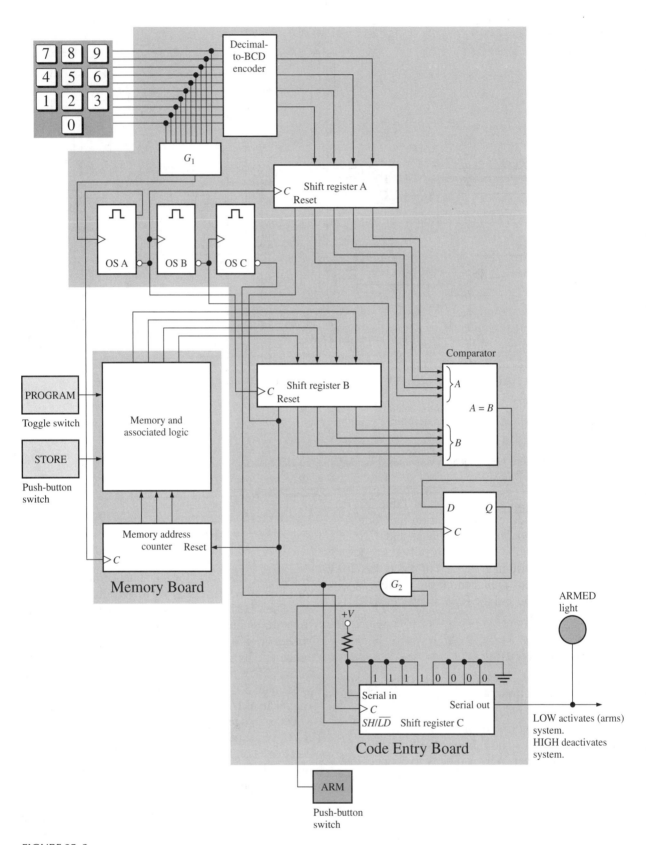

FIGURE 25–3
Security entry system.

FIGURE 25–4
Simplified basic logic diagram of the memory logic.

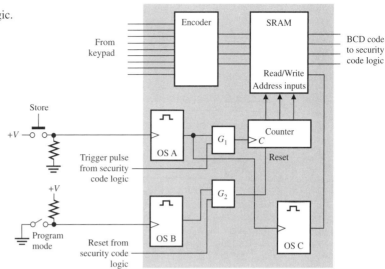

TABLE 25–1
Function table.

$\overline{CE}$	$\overline{WE}$	Operation	Condition of Outputs
L	L	Write	Complement of data inputs
L	H	Read	Complement of selected word
H	L	Inhibit Storage	Complement of data inputs
H	H	Do Nothing	HIGH

3. Program the first five locations of the memory with a 5-digit combination. Unfortunately, the owner is not very clever and decides to use his zip code for the combination. He lives in Cool, CA—ZIP 95614. The starting address for the combination is 0000. Don't forget that the output data will be the complement of the data entered.

4. After you have programmed the combination into the first five locations (0000 through 0100), set the data to cause the display to be blank for address 0101. Then test the circuit by setting the addresses for binary sequence 0000 through 0101 and observing the combination in the seven-segment display followed by the blank display. Demonstrate your working circuit to your instructor.

For Further Investigation

For checking the combination, you would like to see the complete sequence automatically. To do this, you will need to add a counter that cycles the address lines through the five-digit combination and the sixth blank location. Decide how to connect a 7493 counter so that it cycles through the first six memory locations repeatedly. Connect the circuit and write a short description of the counter and your results in the report.

Report for Experiment 25

Name: _____ Date: _____ Class: _____

Data and Observations:

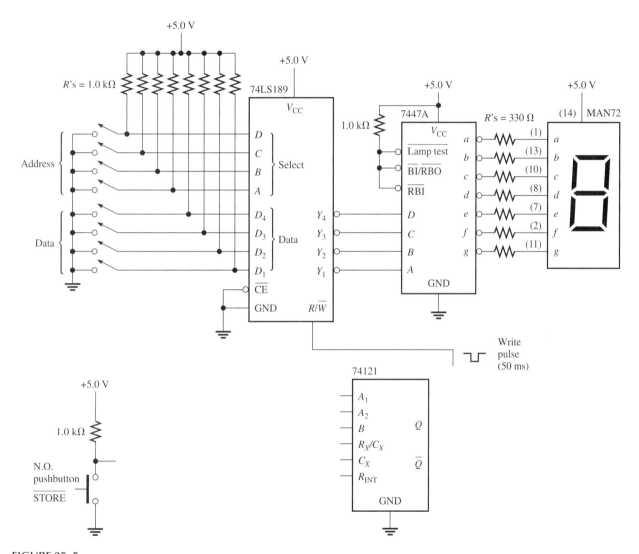

FIGURE 25–5
Schematic of security entry system.

Results and Conclusion:

Further Investigation Results:

Review Questions (TTL)

1. The manufacturer's specification for the minimum width of the write enable pulse is 25 ns, yet in the experiment a 50 ms pulse was specified to avoid switch bounce. Was it really necessary to debounce the START pushbutton? Why or why not?

2. In Step 4, you were directed to store a binary number that would cause the display to be blank for location 0101. What binary number did you store? Why wasn't 1111 the correct data to store?

3. The specification sheet for the 74LS189 indicates that it features full, on-chip decoding.
   a. What does this mean?

   b. According to the specification sheet, what is the minimum amount of time data must be available during a write operation?

318

26

Introduction to the Intel Processors

Objectives

After completing this experiment, you will be able to

☐ Use certain Debug commands to view and change internal registers, view and modify memory contents, compare a block of data, and determine the hardware configuration of the computer.

☐ Use Debug to observe selected assembly language instructions execute.

☐ Assemble and execute a simple assembly language program.

Reference Reading

Floyd, *Digital Fundamentals with VHDL,* Chapter 12, "Introduction to Microprocessors, Computers, and Buses"

Materials Needed

PC

Summary of Theory

The Intel microprocessors are widely used as the heart of computers. The fundamental processor that is a good starting point for understanding microprocessors is the 8086/8088 processors that were introduced in 1978. As newer processors were developed, the family became known as the 80X86 and Pentium processors. Although significant im-

provements have occurred in speed, size, and structure, the concepts of how the processor performs its job are much the same. Code originally written for the 8086/8088 will still execute on the fastest Pentium IV processor available.

Computer programmers that use assembly language are primarily concerned with the register structure of the processor and the instruction set that is available. The register structure is the set of registers made available for the programmer to use for various functions and they often have special functions associated with them. The register structure for processors starting with the 80386 is an expanded version of the original 8086 registers. Figure 26–1 is the register structure for the 80X86 and Pentium processors.

The instruction set is the list of instructions available for programming. The Intel 80X86 and Pentium microprocessors have complex instruction sets, with literally hundreds of variations. This lab exercise will introduce you to the registers and some basic instructions to allow you to execute an assembly language program.

A program that is available on all DOS-based computers is called Debug. Debug is a DOS program that allows you to test and debug executable files. Although Debug only allows you to work with the basic 16-bit register set, it is still a useful program for basic programming tasks such as viewing registers, testing simple programs or making changes to memory. It is a good starting point for understanding more complex assemblers. Table 26–1

FIGURE 26–1

Register structure of the Intel 80X86
and Pentium processors.

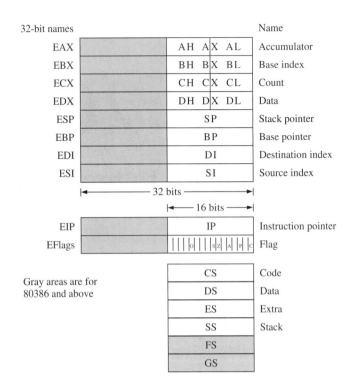

32-bit names			Name
EAX	AH AX AL	Accumulator
EBX	BH BX BL	Base index
ECX	CH CX CL	Count
EDX	DH DX DL	Data
ESP	SP	Stack pointer
EBP	BP	Base pointer
EDI	DI	Destination index
ESI	SI	Source index

|← ——— 32 bits ——— →|

|← —— 16 bits —— →|

EIP | IP | Instruction pointer
EFlags | Flag

Gray areas are for
80386 and above

CS | Code
DS | Data
ES | Extra
SS | Stack
FS |
GS |

shows the common Debug commands with examples of each. To better acquaint you with Debug and assembly language, you will use most of these commands in this exercise.

This experiment has a different format than the others and does not require building hardware; it is more like a tutorial exercise than a traditional lab experiment. The procedure gives many examples of Debug commands with short exercises. Instead of a separate Report section, answers to exercises are entered in the space provided in the Procedure section.

Pre-lab Questions

1. What is the major difference between the registers in the original 8086 and the registers in the 80386 and above processors?
2. What is Debug?

Procedure

1. The Debug program is a feature of the operating system. On your PC, open an MS-DOS Prompt window and type **Debug <cr>**. (**<cr>** stands for "carriage return," which means press the ⃞Enter key). To open an MS-DOS window, click **Start** and **Run**. Enter **Command**, then click OK. You should

be able to access Debug directly by typing the word **Debug**. If for some reason you cannot access Debug, you can find Debug.exe by doing a "search" (enter the command **CD\<cr>**, then type the command **DIR Debug.exe /S<cr>**). When you run Debug, you should see a hyphen (or minus sign) (−), which is the Debug prompt.

Checking System Equipment and ROM BIOS Date

2. You can use Debug to view the contents of selected memory locations within the first 1M of memory and pick out some of the system data for your computer. To do this, use the Dump command to first look at the BIOS data area (part of RAM) as follows:

−D 40:0 <cr>

This tells Debug to dump (display) 8 lines with 16 bytes per line of the memory starting at address 40:0 (in standard segment:offset notation). The results will be similar to the display shown in Figure 26–2(a). To the left side of the display is the address of the first byte in the line, followed by 16 bytes of hexadecimal data that are the contents of the next 16 locations. On the far right is the ASCII representation of those bytes that contain characters that can be displayed.

TABLE 26–1

Common Debug commands.

Debug Command	Examples	Description
A (assemble)	A 100 A 1234:100	Assemble instructions starting at CS:100 Assemble instructions starting at 1234:100
C (compare)	C 200,2FF,600	Compare a block of code from DS:200 to DS:2FF with the block starting at DS:600
D (dump)	D 120 D SS:FFEE FFFD	Dump (or "display") the contents of 128 bytes of memory starting at address DS:120 (DS is default) Dump 16 bytes starting at SS:FFEE
E (enter)	E 120 E:0100:0000	Examine or enter new data into memory starting at DS:120 Examine or enter new data into memory starting at 0100:0000
F (fill)	F 300, 400,FF	Fill memory locations starting at DS:300 and ending at DS:400 with the value FFH
G (go)	G = 100,120	Go (execute instructions) starting at CS:100 and continuing to CS:120. (Note equal sign is required).
H (hex)	H A000, B000	Hexadecimal sum and difference is performed on the numbers A000H and B000H
I (input)	I 300	Input port number 300H (prototype card location)
M (move)	M 200,2FF,600	Move (copy) the block of code from DS:200 to DS:2FF to the block starting at DS:600
O (output)	O 43,36	Out the number 36H to port 43 (timer control register)
P (proceed)	P = 100 10	Proceed, or execute a set of related instructions starting at address CS:100 and doing 10 instructions. It can be used for loops or calls to subroutines as if it were a single instruction.
Q (quit)	Q	Quit Debug
R (register)	R R SI	Display the contents of the 16-bit registers and flags Display the contents of the SI register and allow a new value to be written to it
S (search)	S 100, FFF, 0A	Search locations DS:100 to DS:FFF for the byte 0AH. Address with this byte will be displayed.
T (trace)	T T 5	Trace the execution of one instruction Trace the execution of the next 5 instructions
U (unassemble)	U 100 U 100 110	Unassemble (disassemble) code starting at location CS:100 Unassemble code from CS:100 to CS:110

The data that is shown as a result of this dump command is a "work area" for BIOS and contains lots of information about your computer. For example, location 40:17 has keyboard control information. Bit 7 (the most significant bit) is a 1 if the insert mode is on and bit 6 will indicate if the *caps lock* function is on. Press the caps lock button and repeat the dump command as before. You should observe bit 6 of 40:17 will now be set as shown in Figure 26–2(b). (Reset the caps lock function after observing this.)

Now observe the first two locations at 40:10. These locations contain the equipment status word. To interpret the information, you have to reverse the two bytes and convert them to binary. For example, in Figure 26–2(b) the equipment status

```
                C:\WINDOWS>Debug
                -D 40:0
                0040:0000  F8 03 F8 02 00 00 00 00-78 03 00 00 00 00 0F 02   ........x.......
                0040:0010  27 C2 00 80 02 00 00 20-00 00 38 00 38 00 44 20   '...... ..8.8.D
                0040:0020  65 12 62 30 75 16 67 22-0D 1C 44 20 20 39 34 05   e.b0u.g"..D  94.
                0040:0030  30 0B 3A 27 30 0B 0D 1C-00 00 00 00 00 00 00 C0   0.:'0...........
                0040:0040  00 01 80 00 00 00 00 00-00 03 50 00 00 10 00 00   ..........P.....
                0040:0050  00 0C 00 00 00 00 00 00-00 00 00 00 00 00 00 00   ................
                0040:0060  0E 0D 00 D4 03 29 30 A4-17 3D 85 00 CE 61 0A 00.  .....)0..=...a..
                0040:0070  00 00 00 00 00 01 00 00-14 14 14 3C 01 01 01 01   ...........<....
```

(a)

```
                -D 40:0
                0040:0000  F8 03 F8 02 00 00 00 00-78 03 00 00 00 00 0F 02   ........x.......
                0040:0010  27 C2 00 80 02 00 00 00-2C 00 2C 00 44 20         '......`..,.,.D
                0040:0020  20 39 34 05 30 0B 3A 27-30 0B 0D 1C 20 39 34 05    94.0.:'0... 94.
                0040:0030  30 0B 3A 27 30 0B 0D 1C-0D 1C 0D 1C 0D 1C 00 C0   0.:'0...........
                0040:0040  00 01 80 00 00 00 00 00-00 03 50 00 00 10 00 00   ..........P.....
                0040:0050  00 18 00 00 00 00 00 00-00 00 00 00 00 00 00 00   ................
                0040:0060  0E 0D 00 D4 03 29 30 A4-17 3D 85 00 72 63 0A 00   .....)0..=..rc..
                0040:0070  00 00 00 00 00 01 00 00-14 14 14 3C 01 01 01 01   ...........<....
```

(b)

FIGURE 26–2

word is 27 C2 (read on the second line). Intel shows words in reverse order; the most significant byte is first followed by the least significant byte. Reversing the bytes and converting to binary results in the following:

Bit:	15	14	13	12	11	10	9	8	7	6	5	4	3	2	1	0
Binary:	1	1	0	0	0	0	1	0	0	0	1	0	0	1	1	1

From left to right, this pattern means

15, 14	Number of parallel printer ports attached = 3 (binary 11)
13, 12	Not used
11–9	Number of serial ports attached = 1 (binary 001)
8	Not used
7, 6	Number of diskette devices = 1 (where 00 = 1, 01 = 2, 10 = 3, and 11 = 4)
5, 4	Initial video mode = 80 × 25 color (where 01 = 40 × 25 color, 10 = 80 × 25 color, and 11 = 80 × 25 monochrome)
3, 2	Not used
1	Math coprocessor is present = yes (0 = no, 1 = yes)
0	Diskette drive is present = yes (0 = no, 1 = yes)

In the space provided, write down the bit pattern you see for locations 40:10 and 40:11 in reverse order. Then determine what installed equipment BIOS has found.

Bit:	15	14	13	12	11	10	9	8	7	6	5	4	3	2	1	0
Binary:																

Number of parallel printer ports attached =

_____

Number of serial ports attached =

_____

Number of diskette devices =

_____

Initial video mode = _____

Math coprocessor is present? _____

Diskette drive is present? _____

3. In this step, you can check the date of manufacture of your ROM BIOS recorded as mm/dd/yy which begins at location FFFF:5. Issue a dump command as follows:

−D FFFF: 0 <cr>

The date is encoded as ASCII characters which can be read directly from the right-hand side of the dis-

322

play (starting at offset 5). Indicate the date you found in the space provided:

Date of ROM BIOS: _____

Changing Data in Memory and Comparing a Block

4. In this step, you will change the contents of 256 memory locations to an ASCII zero (30H) by using the Fill command. First check on the contents of the current data segment between offset address 0 and 100 by using the Dump command as follows:

−D 0 100 <cr>

You should observe a random pattern of bytes in the memory. Now fill this region with ASCII zero (30H) by invoking the Fill command as follows:

−F 0,FF,30 <cr>

Next issue the Dump command again and observe the results. Notice the pattern on the right side of the display.

5. Now change one location to a different character by invoking the Enter command as follows:

−E 20 <cr>

Debug will respond with the address (DS:20) and the contents (30) followed by a dot. Enter **31 <cr>** after the dot. This will change the byte at location DS:20 to an ASCII 1.
(You can confirm this with another Dump command.)

6. Issue the following command which will compare two blocks of memory:

−C 0,2F,30 <cr>

Describe the response from Debug.

_____

Examining and Modifying the Internal Registers

7. Issue the register command by typing:

−R <cr>

You should see the contents of the 16 bit register set with their initial values similar to Figure 26–3. The general purpose registers (AX, BX, CX, and DX), the base pointer (BP), and the source and destination index registers (SI and DI) will all show 0000H. The segment registers (DS, ES, SS, and CS) will have a

hex number that depends on where DOS found available address space so will not be the same for different users. The stack pointer (SP) begins near the top of the offset address (FFEE) and the instruction pointer will start at 0100H. Flags are indicated with two-letter codes. Following the register list is an address given in segment:offset notation and an arbitrary instruction.

8. To modify the contents of the AX register, issue the register command for the AX register:

−R AX <cr>

The processor will respond with

AX 0000:

showing the current contents and a colon. The colon indicates it is waiting for your response. Type

:0100 <cr>

The value 0100H will now be entered into the AX register. You can see this by issuing another register command. Type

−R <cr>

and you should see the new contents of the AX register. The other register can be modified by a similar procedure. Use the register command to change the contents of the BX register to 0200H and the CX register to F003H. Indicate in the space below the command you used:

Command to place 0200H in BX register:

_____

Command to place F003H in CX register:

_____

Tracing Instructions

9. In this step, you will assemble some basic assembly language instructions with Debug and then observe the results after they execute. Issue the following Debug command:

−A 100 <cr>

This command tells Debug to assemble instructions beginning at CS:100. The processor responds with the starting address and a blinking dash cursor. Enter the following assembly language instructions. Note that the segment address will be different than

```
-R
AX=0000  BX=0000  CX=0000  DX=0000  SP=FFEE  BP=0000  SI=0000  DI=0000
DS=1E8E  ES=1E8E  SS=1E8E  CS=1E8E  IP=0100    NV UP EI PL NZ NA PO NC
1E8E:0100 BAAB81         MOV    DX,81AB
-
```

FIGURE 26–3

the one shown here, but the offset address should be the same.

```
1E8C:0100 mov cx, 04 <cr>
1E8C:0103 mov ax, 40 <cr>
1E8C:0106 mov ds,ax <cr>
1E8C:0108 mov si, 17 <cr>
1E8C:010B xor byte ptr [si], 40 <cr>
1E8C:010E loop 10B <cr>
1E8C:0110 nop <cr>
```

Press <cr> again to leave the assembler.

10. You can trace this code and observe the registers as each instruction is executed. The first four instructions are all move instructions that are used to preset certain values in registers. An explanation of the code follows. First, make sure the IP is loaded with 0100H. If not, use an **R IP** instruction to set it to the starting address of the code. Then use the **-T** command to trace a single instruction. You should observe that after executing this instruction, the CX register contains 0004H.

Issue three more **-T** commands until you reach the **xor byte ptr [si], 40** instruction. Up to this point you should observe that certain registers are loaded. The register pair DS:SI forms a segment:offset address which points to the location in memory you looked at in step 2. This memory location is the BIOS work area with the keyboard control information. Recall that bit 6 will indicate if the *caps lock* function is on. You may also recall that an XOR gate can be used to pass a bit unchanged or to complement it.* In the instruction, the XOR function is used to selectively complement bit 6 and leave the others unchanged at the location pointed to by DS:SI. Issue another trace command, observe what happens after the XOR instruction executes, and record your observation in the space provided:

_____

_____

11. Following the XOR instruction is the **loop 10B** instruction. The loop instruction is a quick way to repeat a process. Loop decrements the CX register by 1 and transfers control to the instruction at location 10B if CX is not 0; otherwise, the next instruction in line is executed. Since the CX register was initialized to 4, the loop will be repeated 4 times. Continue tracing instructions, watching what happens, until you reach the **nop** ("no operation") instruction on line CS:110. *Note:* if you want to repeat the procedure outlined in this step, you need to reset the IP to 100. You can then trace the program again.

*See Experiment 5.

Observations from step 11:

_____

_____

Assembling and Executing an Assembly Language Program

12. The program for this step is very similar to Example 12–2 given in the text. To make it interesting, we'll change how the data is entered and make it byte-size (instead of word-size). This will require changing several instructions in the code. The problem is to write an assembly language program that will find the largest unsigned number in a list and place it in the last position. Data in this exercise is bytes (8 bits), not words (16 bits). The last data point is signaled with a zero. The flowchart is shown in Figure 26–4 for reference.*

*Although the flowchart is identical to the one in the text, the instructions are not because the data are bytes, not words.

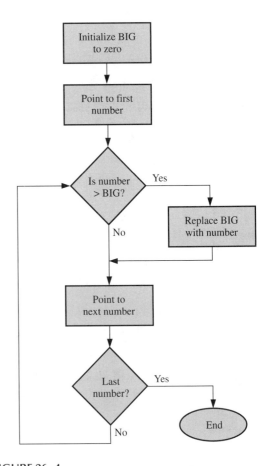

FIGURE 26–4
Flowchart for largest number problem. The variable BIG represents the largest value.

You can use Debug to enter the data into the list. The list will be 16 data points starting at the current data segment (assigned by DOS) and at the offset address of 50. Select 16 random bytes (not in any order) and modify memory by using the Debug Enter command starting at DS:50 (**-E 50**). You can use the space bar after each entry until you reach DS:60. Add zero as a last data indicator for the 17th byte at address DS:60, then press **<cr>**. Check that the data has been correctly entered with the Debug Dump command.

13. The Debug listing of the modified program is given in this step. The program is entered by starting the assembly at location 100. Start by issuing the **-A 100** command. Then type the following. (Note that your segment address will be different).

```
1E8C:0100 mov ax,0 <cr>
1E8C:0103 mov bx,50 <cr>
1E8C:0106 cmp [bx],al <cr>
1E8C:0108 jbe 010c <cr>
1E8C:010A mov al,[bx] <cr>
1E8C:010C inc bx <cr>
1E8C:010D cmp byte ptr [bx],0 <cr>
1E8C:0110 jnz 0106 <cr>
1E8C:0112 mov [bx],al <cr>
1E8C:0114 nop <cr>
```

Check that you have entered the code correctly by unassembling it using the **u** command:

−u 100 114

If the code has been correctly entered, you can execute it with the Go command. (Alternatively, you can trace each instruction if you prefer). Issue the Go command as follows. (Note the = sign!)

−g = 100 114 <cr>

The code will execute and show the registers at the end of the code. Indicate in the space below the values in the three registers listed after executing the code:

AX = _____   BX = _____

CX = _____

Press **<cr>** again to leave the assembler.

14. Dump the memory locations from DS:50 to DS:60. What happened?

_____

_____

For Further Investigation

For the code in step 13, try changing the instruction on line 100 from **mov ax,0** to **mov ax,ffff** and the instruction on line 108 from **jbe 010c** to **jae 010c.** Reenter a zero for the last data point (at DS:50). Run the code and observe the data and the registers. Summarize your findings.

Review Questions

1. Cite evidence from the experiment that the Debug Dump command can be used for looking at both RAM and ROM.

2. Explain what action occurs as a result of the Debug command **-F 1F0,1FF,FA <cr>**.

3. Show the Debug command that would allow you to view the lowest 10 words in memory containing the Intel interrupt vectors.

4. Where is the BIOS "work area" in memory? Cite examples of the type of data that can be found there.

27

D/A and A/D Conversion

Objectives

After completing this experiment, you will be able to
☐ Construct a circuit using a binary counter and a digital-to-analog converter (DAC).
☐ Check the calibration of the circuit, measure its resolution in volts/step, and observe its waveforms on an oscilloscope.
☐ Modify the circuit into a tracking analog-to-digital converter (ADC), and use it to construct a digital light meter.

Reference Reading

Floyd, *Digital Fundamentals with VHDL,* Chapter 13, "Introduction to Digital Signal Processing"

Materials Needed

74191 up/down counter
MC1408 digital-to-analog converter*
7447A BCD-to-seven-segment decoder/driver
MAN-72 seven-segment display
LM741 operational amplifier
3906 PNP transistor
CdS photocell (Jameco 120299 or equivalent)
Resistors: seven 330 Ω, two 1.0 kΩ, two 2.0 kΩ, one 5.1 kΩ, one 10 kΩ

For Further Investigation:
    ADC0804 analog-to-digital converter

*Available at www.garysupply.com

Resistors: two 2.2 kΩ, one 1.0 kΩ
One 1.0 kΩ potentiometer
One SPDT switch (wire can be used)

Summary of Theory

Digital Signal Processing (DSP) has become an important element of many digital designs, especially those that work in *real time. Real time* is defined as a time short enough that required processes are completed without affecting the end result. DSP involves three basic steps. These are conversion of an analog signal to digital, processing the signal in a specialized microprocessor, and (usually) conversion of the digital signal back to analog.

The focus of this experiment is the conversion process from analog to digital and back. Conversion from an analog input into a digital quantity is done by an *analog-to-digital converter* (ADC). A *digital-to-analog converter* (DAC) does the reverse—it converts a digital quantity into a voltage or current that is proportional to the input.

A variety of ADCs are available. The selection of a particular one depends on requirements such as conversion speed, resolution, accuracy, and cost. *Resolution* is the number of steps the full-scale signal is divided into. It may be expressed as a percentage of full-scale, as a voltage per step, or simply as the number of bits used in the conversion. *Accuracy,* which is often confused with resolution, is the percentage difference between the actual and the expected output.

A simple analog device, the potentiometer, can be used as a sensor to produce a voltage proportional to the shaft position. Figure 27–1 shows a simplified circuit that illustrates conceptually how the shaft position of the potentiometer can be converted to a digital number. (Only one digit is shown to keep the system simple.) It is drawn with an ADC0804, an 8-bit ADC. The digital output is scaled to a +5.0 V reference—that is, the output is the maximum value when the input is +5.0 V. With a small modification, the output could be scaled for other input voltages. The circuit could be constructed with either the AD673 or the ADC0804, depending on availability. The actual construction of this circuit is left as a Further Investigation.

In the first part of this experiment, you will test an integrated circuit DAC (the MC1408) using a binary up/down counter for a digital input. A reference current of nearly 1.0 mA is set up by a 5.1 kΩ resistor connected to +5.0 V. This current is used to set the full-scale output in the 2.0 kΩ load resistor.

After testing the DAC, you can convert the circuit to a tracking ADC with the addition of a comparator and interface circuity (see Figure 27–3). The binary output from an up/down counter is converted to an analog quantity by the DAC, which is compared

to the analog input. This circuit is a little more complicated than that shown in Figure 27–1, but better illustrates how a tracking ADC works. In principle, any analog input could be used (such as the antenna tracking system input), but we will use a photocell to construct a simplified digital light meter.

Pre-lab Questions

1. What is the difference between resolution and accuracy when applied to an ADC?
2. For the circuit in Figure 27–1, what is the purpose of the 7447A?

Procedure

Multiplying DAC

1. Construct the circuit shown in Figure 27–2. The MC1408 DAC has 8-bit resolution, but we will use only the 4 most significant bits and not bother with a binary-to-BCD decoder. Note how the input

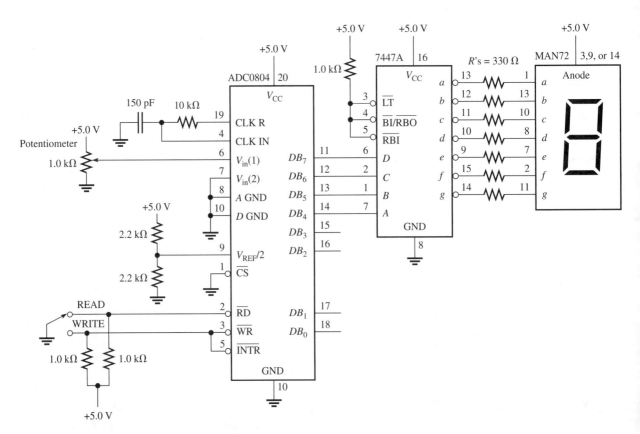

FIGURE 27–1

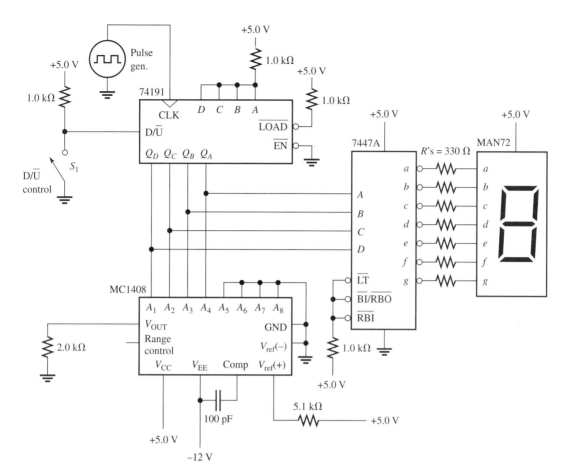

FIGURE 27–2

pins on the DAC are numbered; the MSB is the low-est number. Set the pulse generator for a TTL-level 1 Hz, and close S_1. Observe the waveforms at the output of the counter. Sketch the observed wave-forms in Plot 1 of the report.

2. Open S_1. Observe the waveforms from the counter and draw them in Plot 2.

3. Apply a short to ground on the $\overline{\text{LOAD}}$ input of the counter. This parallel-loads the counter to all 1's. Now check the calibration of the DAC. With the short in place, measure the output voltage on pin 4 of the MC1408. This represents the full-scale output. Determine the volts per step by dividing the full-scale output voltage by 15 (since there are 15 steps present). Record the voltage and the volts per step in Table 27–1.

4. Disconnect the short to ground from the $\overline{\text{LOAD}}$ input of the counter. Speed the pulse gener-ator up to 1 kHz. With an oscilloscope, observe the analog output (pin 4) from the DAC. On Plot 3 sketch the waveform you see. Label the voltage and time on your sketch.

5. Close S_1 and observe the analog output from the DAC. Sketch the observed waveform on Plot 4.

A Digital Light Meter—A Tracking ADC

6. Modify the circuit into a tracking ADC by adding the photocell, operational amplifier (op-amp), and transistor, as shown in Figure 27–3. The circuit senses light, producing a voltage at the non-inverting input (pin 3) of the op-amp. The input voltage from the photocell is compared to the output voltage from the DAC and causes the counter to count either up or down. The purpose of the transistor is to change the op-amp output to TTL-compatible levels for the counter.

7. Set the pulse generator for 1 Hz, and note what happens to the count in the seven-segment dis-play as you cover the photocell with your hand. If a constant light is allowed to strike the photocell, the output still oscillates. This oscillating behavior is characteristic of the tracking ADC. Speed up the generator and observe the analog output of the DAC on the oscilloscope. Describe the signal observed on the scope as you cover the photocell.

8. The modification shown in Figure 27–4 is a simple way to remove the oscillating behavior from the seven-segment display. Note that the Q_D output of the counter is connected to the C input of the 7447A. Try it and explain how it works.

329

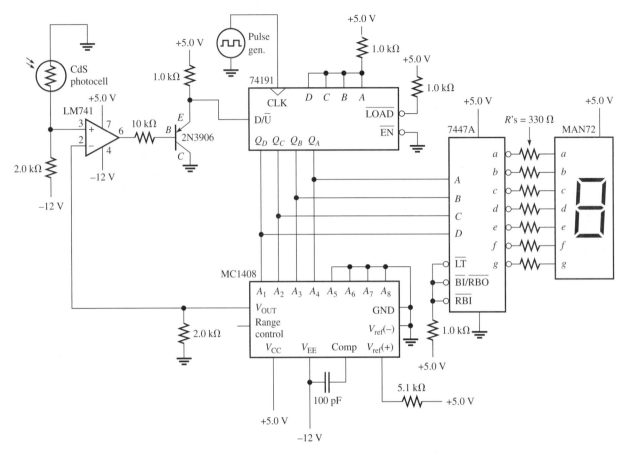

FIGURE 27–3
Simple digital light meter.

For Further Investigation

Construct the simplified antenna positioning system shown in Figure 27–1. To save you time, pin numbers are included on the drawings. After power is applied, the read/write switch is temporarily placed in the write position, then moved to the read position. As you rotate the potentiometer, the output numbers should change. Record the input voltage at each threshold. Is the output a linear function of the input voltage?

FIGURE 27–4

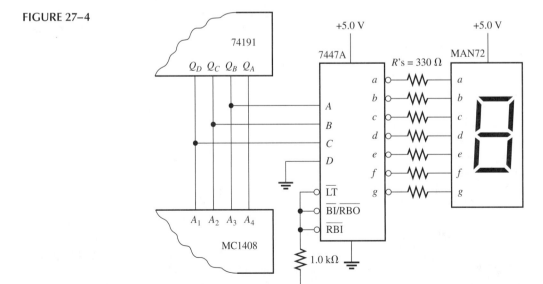

Report for Experiment 27

Name: _____ Date: _____ Class: _____

Data and Observations:

Q_A
Q_B
Q_C
Q_D

Plot 1

Q_A
Q_B
Q_C
Q_D

Plot 2

TABLE 27–1

Quantity	Measured Value
DAC full-scale output voltage	
Volts/step	

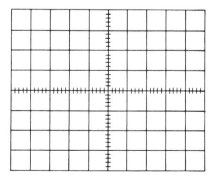

Plot 3

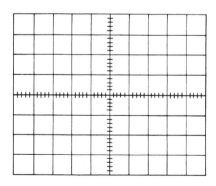

Plot 4

Observations from Step 7:

Observations from Step 8:

Results and Conclusion:

Further Investigation Results:

Review Questions (TTL)

1. a. In Step 4, you observed the analog output from the DAC. What output voltage represents a binary 1010 input?

   b. What is the output frequency of the DAC?

2. If all eight input bits for the DAC were used, what would be the output resolution in volts/step?

3. a. What happens to the output voltage if the 5.1 $k\Omega$ resistor is made smaller?

   b. What happens to the output resolution?

Appendix A

Selected Manufacturers' Data Sheets

SN5400, SN54LS00, SN54S00, SN7400, SN74LS00, SN74S00 QUADRUPLE 2-INPUT POSITIVE-NAND GATES

SDLS025 – DECEMBER 1983 – REVISED MARCH 1988

- **Package Options Include Plastic "Small Outline" Packages, Ceramic Chip Carriers and Flat Packages, and Plastic and Ceramic DIPs**
- **Dependable Texas Instruments Quality and Reliability**

description

These devices contain four independent 2-input-NAND gates.

The SN5400, SN54LS00, and SN54S00 are characterized for operation over the full military temperature range of −55°C to 125°C. The SN7400, SN74LS00, and SN74S00 are characterized for operation from 0°C to 70°C.

FUNCTION TABLE (each gate)

INPUTS		OUTPUT
A	B	Y
H	H	L
L	X	H
X	L	H

logic symbol[†]

1A (1)	
1B (2)	(3) 1Y
2A (4)	
2B (5)	(6) 2Y
3A (9)	
3B (10)	(8) 3Y
4A (12)	
4B (13)	(11) 4Y

&

[†]This symbol is in accordance with ANSI/IEEE Std. 91-1984 and IEC Publication 617-12.

Pin numbers shown are for D, J, and N packages.

SN5400 . . . J PACKAGE
SN54LS00, SN54S00 . . . J OR W PACKAGE
SN7400 . . . N PACKAGE
SN74LS00, SN74S00 . . . D OR N PACKAGE
(TOP VIEW)

1A	1	14	VCC
1B	2	13	4B
1Y	3	12	4A
2A	4	11	4Y
2B	5	10	3B
2Y	6	9	3A
GND	7	8	3Y

SN5400 . . . W PACKAGE
(TOP VIEW)

1A	1	14	4Y
1B	2	13	4B
1Y	3	12	4A
VCC	4	11	GND
2Y	5	10	3B
2A	6	9	3A
2B	7	8	3Y

SN54LS00, SN54S00 . . . FK PACKAGE
(TOP VIEW)

Pin	Signal
4	1Y
5	NC
6	2A
7	NC
8	2B
18	4A
17	NC
16	4Y
15	NC
14	3B

Top: 1B, 1A, VCC, NC, GND
Bottom: 2Y, 3V, NC, 3Y, 3A

NC - No internal connection

logic diagram (positive logic)

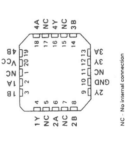

1A, 1B → 1Y
2A, 2B → 2Y
3A, 3B → 3Y
4A, 4B → 4Y

$Y = A \cdot B$ or $Y = \overline{A} + \overline{B}$

---

recommended operating conditions

		SN5400			SN7400			UNIT
		MIN	NOM	MAX	MIN	NOM	MAX	
V_{CC}	Supply voltage	4.5	5	5.5	4.75	5	5.25	V
V_{IH}	High-level input voltage	2			2			V
V_{IL}	Low-level input voltage			0.8			0.8	V
I_{OH}	High-level output current			−0.4			−0.4	mA
I_{OL}	Low-level output current			16			16	mA
T_A	Operating free-air temperature	−55		125	0		70	°C

electrical characteristics over recommended operating free-air temperature range (unless otherwise noted)

PARAMETER	TEST CONDITIONS			SN5400			SN7400			UNIT
			MIN	TYP[‡]	MAX	MIN	TYP[‡]	MAX		
V_{IK}	V_{CC} = MIN,	I_I = −12 mA				−1.5			−1.5	V
V_{OH}	V_{CC} = MIN,	V_{IL} = 0.8 V,	I_{OH} = −0.4 mA	2.4	3.4		2.4	3.4		V
V_{OL}	V_{CC} = MIN,	V_{IH} = 2 V,	I_{OL} = 16 mA		0.2	0.4		0.2	0.4	V
I_I	V_{CC} = MAX,	V_I = 5.5 V				1			1	mA
I_{IH}	V_{CC} = MAX,	V_I = 2.4 V				40			40	µA
I_{IL}	V_{CC} = MAX,	V_I = 0.4 V				−1.6			−1.6	mA
I_{OS}§	V_{CC} = MAX		−20		−55	−18		−55	mA
I_{CCH}	V_{CC} = MAX,	V_I = 0 V			4	8		4	8	mA
I_{CCL}	V_{CC} = MAX,	V_I = 4.5 V			12	22		12	22	mA

[†] For conditions shown as MIN or MAX, use the appropriate value specified under recommended operating conditions.
[‡] All typical values are at V_{CC} = 5 V, T_A = 25°C.
§ Not more than one output should be shorted at a time.

switching characteristics, VCC = 5 V, TA = 25°C (see note 2)

PARAMETER	FROM (INPUT)	TO (OUTPUT)	TEST CONDITIONS		MIN	TYP	MAX	UNIT
t_{PLH}	A or B	Y	R_L = 400 Ω,	C_L = 15 pF		11	22	ns
t_{PHL}						7	15	ns

NOTE 2: Load circuits and voltage waveforms are shown in Section 1.

PRODUCTION DATA information is current as of publication date. Products conform to specifications per the terms of Texas Instruments standard warranty. Production processing does not necessarily include testing of all parameters.

Copyright © 1988, Texas Instruments Incorporated

TEXAS INSTRUMENTS

POST OFFICE BOX 655303 ● DALLAS, TEXAS 75265

SDLS027

SN5402, SN54LS02, SN54S02, SN7402, SN74LS02, SN74S02
QUADRUPLE 2-INPUT POSITIVE-NOR GATES
DECEMBER 1983–REVISED MARCH 1988

- Package Options Include Plastic "Small Outline" Packages, Ceramic Chip Carriers and Flat Packages, and Plastic and Ceramic DIPs
- Dependable Texas Instruments Quality and Reliability

description

These devices contain four independent 2-input-NOR gates.

The SN5402, SN54LS02, and SN54S02 are characterized for operation over the full military temperature range of −55°C to 125°C. The SN7402, SN74LS02, and SN74S02 are characterized for operation from 0°C to 70°C.

FUNCTION TABLE (each gate)

INPUTS		OUTPUT
A	B	Y
H	X	L
X	H	L
L	L	H

SN5402 . . . J PACKAGE
SN54LS02, SN54S02 . . . J OR W PACKAGE
SN7402 . . . N PACKAGE
SN74LS02, SN74S02 . . . D OR N PACKAGE
(TOP VIEW)

1Y	1	14 Vcc
1A	2	13 4Y
1B	3	12 4B
2Y	4	11 4A
2A	5	10 3Y
2B	6	9 3B
GND	7	8 3A

SN5402 . . . W PACKAGE
(TOP VIEW)

1A	1	14 4Y
1B	2	13 4B
1Y	3	12 4A
Vcc	4	11 GND
2Y	5	10 3B
2A	6	9 3A
2B	7	8 3Y

SN54LS02, SN54S02 . . . FK PACKAGE
(TOP VIEW)

NC – No internal connection

logic symbol†

logic diagram (positive logic)

$Y = \overline{A \cdot B}$ or $Y = \overline{A + B}$

† This symbol is in accordance with ANSI/IEEE Std. 91-1984 and IEC Publication 617-12.
Pin numbers shown are for D, J, and N packages.

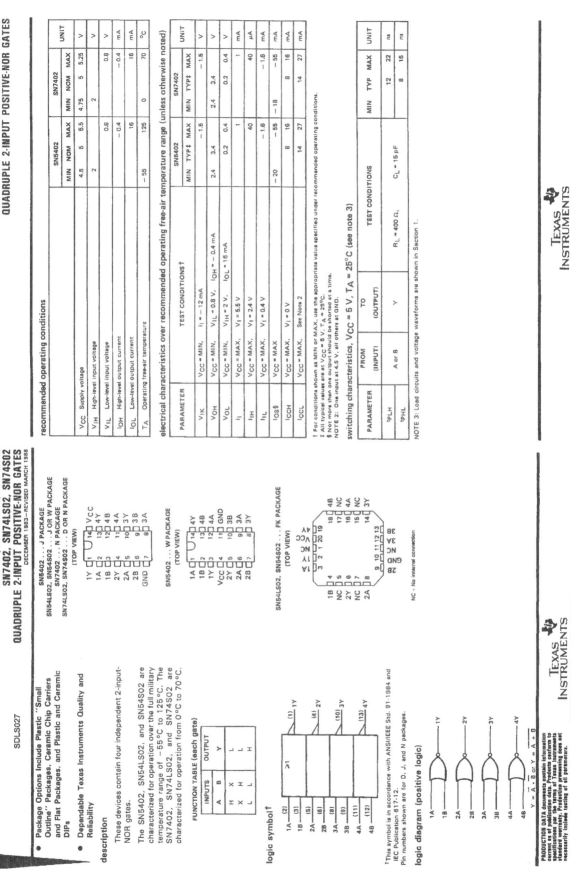

TEXAS INSTRUMENTS
POST OFFICE BOX 655012 • DALLAS, TEXAS 75265

SN5402, SN7402
QUADRUPLE 2-INPUT POSITIVE-NOR GATES

recommended operating conditions

		SN5402 MIN	SN5402 NOM	SN5402 MAX	SN7402 MIN	SN7402 NOM	SN7402 MAX	UNIT
Vcc	Supply voltage	4.5	5	5.5	4.75	5	5.25	V
VIH	High-level input voltage	2			2			V
VIL	Low-level input voltage			0.8			0.8	V
IOH	High-level output current			−0.4			−0.4	mA
IOL	Low-level output current			16			16	mA
TA	Operating free-air temperature	−55		125	0		70	°C

electrical characteristics over recommended operating free-air temperature range (unless otherwise noted)

PARAMETER	TEST CONDITIONS†	SN5402 MIN	SN5402 TYP‡	SN5402 MAX	SN7402 MIN	SN7402 TYP‡	SN7402 MAX	UNIT
VIK	Vcc = MIN, II = −12 mA			−1.5			−1.5	V
VOH	Vcc = MIN, VIL = 0.8 V, IOH = −0.4 mA	2.4	3.4		2.4	3.4		V
VOL	Vcc = MIN, VIH = 2 V, IOL = 18 mA		0.2	0.4		0.2	0.4	V
II	Vcc = MAX, VI = 5.5 V			1			1	mA
IIH	Vcc = MAX, VI = 2.4 V			40			40	µA
IIL	Vcc = MAX, VI = 0.4 V			−1.6			−1.6	mA
IOS§	Vcc = MAX	−20		−55	−18		−55	mA
ICCH	Vcc = MAX, VI = 0 V		8	16		8	16	mA
ICCL	Vcc = MAX, See Note 2		14	27		14	27	mA

† For conditions shown as MIN or MAX, use the appropriate value specified under recommended operating conditions.
‡ All typical values are at Vcc = 5 V, TA = 25°C.
§ Not more than one output should be shorted at a time.
NOTE 2: One input at 4.5 V, all others at GND.

switching characteristics, Vcc = 5 V, TA = 25°C (see note 3)

PARAMETER	FROM (INPUT)	TO (OUTPUT)	TEST CONDITIONS	MIN	TYP	MAX	UNIT
tPLH	A or B	Y	RL = 400 Ω, CL = 15 pF		12	22	ns
tPHL	A or B	Y			8	15	ns

NOTE 3: Load circuits and voltage waveforms are shown in Section 1.

TEXAS INSTRUMENTS
POST OFFICE BOX 655012 • DALLAS, TEXAS 75265

Courtesy of Texas Instruments Incorporated

335

SN5404, SN54LS04, SN54S04,
SN7404, SN74LS04, SN74S04
HEX INVERTERS

SDLS029B – DECEMBER 1983 – REVISED FEBRUARY 2002

- ● Dependable Texas Instruments Quality and Reliability

description

These devices contain six independent inverters.

SN5404 . . . J PACKAGE
SN54LS04, SN54S04 . . . J OR W PACKAGE
SN7404 . . . D, N, OR NS PACKAGE
SN74LS04 . . . D, DB, N, OR NS PACKAGE
SN74S04 . . . D OR N PACKAGE
(TOP VIEW)

1A	1	14	V_CC
1Y	2	13	6A
2A	3	12	6Y
2Y	4	11	5A
3A	5	10	5Y
3Y	6	9	4A
GND	7	8	4Y

SN5404 . . . W PACKAGE
(TOP VIEW)

1A	1	14	1Y
2Y	2	13	6A
2A	3	12	6Y
V_CC	4	11	GND
3A	5	10	5Y
3Y	6	9	5A
4A	7	8	4Y

SN54LS04, SN54S04 . . . FK PACKAGE
(TOP VIEW)

NC – No internal connection

logic diagram (positive logic)

$Y = \overline{A}$

TEXAS
INSTRUMENTS

POST OFFICE BOX 655303 ● DALLAS, TEXAS 75265

TEXAS
INSTRUMENTS

POST OFFICE BOX 655303 ● DALLAS, TEXAS 75265

1

- Package Options Include Plastic "Small Outline" Packages, Ceramic Chip Carriers and Flat Packages, and Plastic and Ceramic DIPs

- Dependable Texas Instruments Quality and Reliability

description

These devices contain four independent 2-input OR gates.

The SN5432, SN54LS32 and SN54S32 are characterized for operation over the full military range of −55°C to 125°C. The SN7432, SN74LS32 and SN74S32 are characterized for operation from 0°C to 70°C.

FUNCTION TABLE (each gate)

INPUTS		OUTPUT
A	B	Y
H	X	H
X	H	H
L	L	L

logic symbol†

† This symbol is in accordance with ANSI/IEEE Std 91-1984 and IEC Publication 617-12.
Pin numbers shown are for D, J, N, or W packages.

SN5432, SN54LS32, SN54S32 . . . J OR W PACKAGE
SN7432 . . . N PACKAGE
SN74LS32, SN74S32 . . . D OR N PACKAGE
(TOP VIEW)

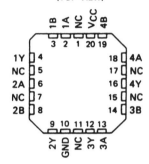

```
1A  [1      14] VCC
1B  [2      13] 4B
1Y  [3      12] 4A
2A  [4      11] 4Y
2B  [5      10] 3B
2Y  [6       9] 3A
GND [7       8] 3Y
```

SN54LS32, SN54S32 . . . FK PACKAGE
(TOP VIEW)

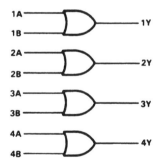

NC - No internal connection

logic diagram

```
1A ─┐
     ├─ 1Y
1B ─┘

2A ─┐
     ├─ 2Y
2B ─┘

3A ─┐
     ├─ 3Y
3B ─┘

4A ─┐
     ├─ 4Y
4B ─┘
```

positive logic

$$Y = A + B \text{ or } Y = \overline{\overline{A} \cdot \overline{B}}$$

2

TTL Devices

TEXAS
INSTRUMENTS

POST OFFICE BOX 655012 • DALLAS, TEXAS 75265

2-137

Courtesy of Texas Instruments Incorporated

SN54LS32, SN74LS32
QUADRUPLE 2-INPUT POSITIVE-OR GATES

recommended operating conditions

		SN54LS32			SN74LS32			UNIT
		MIN	NOM	MAX	MIN	NOM	MAX	
V_{CC}	Supply voltage	4.5	5	5.5	4.75	5	5.25	V
V_{IH}	High-level input voltage	2			2			V
V_{IL}	Low-level input voltage			0.7			0.8	V
I_{OH}	High-level output current			−0.4			−0.4	mA
I_{OL}	Low-level output current			4			8	mA
T_A	Opertating free-air temperature	−55		125	0		70	°C

electrical characteristics over recommended operating free-air temperature range (unless otherwise noted)

PARAMETER	TEST CONDITIONS †			SN54LS32			SN74LS32			UNIT
				MIN	TYP‡	MAX	MIN	TYP‡	MAX	
V_{IK}	V_{CC} = MIN,	$I_I = -18$ mA				−1.5			−1.5	V
V_{OH}	V_{CC} = MIN,	V_{IH} = 2 V,	$I_{OH} = -0.4$ mA	2.5	3.4		2.7	3.4		V
V_{OL}	V_{CC} = MIN,	V_{IL} = MAX,	I_{OL} = 4 mA		0.25	0.4		0.25	0.4	V
	V_{CC} = MIN,	V_{IL} = MAX,	I_{OL} = 8 mA					0.35	0.5	
I_I	V_{CC} = MAX,	V_I = 7 V				0.1			0.1	mA
I_{IH}	V_{CC} = MAX,	V_I = 2.7 V				20			20	µA
I_{IL}	V_{CC} = MAX,	V_I = 0.4 V				−0.4			−0.4	mA
I_{OS}§	V_{CC} = MAX			−20		−100	−20		−100	mA
I_{CCH}	V_{CC} = MAX,	See Note 2			3.1	6.2		3.1	6.2	mA
I_{CCL}	V_{CC} = MAX,	V_I = 0 V			4.9	9.8		4.9	9.8	mA

† For conditions shown as MIN or MAX, use the appropriate value specified under recommended operating conditions.
‡ All typical values are at V_{CC} = 5 V, T_A = 25°C.
§ Not more than one output should be shorted at a time and the duration of the short-circuit should not exceed one second.
NOTE 2: One input at 4.5 V, all others at GND.

switching characteristics, V_{CC} = 5 V, T_A = 25°C (see note 3)

PARAMETER	FROM (INPUT)	TO (OUTPUT)	TEST CONDITIONS		MIN	TYP	MAX	UNIT
t_{PLH}	A or B	Y	R_L = 2 kΩ,	C_L = 15 pF		14	22	ns
t_{PHL}						14	22	ns

NOTE 3: Load circuits and voltage waveforms are shown in Section 1.

TEXAS
INSTRUMENTS

POST OFFICE BOX 655012 • DALLAS, TEXAS 75265

TYPES SN5446A, '47A, '48, '49, SN54L46, 'L47, SN54LS47, 'LS48, 'LS49, SN7446A, '47A, '48, SN74LS47, 'LS48, 'LS49
BCD-TO-SEVEN-SEGMENT DECODERS/DRIVERS

- All Circuit Types Feature Lamp Intensity Modulation Capability

TYPE	ACTIVE LEVEL	DRIVER OUTPUTS				TYPICAL POWER DISSIPATION	PACKAGES
		OUTPUT CONFIGURATION	SINK CURRENT	MAX VOLTAGE			
SN5446A	low	open-collector	40 mA	30 V		320 mW	J, W
SN5447A	low	open-collector	40 mA	15 V		320 mW	J, W
SN5448	high	2-kΩ pull-up	6.4 mA	5.5 V		265 mW	J, W
SN5449	high	open-collector	10 mA	5.5 V		165 mW	W
SN54L46	low	open-collector	20 mA	30 V		160 mW	J
SN54L47	low	open-collector	20 mA	15 V		160 mW	J
SN54LS47	low	open-collector	12 mA	15 V		35 mW	J, W
SN54LS48	high	2-kΩ pull-up	2 mA	5.5 V		125 mW	J, W
SN54LS49	high	open-collector	4 mA	5.5 V		40 mW	J, W
SN7446A	low	open-collector	40 mA	30 V		320 mW	J, N
SN7447A	low	open-collector	40 mA	15 V		320 mW	J, N
SN7448	high	2-kΩ pull-up	6.4 mA	5.5 V		265 mW	J, N
SN74LS47	low	open-collector	24 mA	15 V		35 mW	J, N
SN74LS48	high	2-kΩ pull-up	6 mA	5.5 V		125 mW	J, N
SN74LS49	high	open-collector	8 mA	5.5 V		40 mW	J, N

logic symbols

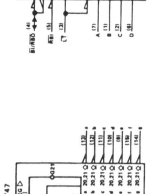

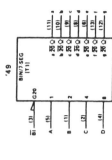

Pin numbers shown on logic notation are for D, J or N packages.

TEXAS
INSTRUMENTS
POST OFFICE BOX 225012 • DALLAS, TEXAS 75265

TYPES SN5446A, '47A, '48, '49, SN54L46, 'L47, SN54LS47, 'LS48, 'LS49, SN7446A, '47A, '48, SN74LS47, 'LS48, 'LS49
BCD-TO-SEVEN-SEGMENT DECODERS/DRIVERS

MARCH 1974 – REVISED DECEMBER 1983

'46A, '47A, 'L46, 'L47, 'LS47 feature	'48, 'LS48 feature	'49, 'LS49 feature
• Open-Collector Outputs Drive Indicators Directly	• Internal Pull-Ups Eliminate Need for External Resistors	• Open-Collector Outputs
• Lamp-Test Provision	• Lamp-Test Provision	• Blanking Input
• Leading/Trailing Zero Suppression	• Leading/Trailing Zero Suppression	

SN54L46, SN54L47 . . . . J PACKAGE
SN5446A, SN5447A, SN54LS47, SN5448,
SN54LS48 . . . . J OR W PACKAGE
SN7446A, SN7447A,
SN7448 . . . . J OR N PACKAGE
SN74LS47, SN74LS48 . . . D, J OR N PACKAGE
(TOP VIEW)

SN54LS47, SN54LS48 . . . . FK PACKAGE
SN74LS47, SN74LS48 . . . . FN PACKAGE
(TOP VIEW)

SN5449 . . . . W PACKAGE
SN54LS49 . . . . J OR W PACKAGE
SN74LS49 . . . D, J OR N PACKAGE
(TOP VIEW)

SN54LS49 . . . . FK PACKAGE
SN74LS49 . . . . FN PACKAGE
(TOP VIEW)

NC — No internal connection

PRODUCTION DATA
This document contains information current as of publication date. Products conform to specifications per the terms of Texas Instruments standard warranty. Production processing does not necessarily include testing of all parameters.

TEXAS
INSTRUMENTS
POST OFFICE BOX 225012 • DALLAS, TEXAS 75265

TYPES SN5446A, SN5447A, SN7446A, SN7447A
BCD-TO-SEVEN-SEGMENT DECODERS/DRIVERS

absolute maximum ratings over operating free-air temperature range (unless otherwise noted)

Supply voltage, VCC (see Note 1) . . . . 7 V
Input voltage . . . . 5.5 V
Current forced into any output in the off state . . . . 1 mA
Operating free-air temperature range: SN5446A, SN5447A . . . -55°C to 125°C
                                       SN7446A, SN7447A . . . . 0°C to 70°C
Storage temperature range . . . . -65°C to 150°C

NOTE 1: Voltage values are with respect to network ground terminal.

recommended operating conditions

		SN5446A			SN5447A			SN7446A			SN7447A			UNIT
		MIN	NOM	MAX	MIN	NOM	MAX	MIN	NOM	MAX	MIN	NOM	MAX	
Supply voltage, VCC		4.5	5	5.5	4.5	5	5.5	4.75	5	5.25	4.75	5	5.25	V
Off-state output voltage, VO(off)	a thru g			30			30			30			15	V
On-state output current, IO(on)	a thru g			40			40			40			40	mA
High-level output current, IOH	BI/RBO			-200			-200			-200			-200	µA
Low-level output current, IOL	BI/RBO			8			8			8			8	mA
Operating free-air temperature, TA		-55		125	-55		125	0		70	0		70	°C

electrical characteristics over recommended operating free-air temperature range (unless otherwise noted)

PARAMETER		TEST CONDITIONS†	SN7447A MIN	TYP‡	MAX	UNIT
V_{IH} High-level input voltage			2			V
V_{IL} Low-level input voltage					0.8	V
V_{IK} Input clamp voltage		VCC = MIN, II = -12 mA			-1.5	V
V_{OH} High-level output voltage	BI/RBO	VCC = MIN, VIH = 2 V, VIL = 0.8 V, IOH = -200 µA	2.4	3.7		V
V_{OL} Low-level output voltage	BI/RBO	VCC = MIN, VIH = 2 V, VIL = 0.8 V, IOL = 8 mA		0.27	0.4	V
$I_{O(off)}$ Off-state output current	a thru g	VCC = MAX, VIH = 2 V, VIL = 0.8 V, VO(off) = MAX			250	µA
$V_{O(on)}$ On-state output voltage	a thru g	VCC = MIN, VIH = 2 V, VIL = 0.8 V, IO(on) = 40 mA		0.3	0.4	V
I_I Input current at maximum input voltage	Any input except BI/RBO	VCC = MAX, VI = 5.5 V			1	mA
I_{IH} High-level input current	Any input except BI/RBO	VCC = MAX, VI = 2.4 V			40	µA
I_{IL} Low-level input current	Any input except BI/RBO	VCC = MAX, VI = 0.4 V			-1.6	mA
	BI/RBO				-4	
I_{OS} Short-circuit output current		VCC = MAX			-4	mA
I_{CC} Supply current		VCC = MAX, See Note 2	SN54' 64		85	mA
			SN74' 64		103	

†For conditions shown as MIN or MAX, use the appropriate value specified under recommended operating conditions.
‡All typical values are at VCC = 5 V, TA = 25°C.
NOTE 2: ICC is measured with all outputs open and all inputs at 4.5 V.

switching characteristics, VCC = 5 V, TA = 25°C

PARAMETER	TEST CONDITIONS	MIN	TYP	MAX	UNIT
toff Turn-off time from A input	CL = 15 pF, RL = 120 Ω, See Note 3			100	ns
ton Turn-on time from A input				100	ns
toff Turn-off time from RBI input				100	ns
ton Turn-on time from RBI input				100	ns

NOTE 3: See General Information Section for load circuits and voltage waveforms. †off corresponds to tPLH and ton corresponds to tPHL.

TEXAS INSTRUMENTS
POST OFFICE BOX 225012 • DALLAS, TEXAS 75265

TYPES SN5446A, '47A, '48, '49, SN54L46, 'L47, SN54LS47, 'LS48, 'LS49, SN7446A, '47A, '48, SN74LS47, 'LS48, 'LS49
BCD-TO-SEVEN-SEGMENT DECODERS/DRIVERS

description

The '46A, 'L46, '47A, and 'LS47 feature active-low outputs designed for driving common-anode VLEDs or incandescent indicators directly, and the '48, '49, 'LS48, 'LS49 feature active-high outputs for driving lamp buffers or common-cathode VLEDs. All of the circuits except '49 and 'LS49 have full ripple-blanking input/output controls and a lamp test input. The '49 and 'LS49 circuits incorporate a direct blanking input. Segment identification and resultant displays are shown below. Display patterns for BCD input counts above 9 are unique symbols to authenticate input conditions.

The '46A, '47A, '48, 'L46, 'L47, 'LS47 and 'LS48 circuits incorporate automatic leading and/or trailing-edge zero-blanking control (RBI and RBO). Lamp test (LT) of these types may be performed at any time when the BI/RBO node is at a high level. All types (including the '49 and 'LS49) contain an overriding blanking input (BI) which can be used to control the lamp intensity by pulsing or to inhibit the outputs. Inputs and outputs are entirely compatible for use with TTL logic outputs.

The SN54246 through '249 and the SN54LS247 through 'LS249 compose the 6 and the 9 with tails and have been designed to offer the designer a choice between two indicator fonts. The SN54249/SN74249 and SN54LS249/SN74LS249 are 16-pin versions of the 14-pin SN5449 and 'LS49. Included in the '249 circuit and 'LS249 circuits are the full functional capability for lamp test and ripple blanking, which is not available in the '49 or 'LS49 circuit.

SEGMENT IDENTIFICATION

NUMERICAL DESIGNATIONS AND RESULTANT DISPLAYS

0 1 2 3 4 5 6 7 8 9 10 11 12 13 14 15

'46A, '47A, 'L46, 'L47, 'LS47 FUNCTION TABLE

DECIMAL OR FUNCTION	LT	RBI	D	C	B	A	BI/RBO†	a	b	c	d	e	f	g	NOTE
0	H	H	L	L	L	L	H	ON	ON	ON	ON	ON	ON	OFF	1
1	H	X	L	L	L	H	H	OFF	ON	ON	OFF	OFF	OFF	OFF	
2	H	X	L	L	H	L	H	ON	ON	OFF	ON	ON	OFF	ON	
3	H	X	L	L	H	H	H	ON	ON	ON	ON	OFF	OFF	ON	
4	H	X	L	H	L	L	H	OFF	ON	ON	OFF	OFF	ON	ON	
5	H	X	L	H	L	H	H	ON	OFF	ON	ON	OFF	ON	ON	
6	H	X	L	H	H	L	H	OFF	OFF	ON	ON	ON	ON	ON	
7	H	X	L	H	H	H	H	ON	ON	ON	OFF	OFF	OFF	OFF	
8	H	X	H	L	L	L	H	ON	ON	ON	ON	ON	ON	ON	
9	H	X	H	L	L	H	H	ON	ON	ON	OFF	OFF	ON	ON	
10	H	X	H	L	H	L	H	OFF	OFF	OFF	ON	ON	OFF	ON	
11	H	X	H	L	H	H	H	OFF	OFF	ON	ON	OFF	OFF	ON	
12	H	X	H	H	L	L	H	OFF	ON	OFF	OFF	OFF	ON	ON	
13	H	X	H	H	L	H	H	ON	OFF	OFF	ON	OFF	ON	ON	
14	H	X	H	H	H	L	H	OFF	OFF	OFF	ON	ON	ON	ON	
15	H	X	H	H	H	H	H	OFF	OFF	OFF	OFF	OFF	OFF	OFF	
BI	X	X	X	X	X	X	L	OFF	OFF	OFF	OFF	OFF	OFF	OFF	2
RBI	H	L	L	L	L	L	L	OFF	OFF	OFF	OFF	OFF	OFF	OFF	3
LT	L	X	X	X	X	X	H	ON	ON	ON	ON	ON	ON	ON	4

H = high level, L = low level, X = irrelevant

NOTES: 1. The blanking input (BI) must be open or held at a high logic level when output functions 0 through 15 are desired. The ripple-blanking input (RBI) must be open or high if blanking of a decimal zero is not desired.
2. When a low logic level is applied directly to the blanking input (BI), all segment outputs are off regardless of the level of any other input.
3. When ripple-blanking input (RBI) and inputs A, B, C, and D are at a low level with the lamp test input high, all segment outputs go off and the ripple-blanking output (RBO) goes to a low level (response condition).
4. When the blanking input/ripple blanking output (BI/RBO) is open or held high and a low is applied to the lamp test input, all segment outputs are on.

†BI/RBO is wire AND logic serving as blanking input (BI) and/or ripple-blanking output (RBO).

TEXAS INSTRUMENTS
POST OFFICE BOX 225012 • DALLAS, TEXAS 75265

SN5474, SN54LS74A, SN54S74
SN7474, SN74LS74A, SN74S74
DUAL D-TYPE POSITIVE-EDGE-TRIGGERED FLIP-FLOPS WITH PRESET AND CLEAR

SDLS119 – DECEMBER 1983 – REVISED MARCH 1988

- Package Options Include Plastic "Small Outline" Packages, Ceramic Chip Carriers and Flat Packages, and Plastic and Ceramic DIPs
- Dependable Texas Instruments Quality and Reliability

description

These devices contain two independent D-type positive-edge-triggered flip-flops. A low level at the preset or clear inputs sets or resets the outputs regardless of the levels of the other inputs. When preset and clear are inactive (high), data at the D input meeting the setup time requirements are transferred to the outputs on the positive-going edge of the clock pulse. Clock triggering occurs at a voltage level and is not directly related to the rise time of the clock pulse. Following the hold time interval, data at the D input may be changed without affecting the levels at the outputs.

The SN54' family is characterized for operation over the full military temperature range of –55°C to 125°C. The SN74' family is characterized for operation from 0°C to 70°C.

SN5474 . . . J PACKAGE
SN54LS74A, SN54S74 . . . J OR W PACKAGE
SN7474 . . . N PACKAGE
SN74LS74A, SN74S74 . . . D OR N PACKAGE
(TOP VIEW)

1CLR	1	14 Vcc
1D	2	13 2CLR
1CLK	3	12 2D
1PRE	4	11 2CLK
1Q	5	10 2PRE
1Q̄	6	9 2Q
GND	7	8 2Q̄

SN5474 . . . W PACKAGE
(TOP VIEW)

1CLR	1	14 1PRE
1D	2	13 1Q
1CLK	3	12 1Q̄
2CLR	4	11 GND
Vcc	5	10 2Q
2D	6	9 2Q̄
2CLK	7	8 2PRE

SN54LS74A, SN54S74 . . . FK PACKAGE
(TOP VIEW)

NC – No internal connection

FUNCTION TABLE

INPUTS				OUTPUTS	
PRE	CLR	CLK	D	Q	Q̄
L	H	X	X	H	L
H	L	X	X	L	H
L	L	X	X	H†	H†
H	H	↑	H	H	L
H	H	↑	L	L	H
H	H	L	X	Q0	Q̄0

† The output levels in this configuration are not guaranteed to meet the minimum levels in V_{OH} if the lows at preset and clear are near V_{IL} maximum. Furthermore, this configuration is nonstable; that is, it will not persist when either preset or clear returns to its inactive (high) level.

logic symbol‡

1PRE	(4)	S
1CLK	(3)	C1
1D	(2)	1D
1CLR	(1)	R
2PRE	(10)	
2CLK	(11)	
2D	(12)	
2CLR	(13)	

(5) 1Q
(6) 1Q̄
(9) 2Q
(8) 2Q̄

‡ This symbol is in accordance with ANSI/IEEE Std 91-1984 and IEC Publication 617-12.
Pin numbers shown are for D, J, N, and W packages.

logic diagram (positive logic)

recommended operating conditions

		SN5474			SN7474			UNIT
		MIN	NOM	MAX	MIN	NOM	MAX	
Vcc	Supply voltage	4.5	5	5.5	4.75	5	5.25	V
VIH	High-level input voltage	2			2			V
VIL	Low-level input voltage			0.8			0.8	V
IOH	High-level output current			–0.4			–0.4	mA
IOL	Low-level output current			16			16	mA
tw	Pulse duration CLK high	30			30			ns
	CLK low	37			37			
	PRE or CLR low	30			30			
tsu	Input setup time before CLK↑	20			20			ns
th	Input hold time-data after CLK↑	5			5			ns
TA	Operating free-air temperature	–55		125	0		70	°C

electrical characteristics over recommended operating free-air temperature range (unless otherwise noted)

PARAMETER		TEST CONDITIONS†	SN5474			SN7474			UNIT
			MIN	TYP‡	MAX	MIN	TYP‡	MAX	
VIK		Vcc = MIN, II = –12 mA			–1.5			–1.5	V
VOH		Vcc = MIN, VIH = 2 V, VIL = 0.8 V, IOH = –0.4 mA	2.4	3.4		2.4	3.4		V
VOL		Vcc = MIN, VIH = 2 V, VIL = 0.8 V, IOL = 16 mA		0.2	0.4		0.2	0.4	V
II		Vcc = MAX, VI = 5.5 V			1			1	mA
IIH	D	Vcc = MAX, VI = 2.4 V			40			40	µA
	CLR				120			120	
	All Other				80			80	
IIL	D	Vcc = MAX, VI = 0.4 V			–1.6			–1.6	mA
	PRE§				–3.2			–3.2	
	CLR§				–3.2			–3.2	
	CLK				–1.6			–1.6	
IOS¶		Vcc = MAX	–20		–57	–18		–57	mA
ICC#		Vcc = MAX, See Note 2		8.5	15		8.5	15	mA

† For conditions shown as MIN or MAX, use the appropriate value specified under recommended operating conditions.
‡ All typical values are at Vcc = 5 V, TA = 25°C.
§ Clear is tested with preset high and preset is tested with clear high.
¶ Not more than one output should be shorted at a time.
# Average per flip-flop.

NOTE 2: With all outputs open, I_{CC} is measured with the Q and Q̄ outputs high in turn. At the time of measurement, the clock input is grounded.

switching charateristics, Vcc = 5 V, TA = 25°C (see note 3)

PARAMETER	FROM (INPUT)	TO (OUTPUT)	TEST CONDITIONS	MIN	TYP	MAX	UNIT
fmax			RL = 400 Ω, CL = 15 pF	15	25		MHz
tPLH	PRE or CLR	Q or Q̄			14	25	ns
tPHL							ns
tPLH	CLK	Q or Q̄			20	40	ns
tPHL							ns

NOTE 3: Load circuits and voltage waveforms are shown in Section 1.

Copyright © 1988, Texas Instruments Incorporated

TEXAS INSTRUMENTS
POST OFFICE BOX 655303 ● DALLAS, TEXAS 75265

Courtesy of Texas Instruments Incorporated

Courtesy of Texas Instruments Incorporated

TYPES SN5476, SN54H76, SN54LS76A, SN7476, SN74H76, SN74LS76A
DUAL J-K FLIP-FLOPS WITH PRESET AND CLEAR

SN5476, SN54H76, SN54LS76A . . . J OR W PACKAGE
SN7476, SN74H76 . . . J OR N PACKAGE
SN74LS76A . . . D, J OR N PACKAGE

REVISED DECEMBER 1983

- **Package Options Include Plastic and Ceramic DIPs**
- **Dependable Texas Instruments Quality and Reliability**

description

The '76 and 'H76 contain two independent J-K flip-flops with individual J-K, clock, preset, and clear inputs. The '76 and 'H76 are positive-edge-triggered flip-flops. J-K input is loaded into the master while the clock is high and transferred to the slave on the high-to-low transition. For these devices the J and K inputs must be stable while the clock is high.

The LS76A contain two independent negative-edge-triggered flip-flops. The J and K inputs must be stable one setup time prior to the high-to-low clock transition for predictable operation. The preset and clear are asynchronous active low inputs. When low they override the clock and data inputs forcing the outputs to the steady state levels as shown in the function table.

The SN5476, SN54H76, and the SN54LS76A are characterized for operation over the full military temperature range of −55°C to 125°C. The SN7476, SN74H76, and the SN74LS76A are characterized for operation from 0°C to 70°C.

(TOP VIEW)

1CLK	1	16 1K
1PRE	2	15 1Q
1CLR	3	14 1$\overline{Q}$
1J	4	13 GND
VCC	5	12 2K
2CLK	6	11 2Q
2PRE	7	10 2$\overline{Q}$
2CLR	8	9 2J

'76, 'H76
FUNCTION TABLE

INPUTS				OUTPUTS	
PRE	CLR	CLK	J	K	Q	$\overline{Q}$
L	H	X	X	X	H	L
H	L	X	X	X	L	H
L	L	X	X	X	H†	H†
H	H	⊓	L	L	Q_0	$\overline{Q}_0$
H	H	⊓	H	L	H	L
H	H	⊓	L	H	L	H
H	H	⊓	H	H	TOGGLE	

'LS76A
FUNCTION TABLE

INPUTS				OUTPUTS	
PRE	CLR	CLK	J	K	Q	$\overline{Q}$
L	H	X	X	X	H	L
H	L	X	X	X	L	H
L	L	X	X	X	H†	H†
H	H	↓	L	L	Q_0	$\overline{Q}_0$
H	H	↓	H	L	H	L
H	H	↓	L	H	L	H
H	H	↓	H	H	TOGGLE	
H	H	H	X	X	Q_0	$\overline{Q}_0$

† This configuration is nonstable; that is, it will not persist when either preset or clear returns to its inactive (high) level.

FOR CHIP CARRIER INFORMATION,
CONTACT THE FACTORY

TEXAS INSTRUMENTS
POST OFFICE BOX 225012 • DALLAS, TEXAS 75265

TYPES SN5476, SN54H76, SN54LS76A, SN7476, SN74H76, SN74LS76A
DUAL J-K FLIP-FLOPS WITH PRESET AND CLEAR

logic diagrams

'76

'H76

TEXAS INSTRUMENTS
POST OFFICE BOX 225012 • DALLAS, TEXAS 75265

- Package Options Include Plastic "Small Outline" Packages, Ceramic Chip Carriers and Flat Packages, and Standard Plastic and Ceramic 300-mil DIPs

- Dependable Texas Instruments Quality and Reliability

TYPE	TYPICAL AVERAGE PROPAGATION DELAY TIME	TYPICAL TOTAL POWER DISSIPATION
'86	14 ns	150 mW
'LS86A	10 ns	30.5 mW
'S86	7 ns	250 mW

SN5486, SN54LS86A, SN54S86 . . . J OR W PACKAGE
SN7486 . . . N PACKAGE
SN74LS86A, SN74S86 . . . D OR N PACKAGE
(TOP VIEW)

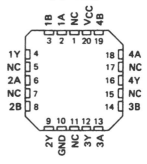

SN54LS86A, SN54S86 . . . FK PACKAGE
(TOP VIEW)

NC - No internal connection

description

These devices contain four independent 2-input Exclusive-OR gates. They perform the Boolean functions $Y = A \oplus B = \overline{A}B + A\overline{B}$ in positive logic.

A common application is as a true/complement element. If one of the inputs is low, the other input will be reproduced in true form at the output. If one of the inputs is high, the signal on the other input will be reproduced inverted at the output.

The SN5486, 54LS86A, and the SN54S86 are characterized for operation over the full military temperature range of −55°C to 125°C. The SN7486, SN74LS86A, and the SN74S86 are characterized for operation from 0°C to 70°C.

exclusive-OR logic

An exclusive-OR gate has many applications, some of which can be represented better by alternative logic symbols.

EXCLUSIVE-OR

These are five equivalent Exclusive-OR symbols valid for an '86 or 'LS86A gate in positive logic; negation may be shown at any two ports.

LOGIC IDENTITY ELEMENT	EVEN-PARITY	ODD-PARITY ELEMENT
The output is active (low) if all inputs stand at the same logic level (i.e., A = B).	The output is active (low) if an even number of inputs (i.e., 0 or 2) are active.	The output is active (high) if an odd number of inputs (i.e., only 1 of the 2) are active.

TEXAS
INSTRUMENTS
POST OFFICE BOX 655012 • DALLAS, TEXAS 75265

2-271

absolute maximum ratings over operating free-air temperature range (unless otherwise noted)

Supply voltage, V_{CC} (see Note 1)	7 V
Input voltage	7 V
Operating free-air temperature range: SN54LS86A	−55°C to 125°C
SN74LS86A	0°C to 70°C
Storage temperature range	−65°C to 150°C

NOTE 1: Voltage values are with respect to network ground terminal.

recommended operating conditions

	SN54LS86A			SN74LS86A			UNIT
	MIN	NOM	MAX	MIN	NOM	MAX	
Supply voltage, V_{CC}	4.5	5	5.5	4.75	5	5.25	V
High-level output current, I_{OH}			−400			−400	μA
Low-level output current, I_{OL}			4			8	mA
Operating free-air temperature, T_A	−55		125	0		70	°C

electrical characteristics over recommended operating free-air temperature range (unless otherwise noted)

PARAMETER		TEST CONDITIONS[†]		SN54LS86A			SN74LS86A			UNIT
				MIN	TYP[‡]	MAX	MIN	TYP[‡]	MAX	
V_{IH}	High-level input voltage			2			2			V
V_{IL}	Low-level input voltage					0.7			0.8	V
V_{IK}	Input clamp voltage	V_{CC} = MIN,	I_I = −18 mA			−1.5			−1.5	V
V_{OH}	High-level output voltage	V_{CC} = MIN, V_{IH} = 2 V, V_{IL} = V_{IL} max, I_{OH} = −400 μA		2.5	3.4		2.7	3.4		V
V_{OL}	Low-level output voltage	V_{CC} = MIN, V_{IH} = 2 V, V_{IL} = V_{IL} max	I_{OL} = 4 mA		0.25	0.4		0.25	0.4	V
			I_{OL} = 8 mA					0.35	0.5	
I_I	Input current at maximum input voltage	V_{CC} = MAX,	V_I = 7 V			0.2			0.2	mA
I_{IH}	High-level input current	V_{CC} = MAX,	V_I = 2.7 V			40			40	μA
I_{IL}	Low-level input current	V_{CC} = MAX,	V_I = 0.4 V			−0.8			−0.8	mA
I_{OS}	Short-circuit output current[§]	V_{CC} = MAX		−20		−100	−20		−100	mA
I_{CC}	Supply current	V_{CC} = MAX,	See Note 2		6.1	10		6.1	10	mA

[†]For conditions shown as MIN or MAX, use the appropriate value specified under recommended operating conditions for the applicable type.
[‡]All typical values are at V_{CC} = 5 V, T_A = 25°C.
[§]Not more than one output should be shorted at a time.
NOTE 2: I_{CC} is measured with the inputs grounded and the outputs open.

switching characteristics, V_{CC} = 5 V, T_A = 25°C

PARAMETER[¶]	FROM (INPUT)	TEST CONDITIONS		MIN	TYP	MAX	UNIT
t_{PLH}	A or B	Other input low	C_L = 15 pF, R_L = 2 kΩ, See Note 3		12	23	ns
t_{PHL}					10	17	
t_{PLH}	A or B	Other input high			20	30	ns
t_{PHL}					13	22	

[¶]t_{PLH} = propagation delay time, low-to-high-level output
t_{PHL} = propagation delay time, high-to-low-level output
NOTE 3: Load circuits and voltage waveforms are shown in Section 1.

TEXAS INSTRUMENTS
POST OFFICE BOX 655012 • DALLAS, TEXAS 75265

Courtesy of Texas Instruments Incorporated

TYPES SN5490A, SN5492A, SN5493A, SN54L90, SN54L93, SN54LS90, SN54LS92, SN54LS93, SN7490A, SN7492A, SN7493A, SN74L90, SN74L93, SN74LS90, SN74LS92, SN74LS93 DECADE, DIVIDE-BY-TWELVE, AND BINARY COUNTERS

MARCH 1974 — REVISED DECEMBER 1983

'90A, 'L90, 'LS90 ... DECADE COUNTERS

'92A, 'LS92 ... DIVIDE-BY-TWELVE COUNTERS

'93A, 'L93, 'LS93 ... 4-BIT BINARY COUNTERS

TYPES	TYPICAL POWER DISSIPATION
'90A	145 mW
'L90	20 mW
'LS90	45 mW
'92A, '93A	130 mW
'LS92, 'LS93	45 mW
'L93	16 mW

description

Each of these monolithic counters contains four master-slave flip-flops and additional gating to provide a divide-by-two counter and a three-stage binary counter for which the count cycle length is divide-by-five for the '90A, 'L90, and 'LS90, divide-by-six for the '92A and 'LS92, and divide-by-eight for the '93A, 'L93, and 'LS93.

All of these counters have a gated zero reset and the '90A, 'L90, and 'LS90 also have gated set-to-nine inputs for use in BCD nine's complement applications.

To use their maximum count length (decade, divide-by-twelve, or four-bit binary) of these counters, the CKB input is connected to the QA output. The input count pulses are applied to CKA input and the outputs are as described in the appropriate function table. A symmetrical divide-by-ten count can be obtained from the '90A, 'L90, or 'LS90 counters by connecting the QD output to the CKA input and applying the input count to the CKB input which gives a divide-by-ten square wave at output QA.

SN5490A, SN54LS90 ... J OR W PACKAGE
SN54L90 ... J PACKAGE
SN7490A ... J OR N PACKAGE
SN74LS90 ... D, J OR N PACKAGE
(TOP VIEW)

CKB	1	14 CKA
R0(1)	2	13 NC
R0(2)	3	12 QA
NC	4	11 QD
VCC	5	10 GND
R9(1)	6	9 QB
R9(2)	7	8 QC

SN5492A, SN54LS92 ... J OR W PACKAGE
SN54L92 ... J OR N PACKAGE
SN74LS92 ... D, J OR N PACKAGE
(TOP VIEW)

CKB	1	14 CKA
NC	2	13 NC
NC	3	12 QA
NC	4	11 QD
VCC	5	10 QC
R0(1)	6	9 QB
R0(2)	7	8 NC

SN5493A, SN54LS93 ... J OR W PACKAGE
SN7493A ... J OR N PACKAGE
SN74LS93 ... D, J OR N PACKAGE
(TOP VIEW)

CKB	1	14 CKA
R0(1)	2	13 NC
R0(2)	3	12 QA
NC	4	11 QD
VCC	5	10 GND
NC	6	9 QB
NC	7	8 QC

SN54L93 ... J PACKAGE
(TOP VIEW)

R0(1)	1	14 CKA
R0(2)	2	13 QA
NC	3	12 QD
VCC	4	11 GND
NC	5	10 QC
NC	6	9 QB
NC	7	8 CKB

NC - No internal connection

For new chip carrier design, use 'LS290, 'LS292, and 'LS293.

'90A, 'L90, 'LS90 BCD COUNT SEQUENCE (See Note A)

COUNT	OUTPUT			
	QD	QC	QB	QA
0	L	L	L	L
1	L	L	L	H
2	L	L	H	L
3	L	L	H	H
4	L	H	L	L
5	L	H	L	H
6	L	H	H	L
7	L	H	H	H
8	H	L	L	L
9	H	L	L	H

'90A, 'L90, 'LS90 BI-QUINARY SEQUENCE (5-2) (See Note B)

COUNT	OUTPUT			
	QA	QD	QC	QB
0	L	L	L	L
1	L	L	L	H
2	L	L	H	L
3	L	L	H	H
4	L	H	L	L
5	H	L	L	L
6	H	L	L	H
7	H	L	H	L
8	H	L	H	H
9	H	H	L	L

'90A, 'L90, 'LS90 RESET/COUNT FUNCTION TABLE

RESET INPUTS				OUTPUT			
R0(1)	R0(2)	R9(1)	R9(2)	QD	QC	QB	QA
H	H	L	X	L	L	L	L
H	H	X	L	L	L	L	L
X	X	H	H	H	L	L	H
X	L	X	L	COUNT			
L	X	L	X	COUNT			
L	X	X	L	COUNT			
X	L	L	X	COUNT			

'92A, 'LS92 COUNT SEQUENCE (See Note C)

COUNT	OUTPUT			
	QD	QC	QB	QA
0	L	L	L	L
1	L	L	L	H
2	L	L	H	L
3	L	L	H	H
4	L	H	L	L
5	L	H	L	H
6	H	L	L	L
7	H	L	L	H
8	H	L	H	L
9	H	L	H	H
10	H	H	L	L
11	H	H	L	H

'92A, 'LS92, '93A, 'L93, 'LS93 RESET/COUNT FUNCTION TABLE

RESET INPUTS		OUTPUT			
R0(1)	R0(2)	QD	QC	QB	QA
H	H	L	L	L	L
L	X	COUNT			
X	L	COUNT			

'93A, 'L93, 'LS93 COUNT SEQUENCE (See Note C)

COUNT	OUTPUT			
	QD	QC	QB	QA
0	L	L	L	L
1	L	L	L	H
2	L	L	H	L
3	L	L	H	H
4	L	H	L	L
5	L	H	L	H
6	L	H	H	L
7	L	H	H	H
8	H	L	L	L
9	H	L	L	H
10	H	L	H	L
11	H	L	H	H
12	H	H	L	L
13	H	H	L	H
14	H	H	H	L
15	H	H	H	H

NOTES: A. Output QA is connected to input CKB for BCD count.
B. Output QD is connected to input CKA for bi-quinary count.
C. Output QA is connected to input CKB.
D. H = high level, L = low level, X = irrelevant

PRODUCTION DATA
This document contains information current as of publication date. Products conform to specifications per the terms of Texas Instruments standard warranty. Production processing does not necessarily include testing of all parameters.

TEXAS INSTRUMENTS
POST OFFICE BOX 225012 ● DALLAS, TEXAS 75265

TEXAS INSTRUMENTS
POST OFFICE BOX 225012 ● DALLAS, TEXAS 75265

Courtesy of Texas Instruments Incorporated

TYPES SN5490A, SN5492A, SN5493A, SN7490A, SN7492A, SN7493A DECADE, DIVIDE-BY-TWELVE, AND BINARY COUNTERS

absolute maximum ratings over operating free-air temperature range (unless otherwise noted)

Supply voltage, V_{CC} (see Note 1)	7 V
Input voltage	5.5 V
Interemitter voltage (see Note 2)	5.5 V
Operating free-air temperature range: SN5490A, SN5492A, SN5493A	-55 C to 125 C
SN7490A, SN7492A, SN7493A	0°C to 70 C
Storage temperature range	-65 C to 150°C

NOTES: 1. Voltage values, except interemitter voltage, are with respect to network ground terminal.
2. This is the voltage between two emitters of a multiple emitter transistor. For these circuits, this rating applies between the two R_0 inputs, and for the '90A circuit, it also applies between the two R_9 inputs.

recommended operating conditions

	SN5490A, SN5492A SN5493A			SN7490A, SN7492A SN7493A			UNIT
	MIN	NOM	MAX	MIN	NOM	MAX	
Supply voltage, V_{CC}	4.5	5	5.5	4.75	5	5.25	V
High-level output current, I_{OH}			-800			-800	µA
Low-level output current, I_{OL}			16			16	mA
Count frequency, fcount (see Figure 1) A input			32			32	MHz
B input			16			16	
Pulse width, t_w A input	15			15			ns
B input	15			15			
Reset inputs	30			30			
Reset inactive-state setup time, t_{su}	25			15			ns
Operating free-air temperature, T_A	-55		125	0		70	C

electrical characteristics over recommended operating free-air temperature range (unless otherwise noted)

PARAMETER[†]	TEST CONDITIONS	'90A MIN	TYP[‡]	MAX	'92A MIN	TYP[‡]	MAX	'93A MIN	TYP[‡]	MAX	UNIT
V_{IH} High-level input voltage		2			2			2			V
V_{IL} Low-level input voltage				0.8			0.8			0.8	V
V_{IK} Input clamp voltage	V_{CC} = MIN, I_I = 12 mA			-1.5			-1.5			-1.5	V
V_{OH} High-level output voltage	V_{CC} = MIN, V_{IH} = 2 V, V_{IL} = 0.8 V, I_{OH} = -800 µA	2.4	3.4		2.4	3.4		2.4	3.4		V
V_{OL} Low-level output voltage	V_{CC} = MIN, V_{IH} = 2 V, V_{IL} = 0.8 V, I_{OL} = 16 mA[#]		0.2	0.4		0.2	0.4		0.2	0.4	V
I_I Input current at maximum input voltage	V_{CC} = MAX, V_I = 5.5 V			1			1			1	mA
I_{IH} High-level input current Any reset	V_{CC} = MAX, V_I = 2.4 V			40			40			40	µA
CKA				80			80			80	
CKB				120			120			80	
I_{IL} Low-level input current Any reset	V_{CC} = MAX, V_I = 0.4 V			-1.6			-1.6			-1.6	mA
CKA				-3.2			-3.2			-3.2	
CKB				-4.8			-4.8			-3.2	
I_{OS} Short-circuit output current[§] SN54	V_{CC} = MAX	-20		-57	-20		-57	-20		-57	mA
SN74		-18		-57	-18		-57	-18		-57	
I_{CC} Supply current	V_{CC} = MAX, See Note 3		29	42		26	39		26	39	mA

[†] For conditions shown as MIN or MAX, use the appropriate value specified under recommended operating conditions.
[‡] All typical values are at V_{CC} = 5 V, T_A = 25 C.
[§] Not more than one output should be shorted at a time.
[#] IOH outputs are tested at I_{OL} = 16 mA plus the limit value for I_{IL} for the CKB input. This permits driving the CKB input while maintaining full fan out capability.
NOTE 3: I_{CC} is measured with all outputs open, both R_0 inputs grounded following momentary connection to 4.5 V, and all other inputs grounded.

TEXAS INSTRUMENTS
POST OFFICE BOX 225012 • DALLAS, TEXAS 75265

TYPES SN5490A, '92A, '93A, SN54L90, 'L93, SN54LS90, 'LS92, 'LS93, SN7490A, '92A, '93A, SN74LS90, 'LS92, 'LS93 DECADE, DIVIDE-BY-TWELVE, AND BINARY COUNTERS

logic diagrams

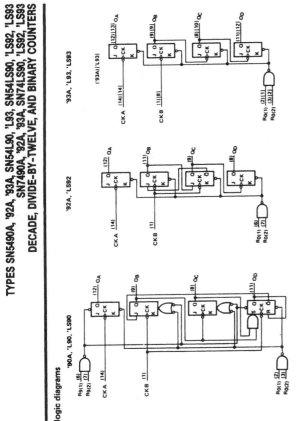

'90A, 'L90, 'LS90

'92A, 'LS92

'93A, 'L93, 'LS93

('93A/'L93')

The J and K inputs shown without connection are for reference only and are functionally at a high level.
Pin numbers shown in ( ) are for the 'LS93 and '93A and pin numbers shown in [ ] are for the 54L93.

schematics of inputs and outputs

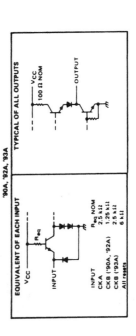

EQUIVALENT OF EACH INPUT   '90A, '92A, '93A

TYPICAL OF ALL OUTPUTS

INPUT	R_{eq} NOM
CKA	2.5 kΩ
CKB ('90A, '92A)	1.25 kΩ
CKB ('93A)	2.5 kΩ
All resets	6 kΩ

TEXAS INSTRUMENTS
POST OFFICE BOX 225012 • DALLAS, TEXAS 75265

TYPES SN54121, SN54L121, SN74121 MONOSTABLE MULTIVIBRATORS WITH SCHMITT-TRIGGER INPUTS

REVISED MAY 1983

- Programmable Output Pulse Width
  With R_{int} ... 35 ns Typ
  With R_{ext}/C_{ext} ... 40 ns to 28 Seconds
- Internal Compensation for Virtual Temperature Independence
- Jitter-Free Operation up to 90% Duty Cycle
- Inhibit Capability

SN54121 . . . J OR W PACKAGE
SN54L121 . . . J PACKAGE
SN74121 . . . J OR N PACKAGE

(TOP VIEW)

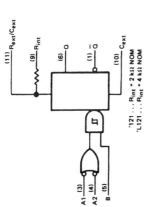

$\overline{Q}$ 1	14 V_{CC}
NC 2	13 NC
A1 3	12 NC
A2 4	11 R_{ext}/C_{ext}
B 5	10 C_{ext}
Q 6	9 R_{int}
GND 7	8 NC

NC - No internal connection.

FUNCTION TABLE

INPUTS			OUTPUTS	
A1	A2	B	Q	$\overline{Q}$
L	X	H	$\overline{\Gamma}$	H†
X	L	H	$\overline{\Gamma}$	H†
X	X	L	$\overline{\Gamma}$	H†
H	H	X	$\overline{\Gamma}$	H†
H	↓	H	⊓	⊔
↓	H	H	⊓	⊔
↓	↓	H	⊓	⊔
L	X	↑	⊓	⊔
X	L	↑	⊓	⊔

For explanation of function table symbols, see page

† These lines of the function table assume that the indicated steady state conditions at the A and B inputs have been setup long enough to complete any pulse started before the setup.

description

These multivibrators feature dual negative-transition-triggered inputs and a single positive-transition-triggered input which can be used as an inhibit input. Complementary output pulses are provided.

Pulse triggering occurs at a particular voltage level and is not directly related to the transition time of the input pulse. Schmitt-trigger input circuitry (TTL hysteresis) for the B input allows jitter-free triggering from inputs with transition rates as slow as 1 volt/second, providing the circuit with an excellent noise immunity of typically 1.2 volts. A high immunity to V_{CC} noise of typically 1.5 volts is also provided by internal latching circuitry.

Once fired, the outputs are independent of further transitions of the inputs and are a function only of the timing components. Input pulses may be of any duration relative to the output pulse. Output pulse length may be varied from 40 nanoseconds to 28 seconds by choosing appropriate timing components. With no external timing components (i.e., R_{int} connected to V_{CC}, C_{ext} and R_{ext}/C_{ext} open), an output pulse of typically 30 or 35 nanoseconds is achieved which may be used as a d-c triggered reset signal. Output rise and fall times are TTL compatible and independent of pulse length.

Pulse width stability is achieved through internal compensation and is virtually independent of V_{CC} and temperature. In most applications, pulse stability will only be limited by the accuracy of external timing components.

Jitter-free operation is maintained over the full temperature and V_{CC} ranges for more than six decades of timing capacitance (10 pF to 10 μF) and more than one decade of timing resistance (2 kΩ to 30 kΩ for the SN54121/SN54L121 and 2 kΩ to 40 kΩ for the SN74121). Throughout these ranges, pulse width is defined by the relationship $t_{w(out)} = C_{ext}R_T\ln2 \approx 0.7\,C_{ext}R_T$. In circuits where pulse cutoff is not critical, timing capacitance up to 1000 μF and timing resistance as low as 1.4 kΩ may be used. Also, the range of jitter-free output pulse widths is extended if V_{CC} is held to 5 volts and free-air temperature is 25°C. Duty cycles as high as 90% are achieved when using maximum recommended R_T. Higher duty cycles are available if a certain amount of pulse-width jitter is allowed.

logic diagram (positive logic)

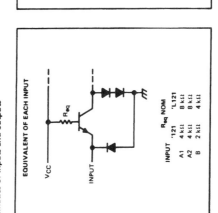

NOTES:
1. An external capacitor may be connected between C_{ext} (positive) and R_{ext}/C_{ext}.
2. To use the internal timing resistor, connect R_{int} to V_{CC}. For improved pulse width accuracy and repeatability, connect an external resistor between R_{ext}/C_{ext} and V_{CC} with R_{int} open-circuited.

Pin numbers shown on logic notation are for J or N packages.

'121 . . . R_{int} = 2 kΩ NOM
'L121 . . . R_{int} = 4 kΩ NOM

schematics of inputs and outputs

EQUIVALENT OF EACH INPUT

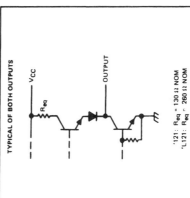

INPUT	R_{eq} NOM	
	'121	'L121
A1	4 kΩ	8 kΩ
A2	4 kΩ	8 kΩ
B	2 kΩ	4 kΩ

TYPICAL OF BOTH OUTPUTS

'121: R_{eq} = 130 Ω NOM
'L121: R_{eq} = 260 Ω NOM

PRODUCTION DATA
This document contains information current as of publication date. Products conform to specifications per the terms of Texas Instruments standard warranty. Production processing does not necessarily include testing of all parameters.

TEXAS INSTRUMENTS
POST OFFICE BOX 225012 ● DALLAS, TEXAS 75265

TEXAS INSTRUMENTS
POST OFFICE BOX 225012 ● DALLAS, TEXAS 75265

Courtesy of Texas Instruments Incorporated

TYPES SN54121, SN54L121, SN74121 MONOSTABLE MULTIVIBRATORS WITH SCHMITT-TRIGGER INPUTS

absolute maximum ratings over operating free-air temperature range (unless otherwise noted)

Supply voltage, V_{CC} (see Note 1) '121	7 V
'L121	8 V
Input voltage	5.5 V
Operating free-air temperature range: SN54121, SN54L121	−55°C to 125°C
SN74121	0°C to 70°C
Storage temperature range	−65°C to 150°C

NOTE 1: Voltage values are with respect to network ground terminal.

recommended operating conditions

		SN54121 SN74121 MIN	NOM	MAX	SN54L121 MIN	NOM	MAX	UNIT
V_{CC} Supply voltage	54 Family	4.5	5	5.5	4.5	5	5.5	V
	74 Family	4.75	5	5.25				
I_{OH} High-level output current				−0.4			−0.2	mA
I_{OL} Low-level output current				16			8	mA
dv/dt Rate of rise or fall of input pulse	Schmitt input, B			1			1	V/s
	Logic inputs, A1, A2			1			1	V/µs
$t_{w(in)}$ Input pulse width		50			100			ns
R_{ext} External timing resistance	54 Family	1.4		30	1.4		30	kΩ
	74 Family	1.4		40				
C_{ext} External timing capacitance		0		1000	0		1000	pF
Duty cycle	R_T = 2 kΩ			67			67	%
	R_T = MAX R_{ext}			90			90	
T_A Operating free-air temperature	54 Family	−55		125	−55		125	°C
	74 Family	0		70				

TYPES SN54121, SN54L121, SN74121 MONOSTABLE MULTIVIBRATORS WITH SCHMITT-TRIGGER INPUTS

electrical characteristics over recommended operating free-air temperature range (unless otherwise noted)

PARAMETER		TEST CONDITIONS†	SN54121 SN74121 MIN	TYP‡	MAX	SN54L121 MIN	TYP‡	MAX	UNIT
V_{T+}	Positive-going threshold voltage at A input	V_{CC} = MIN		1.4	2		1.4	2	V
V_{T-}	Negative-going threshold voltage at A input	V_{CC} = MIN	0.8	1.4		0.8	1.4		V
V_{T+}	Positive-going threshold voltage at B input	V_{CC} = MIN		1.55	2		1.55	2	V
V_{T-}	Negative-going threshold voltage at B input	V_{CC} = MIN	0.8	1.35		0.8	1.35		V
V_{IK}	Input clamp voltage	V_{CC} = MIN, I_I = −12 mA			−1.5			−1.5	V
V_{OH}	High-level output voltage	V_{CC} = MIN, I_{OH} = MAX	2.4	3.4		2.4	3.4		V
V_{OL}	Low-level output voltage	V_{CC} = MIN, I_{OL} = MAX		0.2	0.4		0.2	0.4	V
I_I	Input current at maximum input voltage	V_{CC} = MAX, V_I = 5.5 V			1			1	mA
I_{IH}	High-level input current	A1 or A2	V_{CC} = MAX, V_I = 2.4 V		40			20	µA
		B			80			40	µA
I_{IL}	Low-level input current	A1 or A2	V_{CC} = MAX, V_I = 0.4 V		−1.6			−0.8	mA
		B			−3.2			−1.6	mA
I_{OS}	Short-circuit output current§	54 Family	V_{CC} = MAX	−20		−55	−20		−27	mA
		74 Family	−18		−55				
I_{CC}	Supply current	Quiescent	V_{CC} = MAX		13	25		7	12	mA
		Triggered		23	40		9	20	mA

† For conditions shown as MIN or MAX, use the appropriate value specified under recommended operating conditions.
‡ All typical values are at V_{CC} = 5 V, T_A = 25°C.
§ Not more than one output should be shorted at a time.

switching characteristics, V_{CC} = 5 V, T_A = 25°C

PARAMETER	TEST CONDITIONS	'121 MIN	TYP	MAX	'L121 MIN	TYP	MAX	UNIT
t_{PLH} Propagation delay time, low-to-high-level Q output from either A input	C_L = 15 pF, R_L = 400 Ω for '121, R_L = 800 Ω for 'L121, See Note 2		45	70			140	ns
t_{PLH} Propagation delay time, low-to-high-level Q output from B input			35	55			110	ns
t_{PHL} Propagation delay time, high-to-low-level Q̄ output from either A input			50	80			160	ns
t_{PHL} Propagation delay time, high-to-low-level Q̄ output from B input			40	65			130	ns
$t_{w(out)}$ Pulse width obtained using internal timing resistor	C_{ext} = 80 pF, R_{int} to V_{CC}	70	110	150	70	225	260	ns
$t_{w(out)}$ Pulse width obtained with zero timing capacitance	C_{ext} = 0, R_{int} to V_{CC}		30	50		35	70	ns
$t_{w(out)}$ Pulse width obtained using external timing resistor	C_{ext} = 100 pF, R_T = 10 kΩ	600	700	800	600	700	850	ns
$t_{w(out)}$ Pulse width obtained using external timing resistor	C_{ext} = 1 µF, R_T = 10 kΩ	6	7	8	6	7	8	ms

NOTE 2: See General Information Section for load circuits and voltage waveforms.

TEXAS INSTRUMENTS
POST OFFICE BOX 225012 • DALLAS, TEXAS 75265

TEXAS INSTRUMENTS
POST OFFICE BOX 225012 • DALLAS, TEXAS 75265

CD4069UB Types

TEXAS INSTRUMENTS
Data sheet acquired from Harris Semiconductor
SCHS054A – Revised March 2002

CMOS Hex Inverter
High-Voltage Types (20-Volt Rating)

■ CD4069UB types consist of six CMOS inverter circuits. These devices are intended for all general-purpose inverter applications where the medium-power TTL-drive and logic-level-conversion capabilities of circuits such as the CD4009 and CD4049 Hex Inverter/Buffers are not required.

The CD4069UB-Series types are supplied in 14-lead hermetic dual-in-line ceramic packages (D and F suffixes), 14-lead dual-in-line plastic package (E suffix), 14-lead small-outline package (NSR suffix), and in chip form (H suffix).

Features:

* Standardized symmetrical output characteristics
* Medium Speed Operation—t_{PHL}, t_{PLH} 30 ns (typ.) at 10 V
* 100% tested for quiescent current at 20 V
* Maximum input current of 1 μA at 18 V over full package-temperature range; 100 nA at 18 V and 25°C
* Meets all requirements of JEDEC Tentative Standard No. 13B, "Standard Specifications for Description of 'B' Series CMOS Devices"

Applications:

* Logic inversion
* Pulse shaping
* Oscillators
* High-input-impedance amplifiers

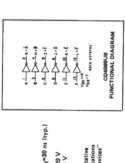

CD4069UB FUNCTIONAL DIAGRAM

RECOMMENDED OPERATING CONDITIONS

For maximum reliability, nominal operating conditions should be selected so that operation is always within the following ranges:

CHARACTERISTIC	LIMITS		UNITS
	Min.	Max.	
Supply-Voltage Range (For T_A = Full Package Temperature Range)	3	18	V

MAXIMUM RATINGS, Absolute-Maximum Values:

DC SUPPLY-VOLTAGE RANGE, (V_{DD})
Voltages referenced to V_{SS} Terminal .... –0.5V to +20V
INPUT VOLTAGE RANGE, ALL INPUTS .... –0.5V to V_{DD} +0.5V
DC INPUT CURRENT, ANY ONE INPUT .... ±10mA
POWER DISSIPATION PER PACKAGE (Pɒ)
 For T_A = –55°C to +100°C 500mW
 For T_A = +100°C to +125°C .... Derate Linearly at 12mW/°C to 200mW
DEVICE DISSIPATION PER OUTPUT TRANSISTOR
 FOR T_A = FULL PACKAGE-TEMPERATURE RANGE (All Package Types) 100mW
OPERATING-TEMPERATURE RANGE (T_A) .... –55°C to +125°C
STORAGE TEMPERATURE RANGE (T_{stg}) .... –65°C to +160°C
LEAD TEMPERATURE (DURING SOLDERING):
 At distance 1/16 ± 1/32 inch (1.59 ± 0.79mm) from case for 10s max .... +265°C

DYNAMIC ELECTRICAL CHARACTERISTICS at T_A = 25°C; Input t_r, t_f = 20 ns.

C_L = 50 pF, R_L = 200 KΩ

CHARACTERISTIC	CONDITIONS V_{DD} V	LIMITS		UNITS
		Typ.	Max.	
Propagation Delay Time, t_{PLH}, t_{PHL}	5	55	110	ns
	10	30	60	
	15	25	50	
Transition Time, t_{THL}, t_{TLH}	5	100	200	ns
	10	50	100	
	15	40	80	
Input Capacitance, C_{IN}	Any Input	10	15	pF

3-180

CD4069UB Types

STATIC ELECTRICAL CHARACTERISTICS

CHARACTER-ISTIC	CONDITIONS			LIMITS AT INDICATED TEMPERATURES (°C)					+25			UNITS
	V_O (V)	V_{IN} (V)	V_{DD} (V)	–55	–40	+85	+125	Min.	Typ.	Max.	
Quiescent Device Current, I_{DD} Max.	–	0,5	5	0.25	0.25	7.5	7.5	–	0.01	0.25	μA
	–	0,10	10	0.5	0.5	15	15	–	0.01	0.5	
	–	0,15	15	1	1	30	30	–	0.01	1	
	–	0,20	20	5	5	150	150	–	0.02	5	
Output Low (Sink) Current, I_{OL} Min.	0.4	0.5	5	0.64	0.61	0.42	0.36	0.51	1	–	mA
	0.5	0.5	5	0.61	0.5	1.1	0.9	1.3	2.6	–	
	1.5	0.15	15	4.2	4	2.8	2.4	3.4	6.8	–	
Output High (Source) Current, I_{OH} Min.	4.6	0.5	5	–0.64	–0.61	–0.42	–0.36	–0.51	–1	–	
	2.5	0.5	5	–2	–1.8	–1.3	–1.15	–1.6	–3.2	–	
	9.5	0.10	10	–1.6	–1.5	–1.1	–0.9	–1.3	–2.6	–	
	13.5	0.15	15	–4.2	–4	–2.8	–2.4	–3.4	–6.8	–	
Output Voltage: Low-Level, V_{OL} Max.	–	5	5	0.05	0.05			–	0	0.05	V
	–	10	10	0.05	0.05			–	0	0.05	
	–	15	15	0.05	0.05			–	0	0.05	
Output Voltage: High-Level, V_{OH} Min.	–	0	5	4.95	4.95			4.95	5	–	
	–	0	10	9.95	9.95			9.95	10	–	
	–	0	15	14.95	14.95			14.95	15	–	
Input Low Voltage, V_{IL} Max.	4.5	–	5	–	–			–	–	2	
	9	–	10	–	2			–	–	–	
	13.5	–	15	2.5	2.5			–	–	2.5	
Input High Voltage, V_{IH} Min.	0.5	–	5	4	4			8	–	–	
	1	–	10	8	8			8	–	–	
	1.5	–	15	12.5	12.5			12.5	–	–	
Input Current I_{IN} Max.	–	0,18	18	±0.1	±0.1	±1	±1	–	±10⁻⁵	±0.1	μA

Fig. 8 – Typical output high (source) current characteristics.

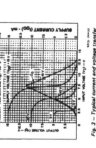

Fig. 10 – Typical propagation delay time vs. load capacitance.

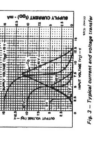

Fig. 9 – Minimum output high (source) current characteristics.

Fig. 4 – Typical output low (sink) current characteristics.

Fig. 5 – Minimum output low (sink) current characteristics.

Fig. 11 – Typical propagation delay time vs. supply voltage.

Fig. 7 – CD4069UB terminal assignment.

Fig. 6 – Schematic diagram of one of six identical inverters.

Fig. 1 – Minimum and maximum voltage transfer characteristics.

Fig. 2 – Typical voltage transfer characteristics as a function of temperature.

Fig. 3 – Typical current and voltage transfer characteristics.

Copyright © 2002, Texas Instruments Incorporated

3-181

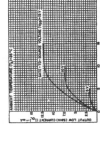

Fig. 1 — Typical voltage transfer characteristics.

Fig. 2 — Typical propagation delay time as a function of load capacitance.

Fig. 4 — Typical output low (sink) current characteristics.

Fig. 6 — Minimum output low (sink) current characteristics.

MAXIMUM RATINGSB, Absolute-Maximum Values:

DC SUPPLY-VOLTAGE RANGE, (V_{DD})
Voltages referenced to V_{SS} Terminal) .... –0.5V to +20V
INPUT VOLTAGE RANGE, ALL INPUTS .... –0.5V to V_{DD} +0.5V
DC INPUT CURRENT, ANY ONE INPUT .... ±10mA
POWER DISSIPATION PER PACKAGE (Pb):
  For T_A = –55°C to +100°C 500mW
  For T_A = +100°C to +125°C .... Derate Linearly at 12mW/°C to 200mW
DEVICE DISSIPATION PER OUTPUT TRANSISTOR
  FOR T_A = FULL PACKAGE-TEMPERATURE RANGE (All Package Types) 100mW
OPERATING-TEMPERATURE RANGE(T_A) .... –55°C to +125°C
STORAGE TEMPERATURE RANGE (T_{stg}) .... –65°C to +150°C
LEAD TEMPERATURE (DURING SOLDERING):
  At distance 1/16 ± 1/32 inch (1.59 ± 0.79mm) from case for 10s max. .... +265°C

DYNAMIC ELECTRICAL CHARACTERISTICS at T_A = 25°C, Input t_r, t_f = 20 ns, and C_L = 50 pF, R_L = 200 KΩ

CHARACTERISTIC	TEST CONDITIONS		ALL TYPES LIMITS		UNITS
	V_{DD} VOLTS		TYP.	MAX.	
Propagation Delay Time, t_{PHL}, t_{PLH}	5		125	250	ns
	10		60	120	
	15		45	90	
Transition Time, t_{THL}, t_{TLH}	5		100	200	ns
	10		50	100	
	15		40	80	
Input Capacitance, C_{IN}	Any Input		5	7.5	pF

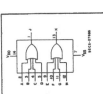

Fig. 3 — Schematic diagram for CD4071B (1 of 4 identical gates).

* ALL INPUTS ARE PROTECTED BY CMOS PROTECTION NETWORK

Fig. 5 —Logic diagram for CD4071B (1 of 4 identical gates).

TEXAS INSTRUMENTS
Data sheet acquired from Harris Semiconductor
SCHS056A – Revised March 2002

CD4071B, CD4072B, CD4075B Types

CMOS OR Gates

High-Voltage Types (20-Volt Rating)

CD4071B Quad 2-Input OR Gate
CD4072B Dual 4-Input OR Gate
CD4075B Triple 3-Input OR Gate

■ CD4071B, CD4072B, and CD4075B

OR gates provide the system designer with direct implementation of the positive-logic OR function and supplement the existing family of CMOS gates. The CD4071, CD4072, and CD4075 types are supplied in 14-lead dual-in-line ceramic packages (D and F suffixes), 14-lead dual-in-line plastic packages (E suffix), 14-lead small-outline package (NSR suffix), and in chip form (H suffix).

Features:

■ Medium-Speed Operation•t_{PLH}, t_{PHL} = 60 ns (typ.) at V_{DD} = 10 V
■ 100% tested for quiescent current at 20 V
■ Maximum input current of 1 μA at 18 V over full package-temperature range; 100 nA at 18 V and 25°C
■ Standardized, symmetrical output characteristics
■ Noise margin (over full package temperature range):
  1 V at V_{DD} = 5 V
  2 V at V_{DD} = 10 V
  2.5 V at V_{DD} = 15 V
■ 5-V, 10-V, and 15-V parametric ratings
■ Meets all requirements of JEDEC Tentative Standard No. 13B, "Standard Specifications for Description of 'B' Series CMOS Devices"

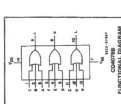

CD4071B
FUNCTIONAL DIAGRAM

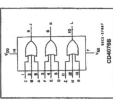

CD4072B
FUNCTIONAL DIAGRAM

CD4075B
FUNCTIONAL DIAGRAM

RECOMMENDED OPERATING CONDITIONS

For maximum reliability, nominal operating conditions should be selected so that operation is always within the following ranges:

CHARACTERISTIC		LIMITS		UNITS
		MIN.	MAX.	
Supply-Voltage Range (For T_A = Full Package-Temperature Range)		3	18	V

STATIC ELECTRICAL CHARACTERISTICS

CHARACTER-ISTIC	CONDITIONS			LIMITS AT INDICATED TEMPERATURES (°C)						+25			UNITS
	V_O (V)	V_{IN} (V)	V_{DD} (V)	–55	–40	+85	+125	Min.	Typ.	Max.			
Quiescent Device Current, I_{DD} Max.	–	0,5	5	0.25	0.25	7.5	7.5	–	0.01	0.25			μA
	–	0,10	10	0.5	0.5	15	15	–	0.01	0.5			
	–	0,15	15	1	1	30	30	–	0.01	1			
	–	0,20	20	5	5	150	150	–	0.02	5			
Output Low (Sink) Current, I_{OL} Min.	0.4	0,5	5	0.64	0.61	0.42	0.36	0.51	1	–			mA
	0.5	0,10	10	1.6	1.5	1.1	0.9	1.3	2.6	–			
	1.5	0,15	15	4.2	4	3.4	2.4	3.4	6.8	–			
Output High (Source) Current, I_{OH} Min.	4.6	0,5	5	–0.64	–0.61	–0.42	–0.36	–0.51	–1	–			mA
	2.5	0,5	5	–2	–1.8	–1.3	–1.15	–1.6	–3.2	–			
	9.5	0,10	10	–1.6	–1.5	–1.1	–0.9	–1.3	–2.6	–			
	13.5	0,15	15	–4.2	–4	–2.8	–2.4	–3.4	–6.8	–			
Output Voltage: Low-Level, V_{OL} Max.	–	0,5	5	0.05	0.05	0.05	0.05	–	0	0.06			V
	–	0,10	10	0.05	0.05	0.05	0.05	–	0	0.05			
	–	0,15	15	0.05	0.05	0.05	0.05	–	0	0.05			
Output Voltage: High-Level, V_{OH} Min.	–	0,5	5	4.95	4.95	4.95	4.95	4.95	5	–			V
	–	0,10	10	9.95	9.95	9.95	9.95	9.95	10	–			
	–	0,15	15	14.95	14.95	14.95	14.95	14.95	15	–			
Input Low Voltage, V_{IL} Max.	0.5, 4.5	–	5	1.5	1.5	1.5	1.5	–	–	1.5			V
	1, 9	–	10	3	3	3	3	–	–	3			
	1.5, 13.5	–	15	4	4	4	4	–	–	4			
Input High Voltage, V_{IH} Min.	4.5	–	5	3.5	3.5	3.5	3.5	–	–				V
	9	–	10	7	7	7	7	–	–				
	13.5	–	15	11	11	11	11	–	–				
Input Current I_{IN} Max.	–	0,18	18	±0.1	±0.1	±1	±1	–	±10⁻⁵	±0.1			μA

Copyright © 2002, Texas Instruments Incorporated

CD4073B, CD4081B, CD4082B Types

TEXAS INSTRUMENTS

Data sheet acquired from Harris Semiconductor
SCHS057A – Revised March 2002

CMOS AND Gates

High-Voltage Types (20-Volt Rating)

CD4073B Triple 3-Input AND Gate
CD4081B Quad 2-Input AND Gate
CD4082B Dual 4-Input AND Gate

■ CD4073B, CD4081B and CD-4082B AND gates provide the system designer with direct implementation of the AND function and supplement the existing family of CMOS gates.

The CD4073B, CD4081B and CD4082B types are supplied in 14-lead dual-in-line ceramic packages (D and F suffixes), 14-lead dual-in-line plastic packages (E suffix), 14-lead small-outline package (NSR suffix), and in chip form (H suffix).

Features:

■ Medium-Speed Operation — t_{PLH}: t_{PHL} = 60 ns (typ.) at V_{DD} = 10 V
■ 100% tested for quiescent current at 20 V
■ Maximum input current of 1 μA at 18 V over full package-temperature range; 100 nA at 18 V and 25°C
■ Noise margin (full package-temperature range) =
 1 V at V_{DD} = 5 V
 2 V at V_{DD} = 10 V
 2.5 V at V_{DD} = 15 V
■ Standardized, symmetrical output characteristics
■ 5-V, 10-V, and 15-V parametric ratings
■ Meets all requirements of JEDEC Tentative Standard No. 13B, "Standard Specifications for Description of 'B' Series CMOS Devices"

MAXIMUM RATINGS, Absolute-Maximum Values:

DC SUPPLY-VOLTAGE RANGE, (V_{DD})
Voltages referenced to V_{SS} Terminal) .... −0.5V to +20V
INPUT VOLTAGE RANGE, ALL INPUTS .... −0.5V to V_{DD} +0.5V
DC INPUT CURRENT, ANY ONE INPUT .... ±10mA
POWER DISSIPATION PER PACKAGE (P_D):
 For T_A = −55°C to +100°C 500mW
 For T_A = +100°C to +125°C .... Derate Linearly at 12mW/°C to 100mW
DEVICE DISSIPATION PER OUTPUT TRANSISTOR
 FOR T_A = FULL PACKAGE-TEMPERATURE RANGE (All Package Types) 100mW
OPERATING-TEMPERATURE RANGE (T_A): .... −55°C to +125°C
STORAGE TEMPERATURE RANGE (T_{stg}): .... −65°C to +150°C
LEAD TEMPERATURE (DURING SOLDERING):
 At distance 1/16 ± 1/32 inch (1.59 ± 0.79mm) from case for 10s max .... +265°C

RECOMMENDED OPERATING CONDITIONS

For maximum reliability, nominal operating conditions should be selected so that operation is always within the following ranges:

CHARACTERISTIC	LIMITS		UNITS
	MIN.	MAX.	
Supply-Voltage Range (For T_A = Full Package Temperature Range)	3	18	V

DYNAMIC ELECTRICAL CHARACTERISTICS at T_A=25°C, Input t_r,t_f=20 ns, and C_L=50 pF, R_L=200 kΩ

CHARACTERISTIC	TEST CONDITIONS	ALL TYPES LIMITS		UNITS
	V_{DD} Volts	TYP.	MAX.	
Propagation Delay Time, t_{PHL}, t_{PLH}	5	125	250	ns
	10	60	120	
	15	45	90	
Transition Time, t_{THL}, t_{TLH}	5	100	200	ns
	10	50	100	
	15	40	80	
Input Capacitance, C_{IN}	Any Input	5	7.5	pF

STATIC ELECTRICAL CHARACTERISTICS

CHARACTERISTIC	CONDITIONS			LIMITS AT INDICATED TEMPERATURES (°C)							UNITS
	V_O (V)	V_{IN} (V)	V_{DD} (V)	−55	−40	+85	+125	+25 Min.	+25 Typ.	+25 Max.	
Quiescent Device Current, I_{DD} Max.	–	–	5	0.25	0.25	7.5	7.5	–	0.01	0.25	μA
	–	0,10	10	0.5	0.5	15	15	–	0.01	0.5	
	–	0,15	15	1	1	30	30	–	0.01	1	
	–	0,20	20	5	5	150	150	–	0.02	5	
Output Low (Sink) Current, I_{OL} Min.	0.4	0,5	5	0.64	0.61	0.42	0.36	0.51	1	–	mA
	0.5	0,10	10	1.6	1.5	1.1	0.9	1.3	2.6	–	
	1.5	0,15	15	4.2	4	2.8	2.4	3.4	6.8	–	
Output High (Source) Current, I_{OH} Min.	4.6	0,5	5	−0.64	−0.61	−0.42	−0.36	−0.51	−1	–	
	2.5	0,5	5	−2	−1.8	−1.3	−1.15	−1.6	−3.2	–	
	9.5	0,10	10	−1.6	−1.5	−1.1	−0.9	−1.3	−2.6	–	
	13.5	0,15	15	−4.2	−4	−2.8	−2.4	−3.4	−6.8	–	
Output Voltage: Low-Level, V_{OL} Max.	–	0,5	5	0.05	0.05	0.05			0	0.05	V
	–	0,10	10	0.05	0.05	0.05			0	0.05	
	–	0,15	15	0.05	0.05	0.05			0	0.05	
Output Voltage: High-Level, V_{OH} Min.	–	0,5	5	4.95	4.95	4.95		4.96	5	–	V
	–	0,10	10	9.95	9.95	9.95		9.95	10	–	
	–	0,15	15	14.95	14.95	14.95		14.95	15	–	
Input Low Voltage, V_{IL} Max.	0.5	–	5	1.5	1.5	1.5	1.5			1.5	V
	1	–	10	3	3	3	3			3	
	1.5	–	15	4	4	4	4			4	
Input High Voltage, V_{IH} Min.	0.5,4.5	–	5	3.5	3.5	3.5	3.5			3.5	
	1,9	–	10	7	7	7	7			7	
	1.5,13.5	–	15	11	11	11	11			11	
Input Current, I_{IN} Max.	–	0,18	18	±0.1	±0.1	±1	±1		±10⁻⁵	±0.1	μA

Fig. 3 — Typical voltage transfer characteristics.

Fig. 4 — Typical propagation delay time as a function of load capacitance.

Fig. 5 — Typical output low (sink) current characteristics.

Fig. 6 — Minimum output low (sink) current characteristics.

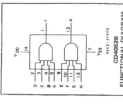

Fig. 1 — Schematic diagram for CD4081B (1 of 4 identical gates).

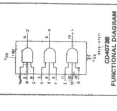

Fig. 2 — Logic diagram for CD4081B (1 of 4 identical gates).

* ALL INPUTS ARE PROTECTED BY CMOS PROTECTION NETWORK

CD4081B FUNCTIONAL DIAGRAM

CD4082B FUNCTIONAL DIAGRAM

CD4073B FUNCTIONAL DIAGRAM

NE555, SA555, SE555
PRECISION TIMERS

SLFS022C – SEPTEMBER 1973 – REVISED FEBRUARY 2002

- Timing From Microseconds to Hours
- Astable or Monostable Operation
- Adjustable Duty Cycle
- TTL-Compatible Output Can Sink or Source up to 200 mA
- Designed To Be Interchangeable With Signetics NE555, SA555, and SE555

description

These devices are precision timing circuits capable of producing accurate time delays or oscillation. In the time-delay or monostable mode of operation, the timed interval is controlled by a single external resistor and capacitor network. In the astable mode of operation, the frequency and duty cycle can be controlled independently with two external resistors and a single external capacitor.

The threshold and trigger levels normally are two-thirds and one-third, respectively, of V_{CC}. These levels can be altered by use of the control-voltage terminal. When the trigger input falls below the trigger level, the flip-flop is set and the output goes high. If the trigger input is above the threshold level and the flip-flop is reset and the output is low. The reset (RESET) input can override all other inputs and can be used to initiate a new timing cycle. When RESET goes low, the flip-flop is reset and the output goes low. When the output is low, a low-impedance path is provided between discharge (DISCH) and ground.

The output circuit is capable of sinking or sourcing current up to 200 mA. Operation is specified for supplies of 5 V to 15 V. With a 5-V supply, output levels are compatible with TTL inputs.

The NE555 is characterized for operation from 0°C to 70°C. The SA555 is characterized for operation from –40°C to 85°C. The SE555 is characterized for operation over the full military range of –55°C to 125°C.

NE555 . . . D, P, PS, OR PW PACKAGE
SA555 . . . D OR P PACKAGE
SE555 . . . D, JG, OR P PACKAGE
(TOP VIEW)

GND	1	8	V_{CC}
TRIG	2	7	DISCH
OUT	3	6	THRES
RESET	4	5	CONT

SE555 . . . FK PACKAGE
(TOP VIEW)

NC – No internal connection

functional block diagram

Pin numbers shown are for the D, JG, P, PS, and PW packages.
NOTE A: RESET can override TRIG, which can override THRES.

FUNCTION TABLE

RESET	TRIGGER VOLTAGE†	THRESHOLD VOLTAGE†	OUTPUT	DISCHARGE SWITCH
Low	Irrelevant	Irrelevant	Low	On
High	$<1/3\ V_{DD}$	Irrelevant	High	Off
High	$>1/3\ V_{DD}$	$>2/3\ V_{DD}$	Low	On
High	$>1/3\ V_{DD}$	$<2/3\ V_{DD}$	As previously established	

† Voltage levels shown are nominal.

AVAILABLE OPTIONS

		PACKAGE				
T_A	V_{THRES} MAX V_{CC} = 15 V	SMALL OUTLINE (D, PS)	CHIP CARRIER (FK)	CERAMIC DIP (JG)	PLASTIC DIP (P)	PLASTIC THIN SHRINK SMALL OUTLINE (PW)
0°C to 70°C	11.2 V	NE555D NE555PS	–	–	NE555P	NE555PW
–40°C to 85°C	11.2 V	SA555D	–	–	SA555P	
–55°C to 125°C	10.6 V	SE555D	SE555FK	SE555JG	SE555P	

The D package is available taped and reeled. Add the suffix R to the device type (e.g., NE555DR). The PS and PW packages are only available taped and reeled.

TEXAS INSTRUMENTS
POST OFFICE BOX 655303 ● DALLAS, TEXAS 75265

Courtesy of Texas Instruments Incorporated